INORGANIC
ISOTOPIC
SYNTHESES

INORGANIC

ISOTOPIC

SYNTHESES

ROLFE H. HERBER, Editor

Contributors:

Henry L. Crespi   L. Lindner
L. Dostrovsky   B. J. Masters
Rolfe H. Herber   F. S. Rowland
Milton Kahn   D. Samuel
Joseph J. Katz   W. Spindel
          Seymour T. Zenchelsky

W. A. Benjamin, Inc.   New York   1962

541.38
H 535

INORGANIC ISOTOPIC SYNTHESES

Library of Congress Catalog Card Number 62-15646
Manufactured in the United States of America

*Final manuscript was received on April 2, 1962:
this volume was published September 14, 1962*

W. A. BENJAMIN, INC.
2465 Broadway, New York 25, New York

Preface

This volume is intended to serve as a guide to the preparation of isotopically labeled inorganic compounds, by providing relevant information in two ways. In many instances, synthetic methods for obtaining a given compound are so unambiguous that a minimum of specific information enables the reader to commence the synthesis in the laboratory. In the present collection, such methods are given in sufficient detail so that no further appeal to the literature will, in general, be required.

In other instances, however, especially when unstable or esoteric compounds are involved, as well as those requiring sophisticated equipment, the chemist interested in the preparation of these materials must be able to refer to the appropriate original publication for specific or elaborate details. To make his task easier, numerous references to the literature are cited in the text, together with an evaluation of the relative merits of competitive methods where this has been feasible.

Finally, the scope of the present information should assist the interested investigator in designing new synthetic methods for the improvement of existing procedures, or for the preparation of isotopically labeled compounds that are still to be born. In this function, the success of this volume will be measured by the time that may elapse until it is outdated. The sooner this occurs, the more useful a function will have been served.

Obviously no material pertaining to scientific information in a vital and growing field can ever be complete. The responsibility for limiting the scope of this volume to the eight nuclides chosen is solely that of the editor. Per contra the high standards of judgment and experience that have contributed to the lucidity and usefulness of the text material are those of the individual authors. The only merit that accrues to the editor lies in the fact that he was able to inveigle the best qualified person in each field to contribute to the present effort and, by continual harrassment, to obtain the individual manuscripts in as short a time as possible.

The editor is grateful for the cooperation of the various contributors in assembling this material. The editorial assistance of Miss Nancy Orban is gratefully acknowledged. Finally, the

ever-present encouragement and assistance of my wife (as well as
of S. A. , K. S. , and S. B. in their own way) deserves to be recorded
here with many thanks.

                                                          R. H. HERBER

New Brunswick, New Jersey
May 1, 1962

Contents

Contents

INORGANIC
ISOTOPIC
SYNTHESES

1

General Procedures

SEYMOUR T. ZENCHELSKY
Rutgers, The State University
New Brunswick, New Jersey

1. INTRODUCTION*

This chapter constitutes a review of background information that will be useful in connection with the discussion of synthetic procedures with the individual nuclides in subsequent chapters. It treats the following subjects: (1) handling of micro and millicurie amounts of radionuclides, (2) general aspects of radiochemical manipulations, (3) radioassay, (4) assay for stable nuclides, (5) review of terms and equations. More detailed information, as well as numerous additional references, can be found in several introductory texts,[1] the reference work of Wahl and Bonner,[2] and various review articles.[3-5]

Although the specific treatment of a particular isotopic nuclide depends upon its individual characteristics as well as upon its state of chemical combination, a major distinction can be made between the stable and radioactive nuclides. This distinction applies to the preparative and manipulative as well as to the assay methods. Thus, while the various radionuclides are prepared by a variety of nuclear reactions, the stable ones are almost exclusively

---

*A review of terms and definitions will be found in Sec. 6 of this chapter.

[1] Overman, R. T., and Clark, H. M., "Radioisotope Techniques," McGraw-Hill, New York, 1960; Choppin, G. R., "Experimental Nuclear Chemistry," Prentice-Hall, Englewood Cliffs, N.J., 1961; Friedlander, G., and Kennedy, J. W., "Nuclear and Radiochemistry," Wiley, New York, 1955; Bleuler, E., and Goldsmith, G. J., "Experimental Nucleonics," Rinehart, New York, 1957.

[2] Wahl, A. C., and Bonner, N. A., "Radioactivity Applied to Chemistry," Wiley, New York, 1951.

[3] Stranks, D. R., and Wilkins, R. G., Chem. Revs., 57, 743 (1957).

[4] Meinke, W. W., Anal. Chem., 32, 104R (1960), and preceding Annual Reviews issues.

[5] Annual Reviews of Nuclear Science, Annual Reviews, Palo Alto, California.

obtained by the altering of naturally occurring isotopic ratios.
Moreover, although the manipulative procedures for the two kinds
of nuclides are identical in principle, more care is required
with radionuclides in practice. This difference results from two
causes: (1) the greater possibility of assay error as a result of
contamination in the case of radionuclides, and (2) the possible
effects of radiation on personnel.

On the other hand, certain considerations apply to both kinds
of nuclides. For example, many radionuclides can be obtained
carrier-free, and stable nuclides may be employed at virtually
carrier-free concentrations, but abnormal behavior has been
reported under these conditions and should be expected.[2,3]
This fact must be considered in manipulation as well as in assaying. Similarly, isotope exchange is possible for stable nuclides
as well as for radionuclides.[2,3] This fact constitutes another
potential source of error; alternatively, this process is extremely
useful for labeling with both kinds of nuclides. Moreover,
kinetic isotope effects are observed for both kinds of nuclides,[2,3]
a fact that must be kept in mind in tracer work, where the identical behavior of corresponding compounds containing isotopic
nuclides is generally assumed.

2. HANDLING OF MICRO- AND MILLICURIE AMOUNTS OF RADIONUCLIDES

A. Radiological Safety

In common with other chemicals, radionuclides present health
hazards when used, or disposed of, improperly. The individual
effects are dependent upon: (1) the type of radiation and its half-
life, (2) the nature of the chemical compound involved, and
(3) the physiological affinity of the particular element. These
hazards may be classified as external or internal, depending
upon whether exposure results from penetrating radiation or
from irradiation by ingested material. The latter hazard is
more likely where volatile or powdered substances are involved,
while the former is important when working with millicurie or
larger quantities of hard gamma or positron emitters, but seldom
with microcurie amounts of beta emitters. A concise summary
of the pertinent factors is given by Overman and Clark,[1] who
list numerous references to the literature. More detailed
treatment of this subject can be found in the various National
Bureau of Standards Handbooks, which are cited below, as well
as in Boursnell's book.[6]

The user of radionuclides should possess at least a general
understanding of the nature and properties of the several kinds of
radiations that he is likely to encounter. In the case of reactor-

---

[6] Boursnell, J. C., "Safety Techniques for Radioactive
Tracers," Cambridge University Press, New York, 1958.

produced nuclides, these consist primarily of beta (plus or minus) and gamma rays, while the fission products decay primarily by beta-minus emission. Such information is available in introductory texts.[1] In addition, the user should have some familiarity with the following subjects: maximum permissible exposure (M. P. E.),[7] use of survey and monitoring instruments,[8] safe handling of radionuclides,[9] design of radioisotope laboratories,[10] shielding and storage,[11] decontamination,[12] and waste disposal.[13]

Although microcurie quantities of certain nuclides are exempt, in domestic laboratories an Atomic Energy Commission license is required for possession of larger amounts or of other nuclides[14]; and users are required to comply with federal regulations.[15] Universities frequently have internal licensing practices as well to facilitate sound health physics discipline. Procurement sources are most often the National Laboratories[16] or foreign atomic-energy agencies, but may be industrial suppliers,[17] both for stable and radionuclides.

---

[7] U.S. National Committee on Radiation Protection, "Permissible Dose from External Sources of Ionizing Radiation: Recommendations," Washington, 1954 (Natl. Bur. Standards Handbook 59, with April 15, 1958, insert).

[8] U.S. National Committee on Radiation Protection, "Radiological Monitoring Methods and Instruments," Washington, 1952 (Natl. Bur. Standards Handbook 51).

[9] U.S. National Committee on Radiation Protection, "Safe Handling of Radioisotopes," Washington, 1949 (Natl. Bur. Standards Handbook 42).

[10] Ward, D. R., "Design of Laboratories for Safe Use of Radioisotopes," U.S.A.E.C. Rep. AECU-2226, 1952; Levy, H.A., Ind. Eng. Chem., 41, 248 (1949).

[11] U.S. National Committee on Radiation Protection, "Protection against Radiations from Radium, Cobalt-60, and Cesium-137," Washington, 1954 (Natl. Bur. Standards Handbook 54).

[12] U.S. National Committee on Radiation Protection, "Control and Removal of Contamination in Laboratories," Washington, 1951 (Natl. Bur. Standards Handbook 48).

[13] U.S. National Committee on Radiation Protection "Recommendations for the Disposal of Carbon-14 Wastes," Washington, 1953 (Natl. Bur. Standards Handbook 53).

[14] "Licensing of Byproduct Material,"Part 30, Chap. I, Title 10, "Federal Register," Vol. 21, No. 6, Jan. 11, 1956

[15] "Standards for Protection against Radiation,"Part 20, Chap. I, Title 10, "Federal Register," Vol. 22, No. 19, Jan. 29, 1957 (amended May 1957).

[16] Oak Ridge National Laboratory, "Radioisotopes, Special Materials and Services," Oak Ridge, Tenn., revised March 1959.

[17] "The Isotope Index: The Complete Purchasing Guide to the Isotopes," Scientific Equipment Company, Indianapolis, Ind.

B. Special Apparatus

Although cumbersome apparatus is often required for work
with higher levels of activity, it is seldom necessary at the
microcurie level, or even millicurie level for some nuclides.
At these lower levels, the special apparatus generally consists of
a modification of commonly used types.[18] The primary purpose
of such apparatus is to avoid ingestion as well as general contamination of other equipment and especially detectors, since even
nonremovable activity may contribute to the background error in
assaying. A secondary purpose of special design equipment is
the conservation of material, since in tracer work the amounts
of chemicals that are manipulated are generally small, and micro
or semimicro techniques are widely employed. These subjects
are treated in several texts.[1,19] Sources of commercially
available apparatus are listed in the annual Buyer's Guide issues
of Nucleonics.[20]

3. GENERAL ASPECTS OF RADIOCHEMICAL MANIPULATION

A. Preparation of Samples for Assay

Radionuclides may be assayed in the solid, liquid, or gaseous
state, the choice in each case depending upon the size of sample
available, its chemical nature, and the detection efficiency for
the radiation emitted by the nuclide in question. This last
criterion will be considered in greater detail in Sec. 4.

Solid samples may be prepared by evaporation of solutions or
slurries, by filtration or centrifugation of precipitates, and by
electrodeposition.[1,21] Great sensitivity can be realized with
the last method, since very thin samples having negligible self-
absorption (for all radiotracers except H^3), are obtainable.
Electrodepostion also has the advangage of greater reproducibility, since sample distribution is potentially more uniform.
Apparatus and procedures are given in the introductory texts
cited above.[1,19,21]

Liquid and gaseous samples are prepared by conventional
methods, with suitable precautions taken to avoid loss of activity.
These will be discussed further in Sec. 4.

---

[18] Bizzell, O. M., "Equipment for Radioisotope Laboratories,"
U.S.A.E.C. Rep. AECU-2875, 1954.

[19] Cook, G. B., and Duncan, J. F., "Modern Radiochemical
Practice," Oxford University Press, New York, 1952.

[20] Nucleonics, Nov. 1960 and preceding November issues.

[21] Chase, G. D., "Principles of Radioisotope Methodology,"
Burgess, Minneapolis, 1959.

B. Separation Procedures

Some separation of the desired compound is generally necessary either prior to, or as part of, the preparation of the sample for assay. For this purpose, the usual analytical techniques are employed.[1,22] They include: (1) precipitation or coprecipitation, (2) electrodeposition, (3) solvent extraction, (4) ion exchange or adsorption chromatography, (5) distillation, and (6) gas generation. These subjects are treated in several texts[1,2,23] and in a review paper.[24] Occasionally, recoil resulting from the decay process will facilitate a separation, e.g., in an isomeric transition accompanied by internal conversion.[25]

C. General Considerations

In a number of cases, carrier-free nuclides may be prepared[26] and used,[2,27] but special precausions are frequently necessary.[28] In many cases, the addition of carrier is required for separation purposes. An isotopic carrier must be in the same chemical form as the tracer nuclide,[1,2] and adequate precautions should be taken to ensure this condition. Nonisotopic carriers are sometimes used where a high specific activity is required for the assay sample or where isotopic carriers are unavailable.

It should be recalled that carrier-free nuclides may behave differently than at macro concentrations, that isotope effects[2,3] may cause a difference in behavior of corresponding compounds containing different nuclides of a given element, and that loss of the label through exchange[2,3] is an omnipresent danger. Another, although less common consideration, is the change in chemical behavior which may result from oxidation-state changes accompanying recoil as a consequence of the decay process.

22 Walton, H. F., "Principles and Methods of Chemical Analysis," Prentice-Hall, New York, 1952.

23 Siri, W. E., "Isotopic Tracers and Nuclear Radiations," McGraw-Hill, New York, 1949.

24 Finston, H. L., and Miskel, J., Ann. Rev. Nuclear Sci., 5, 269 (1955).

25 Sun, K. H., and Pecjak, F. A., Nucleonics, 14 (11), 122 (1956).

*26 Murin, A. N., Nefedov, V. D., and Yutlandov, I. A., Uspekhi Khim., 24, 527 (1955); trans. by T. Turton: AERE-Lib/Trans (British)-722 (U.S. Atomic Energy Comm., Nuclear Sci. Abstr., 11, 470 (1957).)

27 Evans, J. B., and Willard, J. E., J. Am. Chem. Soc., 78, 2908 (1956).

28 Preiss, I. L., and Fink, R. W., Nucleonics, 15 (10), 108 (1957).

4. RADIOASSAY

A number of methods are listed in the review by Stranks and Wilkins[3] as well as in the reviews by Meinke.[4]

A. Detection Instruments and Principles

Geiger-Muller counters. Radionuclides are most commonly determined by the ionization or excitation produced[23] as a result of their interactions with matter.[1, 29] Although very accurate measurements can be made by means of a simple inexpensive electroscope,[1] the time-consuming nature of this procedure limits it to special uses and rather high activity levels. The most widely used instrument is the Geiger-Müller (G. M.) counter, which employs an ionization chamber of such electrode design, and under sufficiently high voltage, as to produce complete breakdown of the gas for each ionizing event within the active volume of the tube.[1, 29, 30] These counters are available with very thin end windows, or as windowless gas-flow counters, for the detection of soft beta and alpha particles from solid and liquid samples.[1, 23] For hard gamma radiation the low percentage of energy lost within the detector is increased by use of a dense filling gas or is compensated for by the use of larger counter tubes[1, 29, 31] than are normally employed in alpha and beta radioassay.

Liquid samples emitting gammas or high-energy betas may be counted with a dipping-type or jacketed-wall counter.[1, 32, 33] Methods for the radioassay of gases will be considered in Sec. 4C.

Proportional counters. Proportional counters are ionization chambers, similar in design to G. M. counters.[29, 31] In contrast with the latter, proportional counters are operated at voltages insufficient to produce complete breakdown while still adequate for ion multiplication. Their name arises from the fact that the size of each resultant pulse is roughly proportional to the energy of the ionizing event producing it. These counters have the advantage of a lower background counting rate for a given volume, and of smaller coincidence loss, and make possible the discrimination of undesired activity on the basis of pulse size. Their disadvantage is cost, as higher voltage power supplies, and frequently linear amplifiers, are required. Proportional counters are

29 Price, W. J., "Nuclear Radiation Detection, " McGraw-Hill, New York, 1958.

30 Taylor, D., "The Measurement of Radio Isotopes, " Methuen, London, 1951.

31 Korff, S. A., "Electron and Nuclear Counters: Theory and Use, " 2nd ed., Van Nostrand, Princeton, 1955.

32 Bruner, H. D., and Perkinson, J. D., Nucleonics, 10 (10), 57 (1952).

33 Solomon, A. K., and Estes, H. D., Rev. Sci. Instr., 19, 47 (1948).

used with those samples already mentioned in connection with
G. M. counters.

Scintillation counters. The greatest detection efficiency for
gamma rays is realized in the use of a scintillation counter, which
can also be used for betas and alphas through choice of the proper
phosphor.[29, 34] The detection principle involved is the phosphor-
escent excitation of a solid or solution as a result of the primary
or secondary ionization produced by the interaction of radiation
with matter.[1, 2] Each ionizing event produces a light pulse which
is detected by means of a photomultiplier tube. Liquid scintillation counting is particularly useful for low-energy beta emitters
and will be discussed below.

Pulse heights are proportional to energy loss, and hence
permit discrimination, as in the case of proportional counters.
Moreover, since gamma rays interact with matter by a number
of processes different from those of alpha and beta radiation, the
resultant light pulses from a given gamma-emitting nuclide have a
characteristic intensity distribution called the scintillation
spectrum, which is useful in identifying the particular nuclide.
As with proportional counters, linear amplifiers are frequently
required. For gamma spectroscopy a single channel analyzer
or similar equipment is needed. Solid, liquid, and even gaseous
samples can be used, either as separate sources, or homo-
geneously or heterogeneously mixed with the scintillator.

Auxiliary apparatus. Pulses from the G. M. counter are of
constant height, independent of the nuclide involved, and generally
of sufficient amplitude to be used directly with a scaler.[29, 35]
Proportional and scintillation counters, on the other hand, almost
always require the use of an amplifier in the circuit before the
pulses are fed into a scaler. Moreover, for pulse-height
measurement, a linear amplifier[29] is required; and finally, if
an energy-distribution measurement is required, a pulse-height
analyzer[29] is needed as well.

Radioautography[23] is seldom used as a routine analytical
method.

B. Assay Errors

Counting errors. Routine assay procedures seldom, if ever,
involve absolute determination of activity[1]; instead, relative
measurements are made. Nevertheless it is necessary to consider the factors that influence the count rate from a given
sample in order to minimize the possible errors.[1, 23, 36] These
include: (1) the intrinsic detector efficiency for the particular
radiation, considering the sensitive volume; (2) the geometry or

[34] "Scintillation Counting-1958," Nucleonics, 16 (6), 54 (1958).

[35] Strong, J., et al., "Procedures in Experimental Physics,"
Prentice-Hall, Englewood Cliffs, N.J., 1943.

[36] Manov, G. G., Ann Rev. Nuclear Sci., 4, 51 (1954).

fraction of 4π solid angle subtended by the detector; (3) the absorption of radiation by the sample, its container, and the detector housing; (5) the dead time or coincidence losses; (6) the statistics of nuclear decay; (7) the background count; and (8) the decay of radioactivity from the sample.

Ionization-chamber instruments, such as the G.M. and proportional counters, are very efficient for alphas and betas. The most serious problem is absorption, especially for alphas and soft betas, where windowless gas-flow counters are preferred.[37] A second problem encountered in end-window detection is the reproducibility of sample location, affecting geometry. This method requires a fair degree of manipulative skill for good precision. Self-absorption is most easily maintained constant by the use of infinite-thickness samples.[1] A similar consideration applies to backscattering,[1,23,38] where infinite-thickness sample cups are used. Background radiation, coincidence loss, and nuclear decay can be measured directly or calculated and taken into account.[1,23,39] Statistical errors are eliminated by accumulating a sufficiently large number of counts.[1] The problems of absorption and scattering are almost negligible for gamma emitters, as is the problem of sample-position reproducibility in jacketed-wall[32,33] or internal gas-flow counters.[37]

Other errors. Further errors in assaying may result from the neglect of possible daughter-product activity, and from loss of the label by exchange[2,3] during the separation process or prior to it.

C. Soft-Beta Emitters

As was mentioned above, the low penetrating power of soft-beta (and alpha) emitters makes absorption the most serious problem in obtaining adequate counting efficiency. Various methods have been employed to minimize or eliminate this difficulty. The sample may be introduced directly into the G.M. or proportional counter as a solid,[40] liquid,[41] or part of the filling gas.[42] Either solids or liquids may be counted by dissolving in

37 Jackson, F. L., and Lampe, H. W., Anal. Chem., 28, 1735 (1956).

38 Müller, R. H., Anal. Chem., 29, 969 (1957); Müller, D. C., Anal. Chem., 29, 975 (1957).

39 Seliger, H. H., and Schwebel, A., Nucleonics, 12 (7), 54, (1954).

40 Robinson, C. V., Science, 112, 198 (1950).

41 Schwebel, A., Isbell, F. S., and Mayer, J. D., J. Research Natl. Bur. Standards, 53, 221 (1954).

42 Bernstein, W., and Ballentine, R., Rev. Sci. Instr., 21, 158 (1950).

a suitable liquid scintillator,[43] and liquids may be counted in a
plastic scintillator dish.[44] Gases may also be assayed in an
ionization chamber[45] using a vibrating-reed or vacuum-tube
electrometer to measure the ionization current, or in a gas
scintillation counter.[44]

Methods for soft-beta emitters are listed in detail in several
texts[1,46] and reviews,[3-5,47] and will be discussed more fully
in connection with the use of H^3 (Chap. 3) and S^{35} (Chap. 7).
It should be noted that while gas counting and liquid scintillation
counting are the most sensitive methods for soft-beta emitters,
they require more manipulation of the sample than does the
assay of solids or liquids by means of an end-window, or windowless, detector.

D. Isotope Dilution

A very important procedure frequently used in the assay of
stable as well as radionuclides is the method of isotope
dilution.[1,48] This procedure permits quantitative determination
of the nuclide content of a sample without quantitative separation,
hence it is useful where otherwise adequate separation methods
are lacking. Isotope dilution can, however, be a source of error
in tracer studies.[49]

5. ASSAY FOR STABLE NUCLIDES

The determination of stable nuclides is accomplished primarily
through the use of the mass spectrometer[23,50] although other
methods are available for the lightest elements, particularly
hydrogen.[3]

---

[43] Rosenthal, D. J., and Anger, H. O., Rev. Sci. Instr., 25,
670 (1954).

[44] Stranks, D. R., J. Sci. Instr., 33, 1 (1956).

[45] Brownell, G. L., and Lockhart, H. S., Nucleonics, 10 (2),
26 (1952).

[46] Calvin, M., Heidelberger, C., Reid, J. C., Tolbert, B. M.,
and Yankwich, P. F., "Isotopic Carbon," Wiley, New York,
1949.

[47] Anderson, E. C., and Hayes, F. N., Ann. Rev. Nuclear
Sci., 6, 303 (1956).

[48] Gest, H., Kamen, M. D., and Reiner, J. M., Arch.
Biochem., 12, 273 (1947); Rosenblum, C., Nucleonics, 14 (5),
58 (1956).

[49] Ropp, G. A., J. Chem. Educ., 34, 60 (1957).

[50] Robertson, A. J. B., "Mass Spectrometry," Methuen,
London, 1954.

A. Mass Spectrometer

Stable-isotope assay by means of the modern mass spectrometer can be accomplished with a precision of $\pm$ 0.1 per cent,
whereas radionuclide assay of 0.5 per cent standard deviation
requires great care. Moreover, the position of an isotopic
nuclide within a molecule can often be deduced from the frag-
mentation pattern of that molecule within the mass spectrometer;
although caution is necessary because a given mass is not always
uniquely associated with a particular fragment.[50]

This method[23] involves the introduction of the sample, in
gaseous form, into the evacuated spectrometer followed by
electron bombardment by accelerated thermionic electrons. The
resultant positively charged molecular fragments are then accelerated and focused according to mass, either electrostatically,
electromagnetically, or by means of radio-frequency pulsing
applied to a series of grids within the spectrometer.[51] Ion
currents are detected and measured by means of various kinds of
electrometers or ion multipliers.[35,52] The measured ion currents
permit the calculation of isotopic ratios, after standardization
with samples of known ratio.[50,51] Solid and liquid samples can
be used if vaporized by means of the appropriate apparatus, but
gaseous samples are most common.[53] Much current information
on apparatus and methods for isotope-ratio measurement can be
found in the annual reviews issues of Analytical Chemistry.[54]

B. Special Methods for Deuterium

Hydrogen occupies a uniquely favorable position because the
mass ratios of its nuclides, H^2:H^1 and H^3:H^1, are larger than
those of the isotopic nuclides of any other element. Thus
differences in properties between the unlabeled and labeled
compound are easily distinguished, a fact that permits the
determination of isotopic ratios by a variety of physical methods
in addition to mass spectrometry. These include: (a) density
measurements, (b) absorption spectrophotometry, (c) thermal
conductivity, and (d) refractometry.[3,23,55,56] For heavy water,

51 Stewart, D. W., Mass Spectrometry, in "Technique of
Organic Chemistry," Vol. 1, Part 4, Interscience, New York,
1960.
52 Kerwin, L., Mass Spectroscopy, in "Advances in Electronics and Electron Physics," Vol. 8, Academic, New York, 1956.
53 Hintenberger, H., Experientia, 12, 449 (1956).
54 Diebler, V. H., and Reese, R. M., Anal. Chem., 32,
211R (1960).
55 Kirshenbaum, I., "Physical Properties and Analysis of
Heavy Water," McGraw-Hill, New York, 1951.
56 Dole, M., Chem. Revs., 51, 263 (1952).

density measurement affords as good precision as routine mass spectrometry and has the advantages of lower cost and greater ease of manipulation. [23]

6. REVIEW OF TERMS AND EQUATIONS

Activity. In a precise sense, the activity, or absolute activity, of a sample is synonymous with its disintegration rate and is usually expressed in millicuries or microcuries. The milli-curie is defined as a disintegration rate of 3.700×10^7 disintegrations per second. [57] Another use of the term activity makes it synonymous with the counting rate observed for a given sample. This latter usage is imprecise because the over-all counting efficiency, which determines the ratio of counting rate to disintegration rate, is a variable, dependent upon many factors, as explained above. [1] The term specific activity [1] is commonly defined as the activity per unit weight (or volume) of sample, although in a precise sense it means the disintegration rate of 1 gram of the nuclide.

Background. The background counting rate is the observed counting rate in the absence of a sample. It is caused by the background radiation, which stems chiefly from two sources-- cosmic rays and the natural radioactivity present in the earth and in the materials of construction, [1] but which may arise also from accidental contamination and should thus be periodically determined.

Backscatter. This term is used to designate that radiation which is reflected (scattered) by the source mount. It is [1, 23, 38] primarily important in the cases of alpha and beta particles. The extent of backscattering depends upon the atomic number and thickness of the source-mount material as well as on the kind of radiation and its energy. At sufficiently great thickness (in-finite thickness) of source mount, the backscatter approaches a maximum value asymptotically.

Carrier. Radionuclides are used at concentrations far too small to permit many ordinary chemical operations; thus a carrier is used in order to facilitate the chemical processing. An isotopic carrier is one that is in the same chemical form as the radionuclide but contains a stable isotope of the radionuclide. [1] A nonisotopic carrier is one that will carry the radionuclide through a particular chemical process, but may be separated from the radionuclide by another chemical process. [1] A nonisotopic carrier has an atomic number (Z) different from that of the radio-nuclide.

---

[57] "Report of the International Commission on Radiological Units and Measurements," Natl. Bur. Standards Handbook 62, 1957.

Cross section. The absolute activity acquired by a given nuclide as a result of a nuclear reaction[1, 23] depends upon several factors; (1) the number of target nuclei, (2) the flux of bombarding radiation (3) the length of irradiation, and (4) the nuclear cross section of the target.[1] It is thus a measure of the activity per unit flux which a single nuclide would acquire in infinite bombardment time. The unit of cross section is the barn and is equal to 10^{-24} cm^2.

Daughter activity. When a nucleus decays, the product is either a stable or radioactive nucleus. In the latter case, the resultant activity is called the daughter activity. The term parent activity is used for that radiation which is emitted in the formation of the daughter.[1]

Decay energy. The process of nuclear decay (disintegration) consists of the formation of a product nucleus from a parent nucleus, accompanied by the emission of radiation. A consequence of the law of mass-energy conservation is the following relationship among the masses of the parent nucleus M_A, the product nucleus M_B, the emitted particle radiation M_C, and the energy evolved (or decay energy) $E_D : M_A - (M_B + M_C) = E_D$. This decay energy consists of the total kinetic energy imparted by the decay process to the nuclei and particle radiation as well as the energy of any accompanying electromagnetic radiation.[58]

Half-life. Nuclear decay (disintegration) is a statistical process and follows first-order kinetics.[1] The number of radioactive nuclei remaining at time t is called N_t and is related to the number present at any arbitrary time t_0 by the equation $N_t = N_0 e^{-\lambda t}$, where λ and t are expressed in the same units. The half-life $t_{1/2}$ is related to the decay constant λ by the equation $t_{1/2} = \ln 2 / \lambda$, and represents the time required for N_t to diminish to $N_0/2$.

Half-time. This term is applied to the process of isotope exchange in the same way that it is used in connection with the kinetics of any chemical reaction, and is analogous to the term, half-life, as applied to radioactive decay. The half-time of exchange $t_{1/2}$ is the time necessary for the fraction of exchange F to assume the numerical value 1/2.[2, 3]

Isotope effect. Differences in properties between a compound containing one isotope of a given element and the corresponding compound containing another isotope of that element are called isotope effects.[2, 23] These differences frequently permit a separation of the nuclides. Differences in behavior of isotopic molecules are expected on both classical and quantum mechanical grounds. The effect diminishes with increasing mass of the isotopic nuclides.

Isotope exchange. When a given nuclide interchanges between two different chemical forms, the reaction is said to be an isotope

58 Lapp, R. E., and Andrews, H. L., "Nuclear Radiation Physics," Prentice-Hall, Englewood Cliffs, N. J., 1954.

exchange reaction. Such exchange is common, but is not detectable in the absence of a tracer nuclide.[2,3]

Isotope dilution. In the absence of a quantitative separation procedure, the amount of a given compound present, x, in a mixture may be determined by adding a known quantity of labeled compound y, whose specific activity A_i is known also. It is then merely necessary to isolate a small, but pure, sample of the desired compound. The result is calculated from a measurement of the final specific activity A_f by means of the equation $x = y[(A_i/A_f)-1]$. An inverse technique may be used to calculate the amount of labeled material present.[1]

Mev. The energies involved in nuclear decay processes are usually expressed in the units electron volts (ev) or million electron volts (Mev). An electron volt represents the energy required to raise 1 electron through a potential difference of 1 volt.[1,58] For 1 mole of electrons, the energy required would be 23.052 kcal.

Nuclide. A nuclide is a particular atomic species, having a unique atomic number and mass number. Nuclides having the same atomic number are said to be isotopes (of the same element).[59]

Radiation. The energetic particles or electromagnetic waves accompanying nuclear decay are broadly referred to as radiation, although the term is used also in other contexts. Radiation due to nuclear decay consists chiefly of alpha particles, beta particles, and gamma rays. The latter two are classified as soft or hard (low energy or high energy), corresponding to the penetrating power of the radiation. Such a designation is quite arbitrary.

Reactor. A device utilizing nuclear fission to produce a high-neutron flux is called a reactor. One important use is the production of radionuclides from stable ones.[1,23,58]

Recoil. The conservation of momentum requires that a nucleus undergoing decay should recoil in a direction opposite to that of the emitted radiation. If the recoil energy is sufficiently large and appropriately directed, a chemical bond may be broken, resulting in ion or radical formation. This is the case for certain n,γ reactions which are referred to as Szilard-Chalmers reactions.[1,2]

Statistics. Counting rates measured on a single sample vary (after correction for decay) because of the statistical nature of the decay process.[1] If a Poisson distribution is assumed for these fluctuations about the true value, then the standard deviation σ of a single observation of N counts is $\sigma = \sqrt{N}$. The probable error will be 0.67σ.[60]

---

59 Kohman, T., Am. J. Phys., 15, 356 (1947).

60 Rainwater, L. J., and Wu, C. S., Nucleonics, 1, 60 (1947).

2

Inorganic Deuterium Compounds

HENRY L. CRESPI and JOSEPH J. KATZ
Argonne National Laboratory
Argonne, Illinois

1. INTRODUCTION

This chapter describes the syntheses of inorganic compounds in which hydrogen is fully replaced by deuterium, the stable hydrogen isotope of mass $2\,(H^2, D)$. This heavy isotope of hydrogen is designated by the symbol D.

Deuterium of high isotopic purity is prepared on a large scale by the U.S. Atomic Energy Commission. Commercial catalogs list a considerable number of compounds of deuterium.* Heavy water, D_2O, is a particularly important chemical and biological reagent, and is available in large quantities at reasonable cost. It is the most important industrial compound of deuterium and the starting point for most syntheses involving deuterium.

The physical properties of heavy water and some methods of analysis have been given in authoritative detail by Kirshenbaum[1]; this review summarizes much of the data obtained during World War II researches. A bibliography of the earlier literature (through 1945 in Chemical Abstracts) has been compiled by Kimball, [2] and this has been followed by bibliographies on deuterium (and tritium) covering the years 1945 through 1954[3,4]

---

* The "Isotope Index" issued by the Scientific Equipment Corporation, Indianapolis, lists all deuterium compounds commercially available.

[1] Kirshenbaum, J., "Physical Properties and Analysis of Heavy Water," McGraw-Hill, New York, 1951.

[2] Kimball, A. H., "Bibliography of Research on Heavy Hydrogen Compounds," McGraw-Hill, New York, 1949.

[3] Brown, L. M., Friedman, A. S., and Beckett, C. W., "Bibliography of Research on Deuterium and Tritium Compounds 1945 to 1952," Natl. Bur. Standards Circ. 562, U.S. Government Printing Office, Washington, 1957.

[4] Johnson, V. R., Brown, L. M., and Friedman, A. S., "Bibliography of Research on Deuterium and Tritium Compounds 1953 and 1954," Natl. Bur. Standards Circ. 562, U.S. Government Printing Office, Washington, 1957.

compiled by the National Bureau of Standards. An early summary
of constants and numerical data is also available.[5] Work on
biological effects of deuterium through 1951 has been reviewed,[6]
and more recent trends in deuterium chemistry and biology have
been the subject of a recent conference.[7] An excellent review of
the chemistry of deuterium and heavy water appears in the
comprehensive treatise of Pascal.[8]

Many deuterio compounds can be made quite simply by exchange
with D_2O. However, one must take care to exchange exhaustively
with a large excess of heavy water in order to obtain a nearly
isotopically pure product. A recent publication[9] gives a useful
theoretical examination of the problem of obtaining deuterated
compounds by repeated exchange, particularly if a number of
equivalent hydrogen atoms are present.

The synthetic methods given in this chapter are grouped
according to the organization of the periodic table, beginning with
D_2 and ending with $DClO_4$. A few miscellaneous compounds not
easily classified are included also. The synthesis of numerous
organic compounds with deuterium has already been described.[10]
Table 1 lists all the compounds whose syntheses are described here.

2, HYDROGEN-D$_2$[11,12]

$$2UD_3 \rightleftarrows 2U + 3D_2$$

A. Procedure

Pure deuterium gas, free of all contaminants including the
noble gases, can be prepared by the decomposition of uranium

---

[5] Champetier, G., "Annual Tables of Constants and Numerical
Data: 1. Deuterium and Deuterium Compounds," Hermann & Cie,
Paris, 1937.

[6] Morowitz, H. J., and Brown, L. M., "Biological Effects of
Deuterium," Natl. Bur. Standards Rep. 2179, U.S. Government
Printing Office, Washington, 1953.

[7] Deuterium Isotope Effects in Chemistry and Biology, Ann.
N.Y. Acad. Sci., 84, Art. 16 (1960).

[8] Pascal, P., "Nouveau Traite de Chemie Minerale," Vol. 1,
Masson & Cie, Paris, 1956.

[9] Buser, E., Burer, T., and Guntherd, H. H., Helv. Chim.
Acta, 43, 161 (1960).

[10] Murray, A., and Williams, D. L., "Organic Syntheses with
Isotopes," Part II, Interscience, New York, 1958.

[11] Newton, A. S., MDDC-724 (Manhattan Project Declassified
Document), Jan. 1, 1947.

[12] Spedding, F. H., Newton, A. S., Warf, J. C., Johnson, O.,
Nottorf, B. W., Johns, I. B., and Daane, A. H., Nucleonics, 4,
4 (1949).

Table 1
Compounds Whose Syntheses are Presented in This Chapter

D_2	LiD	B_5D_9	SiD_4	ND_3	D_2O	DF
	NaD		SiD_3H	PD_3	D_2O_2	DCl
DH	KD		SiD_3Cl	P_2D_4	D_2S	DBr
	RbD		Si_2D_6	AsD_3	D_2Se	DI
	CsD		Si_2OD_6	SbD_3	D_2SO_4	$DClO_4$
	$LiBD_4$		TiD_2	DNO_3	ND_4OD	
	NaOD		GeD_4	D_3PO_3		
	$NaDCO_3$		Ge_2D_6	$Ba(D_2PO_2)_2$		
	KOD		Ge_3D_8	D_3PO_4		
	CuD		GeD_3H			
			$GeDH_3$			
			SnD_4			

Miscellaneous (by exchange)		
D_3BO_3		KD_2AsO_4
$ND_2OD \cdot DCl$		$Ag_2D_3IO_6$
$CuSO_4 \cdot 5D_2O$		$(ND_4)_2D_3IO_6$
$SrCl_2 \cdot 6D_2O$		Metal ammines
KD_2PO_4		Sulfamic acid
$NaDSO_4$		

deuteride. An apparatus that has a capacity of about 1 1/2 moles of deuterium is convenient. About 250 g of uranium turnings (lumps of metal can be used but turnings are more convenient) are cleaned to free them of oil, and treated with 6 N nitric acid to remove all oxide and to leave a bright surface. [Caution: Uranium turnings are subject to spontaneous combustion in air and may be dangerous!] The cleaned turnings are then rinsed thoroughly and dried; a final rinse with acetone to facilitate the drying is convenient. The turnings are then placed in a 300-ml round-bottom flask and sealed to a vacuum system through a medium-porosity fritted-glass disc and a stopcock. (The fritted disc is important; it must be present between the flask and the stopcock since the deuteride powder sometimes blows around in the system if deuterium gas is removed too rapidly. The disc serves as a dust filter and prevents contamination of the stopcock and the remainder of the vacuum system. If necessary, a fine glass-wool filter can be used with equally satisfactory results.) The bulb should be far enough away from the stopcock so that heating the bulb to 450° will not overheat the stopcock. A resistance heater capable of heating the flask to about 450° with fairly uniform heating is provided. A thermocouple in the air space between the flask and the heater is required to measure the temperature. It is convenient to have this connected to a Capacitrol or other temperature regulator, but this is not absolutely necessary since hand control of the temperature by a rheostat or a variable transformer is quite satisfactory.

The glass bulb is first thoroughly evacuated and then flushed by filling with deuterium and evacuating several times. It is then heated to 235° under vacuum to remove the adsorbed gases from the uranium. Deuterium at 1 atm pressure is then admitted to the bulb and the turnings are converted to uranium deuteride. The temperature will rise considerably because of the heat of reaction. After the reaction is finished, excess deuterium is pumped away, while keeping the temperature at about 235° (Note 1). As the decomposition pressure of uranium deuteride is about 6 mm at this temperature, some uranium deuteride will necessarily decompose. The temperature is then raised to 385°, and the flask evacuated a few times by pumping off the gas in the uranium deuteride bulb in short cycles. This procedure removes all extraneous gases from the bulb. All deuterium subsequently removed from the bulb will be pure. The deuterium can be removed from the bulb at any desired pressure by regulating the temperature of decomposition.

When all the uranium deuteride has been decomposed, the uranium deuteride is easily regenerated by connecting it to a deuterium tank (Note 2) and admitting deuterium to the partially sintered mass of uranium metal that remains. This finely divided metal will react with deuterium at low temperatures, and usually no heating is necessary to start the regeneration. After the deuteride is completely re-formed, the system is flushed a few times and is again ready for use.

B. Notes

1. The temperatures for the preparation given here are calculated from the equation given for the decomposition pressure of UD_3:

$$\log P_{mm} = \left[-4500/T(\,^\circ K)\right] + 9.43$$

since the procedure as given in detail in the literature is for the ordinary hydrogen system. The equation gives the decomposition pressure of UD_3 as a function of temperature over most of the composition range between UD_3 and U.

2. A convenient method of preparing uranium deuteride and pure deuterium from heavy water is by reaction of D_2O vapor with uranium turnings at 600 to 700°:

$$D_2O + U \longrightarrow UO_2 + 2D_2$$

The resultant deuterium is converted to uranium deuteride with more uranium metal at 250°. A liquid-air trap between the reducing agent and the uranium collector suffices to keep the uranium deuteride free of oxide.

C. Other Preparations

Deuterium gas can also be prepared by electrolysis[13,14] or by the reaction of D_2O with magnesium[15-17] or sodium.[17]

3. HYDROGEN-d_1[18,19]

$$LiAlH_4 + 4D_2O \rightarrow LiOD + Al(OD)_3 + 4HD$$

---

13 Winn, M. M., J. Sci. Instr., **28**, 152 (1951).

14 Dutt, P. K., J. Sci. Instr., **37**, 352 (1960).

15 Knowlton, T. W., J. Research Natl. Bur. Standards, **19**, 605 (1937).

16 Holding, A. F. LeC., and Ross, W. A., J. Appl. Chem. (London), 8, 321 (1958).

17 Brauer, G., and Baudler, M., "Handbuch der Präparative Anorganischen Chemie," No. 1, Enke, Stuttgart, 1951.

18 Fookson, A., Pomerantz, P., and Rich, E. H., J. Research Natl. Bur. Standards, **47**, 31 (1951)

19 Fookson, A. et al, Science, **112**, 748 (1950).

A. Procedure

Apparatus. Hydrogen deuteride was prepared in the apparatus described by Dibeler,[20] except that the reagent was added with a hypodermic syringe through a Neoprene septum and a magnetic stirrer was included in the flask. The apparatus consists of a 250-ml, two-necked flask, with stirring bar, connected by a ground-glass joint to a reflux condenser that is in turn connected through cold traps to a diffusion pump and 5-liter collecting bulbs. Stopcocks permit evacuation or admission of gas to any part of the system. The free opening of the flask is fitted with a rubber septum. The distillation apparatus of Scott and Brickwedde[21, 22] was used for the low-temperature distillation of the HD. The still consists of a boiler of about 5 ml capacity, a constantan heater, Monel helix section, and cold-finger condenser. The boiler and rectifying section are vacuum-jacketed. The entire still is immersed in liquid hydrogen. A similar distillation method is described by Clusius and Starke.[23]

Preparation. HD was prepared in 5 to 10 liter batches by the method of Wender, Friedel, and Orchin.[24] About 160 ml of purified n-butyl ether is distilled from sodium into the reaction flask. A 30 to 40 per cent excess of $LiAlH_4$ (Note 1) is added. The septum is fitted, the flask attached to the reflux condenser, and the contents frozen with liquid nitrogen. After evacuation, the mixture is heated to reflux for 1.5 hours. The mixture is then frozen, evacuated, and the D_2O added through the septum in three portions (150 per cent excess). The temperature is held at 0° or lower with a liquid nitrogen bath. The evolved gas is collected in 5-liter collecting bulbs and further purified by distillation. In terms of hydrogen isotopes, the final product is 99.8 per cent HD with a small percentage of nitrogen.

B. Notes

1. Available commercially from Metal Hydrides, Inc. Beverly, Massachusetts.

---

[20] Dibeler, V. H., J. Research Natl. Bur. Standards, **44**, 363 (1950).

[21] Brickwedde, F. G., and Scott, R. B., Phys. Rev., **55**, 672 (1939).

[22] Scott, R. B., and Brickwedde, F. G., Phys. Rev., 48, 483 (1935).

[23] Clusius, K., and Starke, K., Z. Naturforsch., 4a, 549 (1949).

[24] Wender, I., Friedel, R. A., and Orchin, M., J. Am. Chem. Soc., 71, 1140 (1949).

4. LITHIUM HYDRIDE-d[25]

$$2Li + D_2 \longrightarrow 2LiD$$

A. Procedure

Apparatus: The apparatus employed is illustrated in Fig. 1.

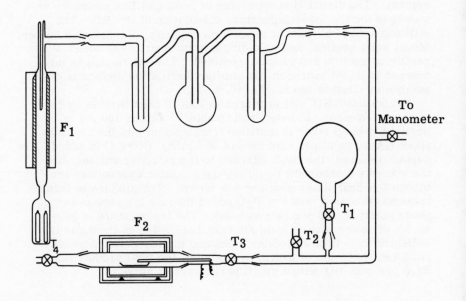

Fig. 1 Apparatus used in the preparation of LiD.

The furnace F_1 for the production of deuterium consists of a
Pyrex tube $(55 \times 2.6$ cm), at the lower end of which indentations
support a perforated iron disc covered with a plug of asbestos wool.
The outside of the tube is enclosed in two layers of asbestos paper,
wound with a heating element, and covered with a layer of fireclay
cement. This tube is then supported centrally in an asbestos
cement pipe, the intervening space being packed with asbestos wool.

[25] Holding, A. F. LeC., and Ross, W. A., J. Appl. Chem.
(London), **8**, 321 (1958).

A bulb containing two ampoules of deuterium oxide is sealed to the lower end of the furnace. This bulb is immersed in an oil bath. A thermocouple pocket is sealed in from the top of the furnace, extending half-way down the tube. Three traps are connected to the top of the furnace through a side arm by standard taper joints, the central trap containing high-vacuum oil to serve as a bubbler, the outer two being immersed in solid carbon dioxide/ alcohol mixture. The trap assembly is connected to a drying tube (P_2O_5) fitted with standard taper joints, a manometer capable of registering up to 95 cm of mercury, a 2-liter gas reservoir, and a stopcock T_2, for connection to a high-vacuum pump. The reservoir can be isolated by means of stopcock T_1.

The furnace F_2 for the production of lithium deuteride consists of a silica tube (46×3 cm) grooved spirally on the outside (10 turns per 2.5 cm) and fitted with standard taper male joints at both ends. A part of this tube (28 cm) is wound with a heating element (resistance 4.26 ohm per yard; total resistance 54 ohms), leaving portions (5 and 13 cm) uncovered at the ends. The covered portion of the tube is held centrally in an asbestos cement pipe (28×10 cm), and the intervening space is packed with asbestos wool. The cement pipe is placed in a heat-resistant box and the intervening space is packed with asbestos wool. The end of the silica tube is fitted with a joint carrying stopcock T_3, which connects this assembly to the rest of the apparatus. The other end of the tube was connected to stopcock T_4. Between the furnace and T_3, thermocouple wires are sealed in (Note 1). These wires extend to the center of the furnace and are insulated by a silica tube, both wires being then enclosed in another silica tube (diam. 5 mm), which is protected by a steel sheath.

The boat (14 cm long) to carry the lithium is constructed from steel tubing (diam. 2 cm), which is halved longitudinally and has welded ends. A steel guard tube (44×2.6 cm) is placed inside the silica tube.

The "dry box" used for the handling of lithium and lithium deuteride was of a conventional type. The desiccating agent is phosphorus pentoxide, and an atmosphere of dry nitrogen is maintained within the box.

Preparation. Furnace F_1 is filled through the side arm with (Grignard) magnesium turnings in the following sequence: 20 mesh (40 g), 30 mesh (30 g), 40 mesh (20 g), and less than 40 mesh (10 g). (If the charge is not graded, the tubes block during operation.) The apparatus is then assembled, and furnaces F_1 and F_2 are slowly heated to their maximum temperatures, 480 and 700°, respectively. At the same time the apparatus is evacuated through stopcock T_4. Furnace F_2 is then allowed to cool to room temperature, and while the apparatus is under vacuum but disconnected from the pump, the ampoules of deuterium oxide are broken by immersing the bulb containing them in a solid carbon dioxide/alcohol mixture. The frozen deuterium

oxide is allowed to warm to room temperature overnight, and is
left for a further day, during which time the pressure in the
apparatus rises to 30 to 40 cm Hg. The temperature of the deuterium oxide is slowly rased to 110 to 115° . When the pressure in the
apparatus is slightly greater than atmospheric, by opening T_4,
a slow stream of deuterium is passed through the furnace F_2, the
temperature of which is slowly raised to 700° . After 2 hours,
T_3 is closed and furnace F_2 is evacuated through T_4. This
process is repeated three times to reduce any oxidized iron in the
metallic components of furnace F_2. T_4 is then closed, T_3
opened, and the deuterium oxide and furnace F_2 cooled to room
temperature overnight, furnace F_1 cooling to 300° . Next day,
T_3 is closed and the steel boat rapidly transferred from furnace
F_2 to the "dry box." A piece of lithium (about 7 g) is cut from
the pure metal, washed three times in dry, light petroleum ether
(b. p. 60-80°), and placed in the steel boat, which is rapidly
returned to furnace F_2. Traces of solvent are removed by evacuating furnace F_2 through T_4 for half an hour. T_3 is opened,
the deuterium oxide heated to 110 to 115° , and the temperature of
furnace F_2 slowly raised to 350 to 440° , when the absoprtion.
of deuterium slowly begins. The temperature of furnace F_2 is
slowly increased, the rate of evolution and absorption of deuterium
being observed from the gas bubbler and manometer, respectively.
The pressure is not allowed to fall below 50 cm, by decreasing
the temperature of furnace F_2 when necessary. As the pressure
in the system increases, the temperature of furnace F_2 is
increased in stages of about 50° to its maximum temperature of
700° . Absorption is regarded as complete when there is no
observable decrease in pressure when furnace F_2 has been
maintained at 700° for 2 hours. The deuterium oxide and furnace
F_2 are allowed to cool to room temperature overnight, and the
temperature of furnace F_1 is reduced to 300° . Next day the
steel boat and guard tube are rapidly transferred to the "dry
box, " and after freeing the boat, the crystalline product is
broken up, using a hammer and chisel (Note 2).

B. Notes

1. Suitable sealing compounds are Edwards Picene, Apiezon Q
wax, or Dekhotinsky cement.
2. The product LiD was analyzed by treating a sample with an
excess of ice at -70° , warming to room temperature and filtering to remove traces of metallic iron ($<$ 0. 5 per cent). The LiOH
content was determined by titration and as the sulfate. Unreacted
Li was found to be less than 0. 5 per cent.

5. NaD, KD, RbD, CsD[26]
$$M + (1/2)D_2 \rightarrow MD$$

A. Procedure

All four alkali deuterides can be prepared by the direct reaction of deuterium gas on the heated metal. A nickel boat is first filled with the metal, using the apparatus shown in Fig. 2. An ampoule

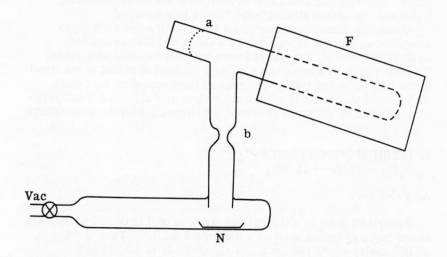

Fig. 2 Apparatus used in the preparation of NaD, KD, RbD, and CsD.

of redistilled metal is placed at the bottom of a glass tube that is then sealed into place at "a" and placed into an electric furnace "F." Under vacuum, the furnace is slowly heated so that the metal distills to "a" and falls into the boat at "N." In this way the metal is prevented from spreading on the glass walls and out of the boat. The filling ended, the vessel is sealed at "b" and displaces the boat to the end of the tube near the stopcock. The tube can then be attached to a source of dry, oxygen-free deuterium.

Deuterium gas is introduced into the tube and the metal heated by means of an electric furnace fitted about the lower part of the tube. When sodium is used, needles of NaD will grow from the

[26] Hackspill, L., and Borocco, A., Bull. soc. chim. Belges, 6, 91 (1939).

metal at 350°. By cooling the top part of the tube with a jet of
air, needles are deposited on the cold part of the tube. Heating
may be continued for 5 or 6 days at the following temperatures
at the lower part of the tube:

310°	for CsD	340°	for KD
320°	for RbD	350°	for NaD

The reaction goes faster at higher temperatures, but metal
will be deposited with the deuteride. Pressure favors the reaction, but with the apparatus described a pressure exceeding
5 to 6 cm Hg above atmospheric cannot be employed.

Under the conditions described the reaction does not go to
completion, since a layer forms on the metal that is neither
volatile or porous, and the reaction therefore essentially stops.
To obtain pure deuteride the boat with unreacted metal is returned
to the bottom of the tube. The tube is then sealed at its center
with a hand torch. It is necessary to be careful during this operation in order to maintain pressure equilibrium with the atmosphere.

6. LITHIUM BOROHYDRIDE-d_4 [27]

$$B_2D_6 + 2LiD \longrightarrow 2LiBD_4$$

A. Procedure

Described here is a typical preparation of $LiBD_4$. The hydride
is not isolated but is used as a diglyme solution. Then 2.35 g
(0.058 mole) of 98 per cent $LiAlD_4$ (Note 1) is placed in a
100-ml three-necked flask fitted with a stopper, a dropping funnel,
and a delivery tube. Stirring is accomplished by a magnetic
stirrer. Fifty milliliters of dry ether (distilled from $LiAlH_4$)
is placed in the reaction flask. A delivery tube connects this
flask with a 300-ml flask containing 0.723 g (0.0775 mole) of
LiD (Metal Hydrides, Inc., 96.5 per cent) suspended in 200 ml
of diglyme. Exit gases are passed into an acetone wash bottle.

Next 5.26 g (0.0776 mole, 10 ml) of boron trifluoride-
diethyl etherate in 50 ml of dry ether is slowly added to the
$LiAlD_4$ over a period of 90 minutes. The LiD suspension is
cooled in an acetone-dry ice bath during absorption of the generated
B_2D_6. Yield 69 per cent.

B. Notes

1. Lithium aluminum deuteride can be obtained from commercial
sources (i.e., Metal Hydrides, Inc., Beverley, Mass.) in small

---

[27] Grannen, E., and Dessy, B. E., Univ. Cincinnati, personal
communication.

quantities. It can be prepared in the laboratory according to the method of Finholt et al.,[28] using the reaction

$$4LiD + AlCl_3 \longrightarrow LiAlD_4 + 3LiCl$$

The lithium deuteride can be obtained commercially, or prepared either by the method of Zintl and Harder[29,30] or by that given above.

7. SODIUM HYDROXIDE-d[31]

$$NaO_2 + D_2O \longrightarrow NaOD + D_2O_2 \xrightarrow{\Delta} NaOD + D_2O + O_2$$

A. Procedure

The apparatus shown in Fig. 3 is used (Note 1). The three-necked flask containing a magnetic stirring bar is loaded in a dry box with about 2 moles (150 g) of reagent-grade sodium peroxide (Note 2). The apparatus is then flushed with dry nitrogen and the flask fixed quickly in place. All joints are lubricated with halocarbon grease. A stream of dry nitrogen at a positive pressure of about 1 cm Hg is passed through the system.

The reaction flask is cooled by complete immersion in an ice bath while 400 ml of heavy water is added dropwise from the dropping funnel "D." The slightly yellow solution is then refluxed for about 15 minutes until evolution of oxygen gas ceases. A sample should then be removed through the capped neck and tested for peroxide by titration with acid $KMnO_4$ solution. Heating is continued until all the peroxide has been decomposed.

At this point the solution is colorless, but it may contain white flocculent solids that can be removed by filtration or, better, by centrifugation. The resulting NaOD solution will be about 10 $\underline{N}$, and may be stored in a polyethylene bottle in an empty desiccator. Storage should be in a closed vessel as polyethylene is somewhat permeable to CO_2.

---

[28] A. E. Finholt, A. C. Bond, Jr., and H. I. Schlesinger, J. Am. Chem. Soc., 69, 1199 (1947).

[29] E. Zintl, and A. Harder, Z. Physik. Chem. (Leipzig), 14B, 265 (1931).

[30] E. Zintl, and A. Harder, Z. Physik. Chem. (Leipzig), 28B, 478 (1935).

[31] This reference number will indicate a procedure routinely used at Argonne National Laboratory. Such procedures have generally been based on standard literature procedures, but the details have been worked out by L. P. Mergenthaler, G. F. Mitchell, J. Petrovich, H. H. Hyman, R. M. Adams, H. L. Crespi, and J. J. Katz.

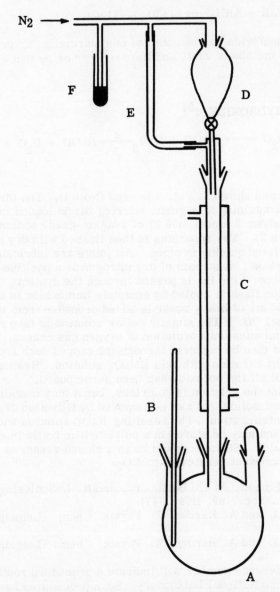

Fig. 3 Apparatus for the preparation of NaOD and D_3PO_4. A, reaction flask; B, thermometer; C, condenser; D, dropping funnel; E, Tygon tubing; F, blowoff with about 1 cm Hg.

B. Notes

1. A single-necked 1-liter flask with a thermometer well may be used in place of the three-necked flask.

2. Caution should be exercised in handling Na_2O_2, since it is very reactive toward water and organic material.

C. Other Preparations

NaOD has also been prepared by reaction of metallic sodium and D_2O.

8. SODIUM BICARBONATE-d[34]

$$Na_2CO_3 + D_2O + CO_2 \longrightarrow 2NaDCO_3$$

A. Prodedure

Na_2CO_3 is heated to about 500 and cooled in a desiccator over P_2O_5. A 15 per cent solution is then prepared in 99.6 per cent D_2O. CO_2 is then prepared from Na_2CO_3, dried by passage through several traps cooled with a CO_2-alcohol mixture, and bubbled through the solution for about 5 hours. Precautions should be taken to exclude atmospheric moisture. The solution is decanted and the precipitate dried in a stream of air that has been dried by passage through a liquid-air-cooled trap. The composition of the powder was established by ignition to sodium carbonate to ensure that no sesquicarbonate is precipitated together with the bicarbonate.

9. POTASSIUM HYDROXIDE-d[35]

$$K + D_2O \longrightarrow KOD + (1/2)D_2$$

A. Procedure

Sixty-seven grams of pure K (Note 1) is melted under nitrogen in reaction tube "A" (Fig. 4); by rotating the tube the metal is allowed to solidify as a thin layer on the walls. The reaction

[32] Halla, F., and Tompa, H., Z. anorg. u. allgem. Chem., 219, 321 (1934).

[33] Weldon, L. H. P., and Wilson, C. L., J. Chem. Soc., 1946, 244.

[34] Robertson, J. M., and Ubbelohde, A. R., Proc. Roy. Soc. (London), A170, 222 (1939).

[35] Hoyer, H., Chem. Ber., 83, 131 (1950).

vessel is then fixed to the apparatus shown in Fig. 4, evacuated,

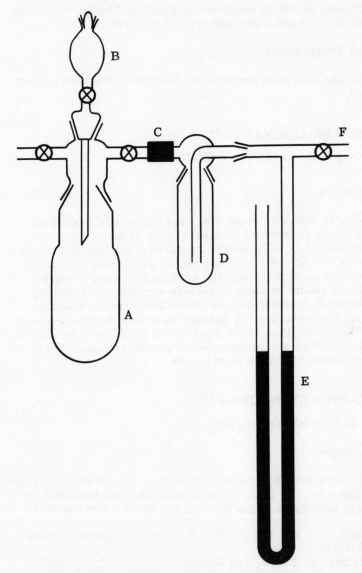

Fig. 4 Apparatus for the preparation of KOD. A, reaction tube;
B, dropping funnel; C, heavy rubber tubing; D, trap; E, mercury manometer; F, stopcock.

and heavy water added slowly from dropping funnel "B." When the manometer indicates a pressure that is somewhat over 1 atm, the liberated deuterium is discharged (Note 2). The reaction tube is made moveable by attachment with a piece of rubber tubing, so that by gentle shaking the aqueous phase is brought into contact with all the potassium.

After the completion of the reaction between K and D_2O, enough additional heavy water is added so that when the hot KOD solution is cooled the crystallized KOD deuterate dissolves (Note 3).

B. Notes

1. Metallic K is thrice purified before use by melting under nitrogen in a vertical tube and allowing the melt to drain into a lower tube. The tubes are evacuated before filling with nitrogen.

2. The liberated deuterium may be discharged into a hood. Hoyer[35] actually collected the deuterium gas on charcoal in a steel cylinder.

3. For the preparation of solid KOD, a method also outlined by Hoyer[35] may be used. In this procedure aqueous KOD is dehydrated by the circulation of hot nitrogen gas through the solution and subsequent removal of the D_2O in a cold trap in the closed system.

10. COPPER (I) HYDRIDE-d[36]

$$2Cu^{++} + 3D_2PO_2^- + 2D_2O \longrightarrow 2CuD + 3D_2PO_3 + 4H^+$$

A. Procedure

Anhydrous copper sulfate is dissolved in D_2O to give a 0.6 $\underline{M}$ $CuSO_4$ solution. To this solution is added an equal volume of 2.4 $\underline{M}$ D_3PO_2 in D_2O, and, under an atmosphere of nitrogen, the solution is heated to 45°. Precipitation is complete in a few minutes (Note 1). The apparatus used should allow washing with D_2O and decantation in a nitrogen atmosphere. The product is somewhat unstable (Note 2).

B. Notes

1. The time required for precipitation of CuD depends on the temperature as follows: 0°, 24 hours; room temperature, 100 minutes; 45°, 90 seconds; 90°, 15 seconds.

2. At 30°, under water, CuH decomposes with a half-time of 30 hours. No similar data for CuD are given. If the dry material

---

[36] Warf, J. C., and Feitknecht, W., Helv. Chim. Acta, **33**, 613 (1950).

is heated to about 100°, it explodes. Decomposition is rapid and complete in alkaline media.

11. PENTABORANE-d$_9$[37]

$$B_2D_6 \xrightarrow[D_2]{225°} B_5D_9$$

A. Procedure

Deuterated diborane was prepared from LiAlD$_4$ and BF$_3$ in diethyl ether solution in the usual way.[38] The B$_2$D$_6$ so prepared was further enriched (Note 1) by exchange[39] with deuterium gas by mixing B$_2$D$_6$ and D$_2$ in a closed system at 70° for 4 hours. The deuterio-diborane was then frozen out with liquid nitrogen and the D$_2$ (with accompanying hydrogen) pumped off. This process was repeated several times until the mass spectrum showed no further enrichment of the B$_2$D$_6$. The B$_2$D$_6$ is then diluted fivefold with D$_2$ and pyrolyzed by circulating through a furnace at 225°.[40] The resulting B$_5$D$_9$ is condensed with a dry ice bath. A product of 99.6 per cent purity is obtained (Note 2).

B. Notes

1. The LiAlD$_4$ used in this preparation contained 95 atom per cent D, so that repeated exchange was necessary to obtain B$_2$D$_6$ of 99.5 per cent isotopic purity.
2. Analysis showed 3.9 per cent B$_5$D$_8$H. Even traces of hydrogen are critical, as its presence is magnified nine times in B$_5$D$_9$. The equipment used in the preparation of the B$_5$D$_9$ was baked with deuterium gas before use. The melting point of the B$_5$D$_9$ was -47.0 ± 0.1° as compared to -46.8 ± 0.1° for B$_5$H$_9$.

[37] Shapiro, I., and Ditter, J. F., J. Chem. Phys., 26, 798 (1957).

[38] Shapiro, I., Weiss, H. G., Schmich, M., Skolnik, S., and Smith, G. B. L., J. Am. Chem. Soc., 74, 901 (1952).

[39] Maybury, P. C., and Koski, W. S., J. Chem. Phys., 21, 742 (1953).

[40] Shapiro, I., and Landesman, H., Rev. Sci. Instr., 26, 652 (1956).

12. SILANE-d$_4$[41]

$$SiCl_4 + LiAlD_4 \longrightarrow SiD_4 + LiCl + AlCl_3$$

A. Procedure

The method used is the same as that for SiH_4 described by Finholt, Bond, Wilzbach, and Schlesinger.[42] In this procedure 0. 348 g of lithium aluminum hydride (or deuteride) in 12. 5 g of diethyl ether is placed in a reaction vessel connected to a vacuum system. Somewhat less than the equivalent amount of $SiCl_4$, 175. 2 cc, is condensed into the flask after the latter is cooled with liquid nitrogen and evacuated. The reaction is allowed to warm slowly to about 0°, at which temperature gas is rapidly evolved (Note 1). The evolved silane is fractionated through an isopentane bath (-159°) and collected at liquid nitrogen temperature.

B. Notes

1. Silane boils at about -112°. It is spontaneously flammable on exposure to air.

C. Other Methods

Silane-d$_4$ can also be prepared from Mg_2Si and aqueous DCl.[43]

13. SILANE-d$_3$[44]

$$4SiCl_3H + 3LiAlD_4 \longrightarrow 4SiD_3H + 3LiCl + 3AlCl_3$$

Silane-d$_3$ may be prepared by this reaction in a manner completely similar to that employed in the synthesis of silane-d$_4$.[39]

---

[41] Lord, B. C., Robinson, D. W., and Schumb, W. C., J. Am. Chem. Soc., 78, 1327 (1956).

[42] Finholt, A. E., Bond, Jr., A. C., Wilzbach, K. E., and Schlesinger, H. I., J. Am. Chem. Soc., 69, 2692 (1947).

[43] Bak, B., Bruhn, J., and Rastrup-Andersen, J., Acta Chem. Scand. 8, No. 1, 367 (1954).

[44] Boyd, D. R. J., J. Chem. Phys., 23, 922 (1955).

14. MONOCHLOROSILANE-d$_3$[41, 43]

$$SiD_4 + DCl \longrightarrow SiD_3Cl + D_2$$

A. Procedure

A modification of the method of Stock and Somieski[46] for the preparation of SiH$_3$Cl was used to prepare SiD$_3$Cl. SiD$_4$ was chlorinated with DCl (Note 1) by heating to 100° in the presence of AlCl$_3$ for 1 to 3 hours (Note 2). The monochlorosilane-d$_3$ is then separated from deuterium, unreacted silane, and DCl by fractionation of these more volatile compounds through a trap immersed in allyl chloride slush, at a temperature of about -136°. The product was separated from dichlorosilane-d$_2$ by repeated fractionation through a trap immersed in carbon disulfide slush (Note 3) at about -111°.

B. Notes

1. If HCl is used there is H-D exchange on the silicon atom. Stock and Somieski[45] used a 10 per cent excess of silane.
2. Longer heating favors the formation of SiD$_2$Cl$_2$. The proportion of SiD$_2$Cl$_2$ was always at least 20 per cent in these experiments.
3. Some pertinent melting points: SiH$_4$, -185°; SiH$_3$Cl, -118°; SiH$_2$Cl$_2$, -122°. Boiling points: SiH$_4$, 112°; SiH$_3$Cl, -30°; SiH$_2$Cl$_2$, +8°.[46] SiD$_3$Cl can be stored in glass at -78°. At room temperature at pressures of 0.5 to 1 atm the compound is stable for 1 to 2 hours. It reacts quickly with water to give disiloxane.

15. DISILANE-d$_6$[46,47]

$$2Si_2Cl_6 + 3LiAlD_4 \longrightarrow 2Si_2D_6 + 3AlCl_3$$

A. Procedure

A 15 per cent excess of dry powdered LiAlD$_4$ (Note 1, page 24) is slowly sprinkled, in vacuum, into a stirred 0.4 M solution of Si$_2$Cl$_6$ in di-n-butyl ether which has previously been dried by distillation from LiAlD$_4$. Prior to this, hydrogen chloride is removed from the starting Si$_2$Cl$_6$ by distillation or by pumping in a vacuum at 0° for several minutes. Most of the reaction is carried out at 0° (at 2.5 mm Hg pressure) and the evolved

[45] Stock, A., and Somieski, C., Ber., 52, 695 (1919).
[46] Bethke, G. W., and Wilson, M. K., J. Chem. Phys., 26, 1107 (1957).
[47] Meal, J. H., and Wilson, M. K., J. Chem. Phys., 24, 385 (1956).

gases are passed over a -80° cold finger and through a -195°
"U" trap. After the LiAlD$_4$ is added and the reaction has ceased,
the reaction mixture is warmed to room temperature and pumped
on until it starts to boil. Based on the hexachlorodisilane used,
a yield of 80 per cent of disilane plus 7 per cent silane is obtained.

The crude reaction product is purified first by trap-to-trap
distillation from -130° to -195°. The silane distills away and
the disilane remains at -130°. The disilane fraction is then
maintained at -80° while condensing almost all the volatile
disilane at -195°. Deuterio-disilane so prepared contained 1.6
atom per cent H, from which the composition is calculated to be
90.5 per cent Si$_2$D$_6$, 9.0 per cent Si$_2$HD$_5$, and 0.37 per cent
Si$_2$H$_2$D$_4$. The effect of a small isotopic impurity is thus greatly
magnified and illustrates the extreme precautions necessary to
obtain pure products if the molecular content of deuterium is high.

B. Other Methods

The procedure outlined for silane-d$_4$[41] can also be used.
The yields obtained appear to be somewhat less than in the above
procedure.

16. DISILOXANE-d$_6$[41]
$$2SiD_3Cl + D_2O \rightarrow D_3SiOSiD_3 + 2DCl$$

A. Procedure

The method used is that of Stock and Somieski.[46] Monochloro-
silane-d$_3$, m.p. -118°, b.p. -30°, is hydrolyzed in vacuum with
twice the theoretical amount of D$_2$O at 30°. The resulting
disiloxane, m.p. -144°, b.p. -15°, is then washed with about 50
times as much D$_2$O at 0°. The yield is the order of 90 per cent.

17. TITANIUM HYDRIDE-d$_2$[48]
$$Ti + D_2 \rightarrow TiD_2$$

A. Procedure

High-purity crystal-bar titanium in a molybdenum boat is
outgassed in vacuum at 350 and 1000°. Deuterium, purified by
passage over uranium at 700°, is allowed to enter the reaction
chamber at 1000°, after which the system is slowly cooled to
400° and maintained at this temperature for several hours. A
pressure of deuterium of slightly more than 1 atm is maintained

[48] Yakel, H. L., Jr., Acta Cryst., 11, 46 (1958).

in the apparatus during cooling. The system is then re-evacuated, again brought to 1000°, and 1 atm of purified D_2 again admitted. The system is finally cooled slowly to room temperature in a deuterium atmosphere. The titanium deuteride is easily crushed to a metallic black powder. Analysis indicates a composition $TiD_{1.98}$.

18. DEUTERIO-GERMANES[49]

$$DCl + Mg_2Ge \rightarrow GeD_4 + Ge_2D_6 + Ge_3D_8$$

A. Procedure

The method of preparation is essentially that of Dennis et al.,[50] which has been used for the preparation of the ordinary hydrogen-containing germanes.

A 4-N DCl solution in D_2O is added dropwise to magnesium germanide, Mg_2Ge, with frequent shaking. The resultant gaseous products are swept through a drying and purification train with dry helium gas. To prevent exchange with the scrubbing solutions, heavy water is used in the scrubbing towers to separate DCl and $GeDCl_3$ from the reaction products. The scrubbed gases are then passed in succession over anhydrous calcium chloride and phosphorus pentoxide to remove D_2O vapor. The products are collected in a liquid-nitrogen-cooled cold trap, and the helium is allowed to escape. The collected products are then subjected to a further fractionation in an all-glass vacuum system, using mercury Stock valves instead of lubricated stopcocks where possible.

Purified GeD_4 can be obtained from the crude reaction products by applying a vacuum to a mixture of germanes maintained at -155° by means of a Freon cold trap. Although this procedure results in the loss of some GeD_4, it yields a purer product. The mixture of germanes is then allowed to warm from -155 to -145°, at which temperature the vapor pressure of GeD_4 is about 10 mm. The distilled GeD_4 that volatilizes under these conditions is then collected in a bulb cooled with liquid nitrogen. This fractionation should be repeated twice, or until a satisfactory product results as indicated by vapor-pressure measurements.

Pure Ge_2D_6 can be obtained by a similar procedure; the residual mixture of higher boiling germanes is then used as starting material. The residue is allowed to warm to -75°, while immersed in a $CHCl_3$-CCl_4 eutectic cooling mixture.

---

49 Zeltmann, A. H., and Fitzgibbon, G. C., J. Am. Chem. Soc., **76**, 2021 (1954).
50 Dennis, L. M., Corey, R. B., and Moore, R. W., J. Am. Chem. Soc., **46**, 657 (1924).

The distillate is collected in a bulb cooled with liquid nitrogen. This fractionation may be repeated several times to attain higher purity.

Pure Ge_3D_8 can be obtained by maintaining the mixture at -50° in a $CHCl_3$-CCl_4 bath while applying a vacuum. A large portion of the product is lost, but this procedure appears to be necessary in order to remove the last traces of the lower boiling Ge_2D_6. The temperature is then allowed to increase to -20°, and the Ge_3D_8 collected in a liquid-nitrogen cold trap. This fractionation is likewise repeated several times to yield a satisfactory product. An unidentified oily residue remains. Clearly, an efficient low-termperature distillation column or the application of preparative vapor-phase chromatography should do much to simplify these procedures.

19. GERMANE-d₃ AND GERMANE-d₁[51]
GeD_3H and GeH_3D

The preparative method is based on that of Finholt et al.[42] The reaction is carried out at room temperature by slowly adding a slurry of $LiAlH_4$ and $LiAlD_4$ to $GeDCl_3$[52] and $GeHCl_3$, dissolved respectively, in diethyl ether or tetrahydrofuran. The products are separated by fractional distillations.

A. Other Methods

Pure GeH_3D may also be prepared by the reduction of sodium germanyl with DCl gas in di-n-butyl ether.[53]

20. STANNANE-d₄[54, 55]
$SnCl_4 + LiAlD_4 \rightarrow SnD_4 + LiCl + AlCl_4$

The method is essentially that of Finholt et al.[42] for the preparation of hydrides of elements of the fourth group of the periodic system.

Pure anhydrous stannic chloride is added to a solution of $LiAlD_4$ (note 1, page 24) in ethylene glycol dimethyl ether in

[51] Lindeman, L. P., and Wilson, M. K., Z. Physik. Chem. (Leipzig), 9 (N. F.), 29 (1956).
[52] Dennis, L. M., Orndorff, W. R., and Tabern, D. L., J. Phys. Chem., 30, 1049 (1926).
[53] Piper, T. S., and Wilson, M. K., J. Inorg. & Nuclear Chem., 4, 22 (1957).
[54] Tamaru, K., J. Phys. Chem., 60, 610 (1956).
[55] Schaeffer, G. W., and Emilias, M., J. Am. Chem. Soc., 76, 1230 (1954).

a dry nitrogen atmosphere. The solution of $LiAlD_4$ is cooled
with liquid nitrogen as the $SnCl_4$ is added. After the addition is
completed, the liquid nitrogen is removed to allow the reaction
mixture to warm very slowly to room temperature. The SnD_4
evolved is condensed in a liquid nitrogen trap and is purified by
trap-to-trap distillation.

21. AMMONIA-d_3[56-59]

$$Mg_3N_2 + 6D_2O \rightarrow 2ND_3 + 3Mg(OD)_2$$

The reaction is carried out in a vacuum system such as the
one shown in Fig. 5. The D_2O is degassed and then distilled into
one of the two tubes containing Mg_3N_2 (Note 1). The Mg_3N_2
has previously been evacuated for about 5 hours at 300°.
Because the hydrolysis reaction is slow even at 100 to 150°, the
water must be passed repeatedly through the heated Mg_3N_2
beds. The reaction is complete when the pressure of ammonia
in the apparatus ceases to increase. The ammonia is then sublimed (Note 2) with the traps open to the pump. The ND_3 product
is subsequently dried with BaO (Note 3) to remove water and
traces of CO_2 that may be present. The final product may still
contain traces of water; these can only be removed by more
rigorous methods (Note 4).

A. Notes

1. The Mg_3N_2 is prepared from pure magnesium turnings and
nitrogen at 1 atm pressure in a tube at a maximum temperature
of 800°. A closed system with a 20-liter reservoir of N_2 is
used for this preparation.
2. The sublimation can be carried out from a tube cooled with
a slush of solid CO_2 in toluene to a trap cooled with liquid
nitrogen.[57]
3. The BaO is prepared by the thermal decomposition of
water-free barium peroxide at 400° in a vacuum.
4. It has been suggested that final traces of impurities in
the ammonia be removed by decomposing and then reforming the
ammonia with an iron catalyst.

―――――――
[56] Groth, D. W., Ihle, H., and Murrenhoff, A., Angew.
Chem., 68, 605 (1956).
[57] DeBruyne, J. M. A., and Smyth, C. P., J. Am. Chem.
Soc., 57, 1203 (1935).
[58] Kirshenbaum, I., and Urey, H. C., J. Chem. Phys.,
10, 706 (1942).
[59] Brauer, G., and Baudler, M., Handbuch der Präparativen
Anorganischen Chemie, No. 1, Enke, Stuttgart, 1951.

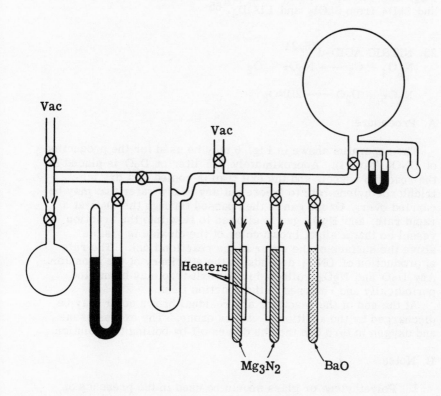

Fig. 5 Apparatus used in the preparation of ND$_3$. See text for
details.

B. Other Methods

Ammonia-d$_3$ has also been prepared by reaction of Li$_3$N
and D$_2$O.[60]

22. PHOSPHINE-d$_3$, ARSINE-d$_3$, AND STIBINE-d$_3$

These compounds have been prepared by methods identical
to those used for the preparation of the (light) hydrogen analogs.
Thus PD$_3$ and P$_2$D$_4$ are obtained from the reaction of D$_2$O

[60] Clusius, K., and Huber, M., Z. Naturforsch., **10a**,
556 (1955).

and calcium phosphide,[61] PD_3 from D_2O and PI_3[62] and from PD_4I and NaOD,[63] AsD_3 from D_2O and sodium arsenide,[64] and SbD_3 from $SbCl_3$ and $LiAlD_4$.[65]

23. NITRIC ACID-d[66, 31]

$$N_2O_4 + O_3 \longrightarrow N_2O_5 + O_2$$

$$N_2O_5 + D_2O \longrightarrow 2DNO_3$$

A. Procedure

The apparatus shown in Fig. 6 may be used for the production of DNO_3 (Note 1). Approximately 0.5 liter of D_2O is placed in the reaction vessel, and the exit trap is cooled in a dry ice-trichloroethylene bath to freeze out any heavy water that may be carried over. Ozone gas is then passed through the D_2O at a rapid rate, and N_2O_4 gas is allowed to flow into the reaction vessel so that a slight brown color of the dioxide is visible above the surface of the water in the reaction flask. The rate of production of DNO_3 depends on the efficiency of the ozonator. Any D_2O and N_2O_4 collected in the exit trap may be melted periodically and returned to the reaction flask.

At the end of the reaction, any residual brown color may be discharged by the addition of excess ozone. The excess ozone and oxygen in turn can then be driven off by boiling the solution.

B. Notes

1. Polyethylene or glass should be used in the presence of N_2O_4. Tygon tubing may be used to carry the ozonated oxygen. There should be no rubber in the reaction system.

C. Other Methods

A method similar to that given above is outlined by Tronstad and Stokland.[67]

---

[61] Nixon, E. R., J. Phys. Chem., 60, 1054 (1956).

[62] Ramsey, D. A., Nature, 178, 374 (1956).

[63] DeHemptinne, M., and Delfosse, J. M., Bull. sci. acad. roy. Belg., 21, 793 (1935).

[64] Delfosse, J. M., Nature, 137, 868 (1936).

[65] Tamaru, K., J. Phys. Chem., 59, 1084 (1955).

[66] Redlich, O., and Nielsen, L. E., J. Am. Chem. Soc., 65, 654 (1943).

[67] Tronstad, L., and Stokland, K., Kgl. Norske Videnskab. Selskabs Forh., 10, 129 (1937).

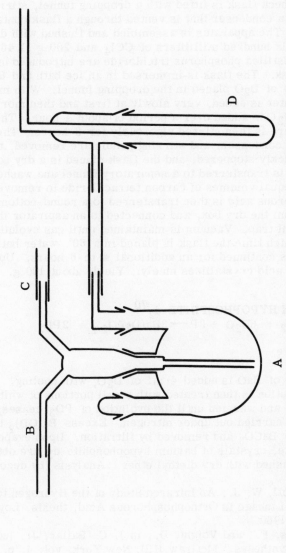

Fig. 6. Apparatus for the preparation of DNO_3. A, 1-liter reaction flask; B, from ozonator (use Tygon tubing); C, from N_2O_4 source (use polyethylene tubing); D, trap.

24. PHOSPHOROUS ACID-d$_3$[68, 69]

$$PCl_3 + 3D_2O \rightarrow D_3PO_3 + 3DCl$$

A. Procedure

A three-neck flask is fitted with a dropping funnel, stirring paddle, and a condenser that is vented through a flask containing solid KOH. The apparatus is assembled and flushed with dry nitrogen. Six hundred milliliters of CCl_4 and 200 g (1.46 moles) of freshly distilled phosphorus trichloride are introduced into the reaction flask. The flask is immersed in an ice bath and 83 g (4.15 moles) of D_2O placed in the dropping funnel. With moderate stirring, water is added, very slowly at first and then more rapidly; all the D_2O is added over a period of about 1 hour. The reaction mixture is then stirred vigorously for 2 hours. The dropping funnel, condenser, and stirring paddle are removed, the openings quickly stoppered, and the flask placed in a dry box. The syrupy acid is transferred to a separatory funnel and washed four times with equal volumes of carbon tetrachloride to remove DCl. The phosphorous acid is then transferred to a round-bottom flask, removed from the dry box, and connected to an aspirator through a solid NaOH trap. Vacuum is maintained until gas evolution stops, at which time the flask is placed in a 60° water bath. Aspiration is continued for an additional 4 to 6 hours. Upon cooling, the acid crystallizes nicely. Yield, about 100 g.

25. BARIUM HYPOPHOSPHITE-d$_2$[70]

$$3Ba(OD)_2 + 6D_2O + 8P \rightarrow 3Ba(D_2PO_2)_2 + 2PD_3$$

A. Procedure

To 1.5 g of BaO is added 4 ml of D_2O, with cooling. The $Ba(OD)_2$ solution is then treated with small portions of white phosphorus, and warmed until the evolution of PD_3 ceases; the operation is carried out under nitrogen. Excess $Ba(OD)_2$ is converted to $BaCO_3$ and removed by filtration. Upon evaporation of the filtrate, crystals of barium hypophosphite-d$_2$ are obtained; these are washed with dry diethyl ether. Analysis (by decomposi-

[68] Driscoll, W. J., An Infrared Study of the Hydrogen to Phosphorus Linkage in Orthophosphorous Acid, thesis, Loyola University, 1960.

[69] Gallias, F., and Voight, D., in J. C. Bailar, Jr. (ed.), "Inorganic Syntheses," McGraw-Hill, New York, vol. 4, p. 55, 1953.

[70] Erlenmeyer, H., Schoenauer, W., and Schwarzenbach, G., Helv. Chim. Acta, 20, 726 (1937).

tion in acid permanganate and recovery of the water) indicates
3.97 atoms of D per molecule in the preparation.

26. PHOSPHORIC ACID-d$_3$[71, 31]

$$3D_2O + P_2O_5 \longrightarrow 2D_3PO_4$$

The apparatus shown in Fig. 3 may be used for the preparation
of deuterio-phosphoric acid. The ground-glass joints should be
lubricated with halocarbon grease. The desired amount of P_2O_5
(from a freshly opened bottle) is placed into the tared reaction
flask in a dry box, and a magnetic stirring bar is added. The flask
is then stoppered, weighed again, and attached to the reaction
system after flushing the system with dry nitrogen. If pure
D_3PO_4 is desired, the stoichiometric amount of D_2O is placed in
the dropping funnel. A stream of dry nitrogen is then allowed to
impose a slight pressure (1 cm Hg above atomspheric) on the
system to prevent air from sucking back into the system when the
reaction flask is cooled.

The reaction flask is surrounded with an ice bath and the D_2O
is added cautiously. The temperature in the flask should not be
allowed to exceed 80°. When about three-fourths of the water
has been added the ice bath can be removed and gentle heat applied
to the flask in the vicinity of the stirring bar. With the bar released from the gummy reaction mass, the mixture may then be
mixed and the remainder of the water added. During this procedure, it will be necessary to use the cooling bath occasionally.

When all the D_2O is added, the mixture is refluxed for about
20 minutes to ensure complete hydration to D_3PO_4 (Note 1).

A. Other Methods

Deuterio-phosphoric acid can be prepared by the same reaction
in a closed system under vacuum.[72] A 1-liter round-bottom
flask containing P_2O_5 is fitted with a dropping funnel and a three-
way stopcock. After evacuating, the system is closed and D_2O
added dropwise. During this procedure the flask is cooled by an
ice bath. This reaction has been carried out with as much as
400 g of P_2O_5. After complete solution of the P_2O_5, the mixture
is allowed to stand 5 hours at 50° to complete the formation of
D_3PO_4. Before making physical measurements on the acid, these
authors allowed it to stand for 2 months. The melting point of the

---

[71] Bantle, W., Helv. Phys. Acta, 15, 373 (1942).
[72] Pannetier, G., and Guenebaut, H., Bull. soc. chim.
France, 1955, 636.

D_3PO_4 prepared by this method was reported as 38.4°. Greenwood and Thompson[73] obtained a value of 46.0° after repeated recrystallization of the acid prepared from purified P_2O_5 and D_2O. These latter authors have also outlined a method for the vacuum preparation of small amounts of D_3PO_4 from P_2O_5 and D_2O[74] (Note 2). Other preparations using P_2O_5 and D_2O have also been reported.[75, 76]

B. Notes

1. The hydration of P_2O_5 is not a simple reaction. Various polyphosphoric acids can be obtained, and detailed examination is required before the composition of the concentrated product can be specified.

2. The density of D_3PO_4 at various temperatures is given[73] by the equation

$$d_4^t = 1.9279 - 7.83 \times 10^{-4}t$$

27. DEUTERIUM OXIDE

D_2O is widely available commercially (Note 1) and its method of production will not be outlined here. Benedict has recently surveyed production processes.[77] Before use in the laboratory it is judicious to distil the heavy water, preferably from alkaline permanganate. In this way impurities such as heavy metals and corrosion inhibitors are essentially eliminated. Table 2 lists some physical constants of D_2O.

A. Notes

1. Among commercial suppliers of D_2O and D_2 are the Stuart

[73] Greenwood, N. N., and Thompson, A., J. Chem. Soc., 1959, 3485.

[74] Greenwood, N. N., and Thompson, A., in E. G. Rochow (ed.),"Inorganic Syntheses," McGraw-Hill, New York, vol. 6, p. 81, 1960.

[75] Brauer, G., and Klement, R., Handbuch der Präparativen Anorganischen Chemie, No. 3, Enke, Stuttgart, 1951.

[76] Simon, A., and Schulze, G., Z. anorg. allgem. Chem., 242, 326 (1939).

[77] Benedict, M., "Survey of Heavy-Water Production Processes," Proceedings of the International Conference on the Peaceful Uses of Atomic Energy, Geneva, 1955, Vol. 8, p. 377, United Nations, New York, 1956.

Table 2
Some Physical Constants of D_2O

	H_2O	D_2O
Density, d_4^{20}	0.9982	1.1056
Molecular volume, $(V)^{20}$	18.05	18.12
Viscosity, ^{20}	1.005	1.25
Melting point	0	3.82
Boiling point	100	101.72
Temp. of max. density	4	11.6
Ion product (25°)	10^{-14}	0.3×10^{-14}

Oxygen Co., San Francisco; Nichem, Inc., Bethesda, Md.; Volk Radiochemical Co., Chicago; Isotopes Specialties Corp., Burbank, Calif.; Tracerlab, Inc., Waltham, Mass.; Isomet Corp., Palisades Park, N.J.

28. HYDROGEN PEROXIDE-d_2

Relatively large quantities of D_2O_2 have been produced from the reaction of potassium persulfate and D_2SO_4[78, 79] and from water vapor in the electrodeless discharge.[79,80] In the latter method D_2O is dissociated in a high-frequency (20Mc/sec) electrodeless discharge. The dissociated gas is conducted directly to a large liquid-air trap, where it forms a glassy deposit. On warming, first deuterium and then oxygen gases are evolved. The peroxide solution, about 50 per cent D_2O_2, is then distilled in vacuum. Martius and Schorre[81] prepared a small quantity (3.8 ml) of 29 per cent D_2O_2 from D_3PO_4 and sodium peroxide.

29. HYDROGEN SULFIDE-d_2[82]

$$Al_2S_3 + 6D_2O \longrightarrow 3D_2S + 2Al(OD)_3$$

A. Procedure

Deuterium sulfide can be conveniently made from freshly pre-

[78] Feher, F., Ber., 72B, 1789 (1939).
[79] Phibbs, M. K., and Giguere, P. A., Can. J. Chem., 29, 173 (1951).
[80] Giguere, P. A., Secco, E. A., and Eaton, R. S., Disc. Faraday Soc., 14, 104 (1953).
[81] Martius, C., and Schorre, G., Ann., 570, 140 (1950).
[82] Brauer, G., and Baudler, M., Handbuch der Präparativen Anorganischen Chemie, No. 1, Enke, Stuttgart, 1951.

pared aluminum sulfide and heavy water (Note 1). Ampoules
containing about 20 g of Al_2S_3 and 7 g of D_2O are placed in a
5-liter flask equipped with a ground-glass joint and stopcocks.
The flask is evacuated, closed, removed from the vacuum line,
and shaken to break the two ampoules. The flask is then left in
the dark for 1 week with occasional shaking. Water will condense
on the sides of the flask and must be brought back into contact
with the Al_2S_3. When the reaction is complete, the D_2S is
collected in a trap at liquid-air temperature. The products are
then slowly distilled from a CO_2 bath to a liquid-air bath, and
transferred to a storage vessel.

B. Other Methods

D_2S has also been prepared from CaS and D_2O in the presence
of $MgCl_2$.[83]

C. Notes

1. Al_2S_3 can be prepared [84] by heating aluminum powder and
sulfur in a clay crucible. Caution must be exercised when mixing
the reagents in order to avoid premature reaction. The aluminum
is washed free of oil with reagent-grade benzene and exhaustively
dried in vacuum at 150°. The stoichiometric mixture of aluminum
and sulfur is ignited with a magnesium ribbon and the crucible
covered as soon as reaction starts. Caution! The reaction is
very vigorous. While still quite warm, the product Al_2S_3 is
crushed and outgassed several hours at 150 to 180° in a tube that is
then sealed under vacuum. The necessary D_2O is also sealed in
an ampoule.

30. HYDROGEN SELENIDE-d_2[85]
$$Al_2Se_3 + 6D_2O \rightarrow 3D_2Se + 2Al(OD)_3$$

A. Procedure

D_2O is frozen onto Al_2Se_3 in an evacuated system. D_2Se
is evolved fairly rapidly when the water is allowed to melt. Excess water can be removed by fractionation. The Al_2Se_3 can
be prepared by heating stoichiometric quantities of aluminum and
selenium in an evacuated Vycor tube until reaction occurs.

[83] Larsen, T., Z. Physika, 111, 391 (1938).
[84] Waitkins, G. R., and Shutt, R., in W. C. Fernelius (ed.),
"Inorganic Syntheses," McGraw-Hill, New York, vol. 2, p. 183,
1946.
[85] Jacke, A. W., Moser, P. W., and Gordy, W., J. Chem.
Phys., 25, 209 (1956).

The preparation of Al_2Se_3 is carried out as detailed[84] in the preceeding synthesis.

31. SULFURIC ACID-d_2[86,31]

$$SO_3 + D_2O \rightarrow D_2SO_4$$

A. Procedure

The apparatus shown in Fig. 7 is used for the preparation

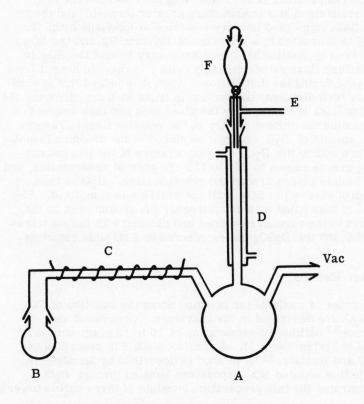

Fig. 7 Apparatus for the preparation of D_2SO_4. A, 1-liter reac-
action flask; B, 500-ml flask; C, heating coil; D, condenser;
E, exit to hood; F, dropping funnel.

86 Ingold, C. K., Raisin, C. G., and Wilson, C. L., J. Chem.
Soc., **1936**, 915.

of deuterio-sulfuric acid. It is essential that the reaction vessel
be made entirely of glass, with as few joints as possible and
these preserved as far as feasible from attack by SO_3. Halocarbon
grease is used to lubricate all joints. Ordinary greases must be
scrupulously avoided. The reaction flask may contain a Teflon
stirring bar (Note 1).

First, a (glass) plug is inserted in the line in place of the
500-ml flask and the system evacuated. SO_3 (Note 2) is added
to a tared 500-ml flask in a good dry box, and the flask is
stoppered. The capped flask containing SO_3 is weighed again and
attached to the apparatus by filling the entire system with dry
nitrogen gas and attaching the flask as indicated in the figure.
With the temperature of the connecting arm between the two
flasks maintained at a temperature greater than 90° and the reaction flask immersed in a dry ice-trichloroethylene bath, the
system is evacuated to a pressure of 130 mm Hg and the SO_3
transferred by distillation. It is necessary to heat the SO_3 in
the distilling flask rather strongly (with a burner) to keep it from
solidifying during the distillation. When it is judged that enough
SO_3 has been distilled, the system is filled with dry nitrogen, the
distilling flask is replaced by the glass plug and then weighed
to determine the amount of SO_3 in the reaction flask. The re-
quisite amount of D_2O can then be placed in the dropping funnel.

Before adding the D_2O, the temperature of the plugged connecting arm is raised to 140 to 150° to prevent condensation, and
an ice bath is placed around the reaction flask. D_2O is then
added dropwise to the SO_3 until the reaction is completed. The
system is then filled with dry nitrogen, the ground joint on the
side arm to the vacuum is opened and cleaned with carbon tetrachloride, and the D_2SO_4 is transferred to a suitable container.

B. Other Methods

A number of methods for bringing about the reaction of SO_3
with D_2O are described in the literature. Greenwood and
Thompson[87] outline the preparation of 10 to 12 g amounts in an
evacuated system (Note 3). A similar method is described by
Brauer and Baudler.[88] A method is described by Shudde[89] in
which helium-diluted SO_3 vapors are bubbled through D_2O.
The apparatus for this preparation consists of three bubble towers,

---

[87] Greenwood, N. N., and Thompson, A., in E. G. Rochow
(ed.), "Inorganic Synthesis," McGraw-Hill, New York, vol. 6,
p. 121, 1960.

[88] Brauer, G., and Baudler, M., Handbuch der Präparativen
Anorganischen Chemie, No. 1, Enke, Stuttgart, 1951.

[89] Shudde, R. H., North American Aviation Report SR-2158,
March 1958.

three traps, and an SO_3 reservoir with a heating mantle. The helium is passed through a trap, 30 per cent oleum bubble tower, SO_3 reservoir (Sulfan B) at 30 to 35°, a warmed trap, D_2O bubble tower, trap, and H_2SO_4 bubble tower. Starting with 60 ml of D_2O, about 200 ml of D_2SO_4 can be prepared in 5 to 6 days by this procedure.

Methods involving the electrolysis of copper sulfate and the reaction of sulfuryl chloride with D_2O for the preparation of D_2SO_4 have also been described.[90]

C. Notes

1. The equipment must be clean and free of organic matter. Organic matter will be oxidized and the acid acquires a pink or brown coloration.

2. The gamma form of sulfur trioxide is available as a stabilized liquid (Sulfan B - General Chemical Division of Allied Chemical Corporation).

3. The density of the D_2SO_4 obtained by Greenwood and Thompson[87] is given by:

$$d_4^t = 1.8816 - 0.980 \times 10^{-3}t.$$

32. AMMONIUM HYDROXIDE-d₅[31]

$$ND_3 + D_2O \rightarrow ND_4OD$$

A. Procedure

An apparatus similar to that for the synthesis of DCl (Fig. 8) may be used. Excess magnesium nitride (Metal Hydrides, Inc.) is placed in the reaction flask, the flask is cooled in an ice bath, and D_2O is added dropwise. The reaction proceeds at a moderate rate. When all the D_2O has been added and the evolution of ND_3 slows, the cooling bath is heated to boiling until no more ammonia is evolved.

[90] Freeman, J. H., and Richard, C. E. C., AERE GP/R 2479, Harwell, 1958.

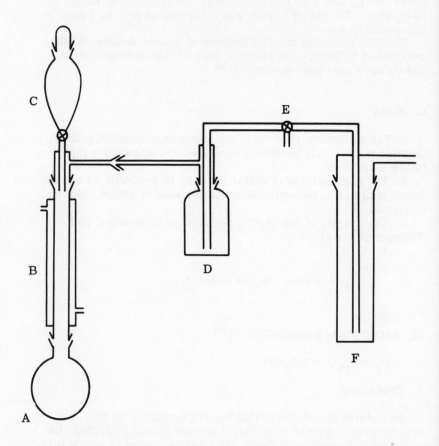

Fig. 8 Apparatus for the preparation of DCl and ND₄OD. A,
        1-liter flask; B, condenser; C, dropping funnel; D, trap; E,
        three-way stopcock; F, trap.

33. HYDROFLUORIC ACID-d[91]

$$Ag + F_2 \longrightarrow AgF_2$$

$$D_2 + AgF_2 \longrightarrow 2DF + Ag$$

---

[91] Long, R. W., Hildebrand, J. H., and Morrell, W. E.,
J. Am. Chem. Soc., 65, 182 (1943).

A. Procedure

The reaction is carried out in a vacuum system constructed of metal and Kel-F (polytrifluorochloroethylene). Very finely divided (molecular) silver metal in a nickel tray is placed in a nickel furnace (Note 1). After degassing for several hours at about 100°, fluorine gas is slowly admitted. The temperature of the reaction mixture is kept below 100°; the fluorination reaction evolves considerable heat. If fluorine is allowed to enter too rapidly, the silver may fuse and the reaction will be incomplete. When there is no longer any pressure drop on standing, the excess fluorine is removed by evacuation and heating to 150°. Deuterium gas is then allowed to fill the system to a pressure of about 1/3 atm. After 15 to 30 minutes the gases are pumped out through a Kel-F trap at liquid nitrogen temperature to freeze out the DF that forms. The entire cycle is then repeated until the desired amount of DF is obtained. About 1 mole of DF can be prepared 8 hours (Note 2) by alternate fluorination and hydrogenation of 115 g of silver.

B. Other Methods

Brauer and Baudler[59] outline a preparation beginning with AgF. Olah and Kuhn[92] survey various preparative possibilities and describe a preparation using benzoyl fluoride and D_2O.

C. Notes

1. About 115 g of silver is placed in a tray in the cylinder. One end of the cylinder is fitted with a cap about 2 inches in diameter. Each end is fitted with quarter-inch copper tubing.
2. AgF_2 can be regenerated, but the efficiency of regeneration gradually decreases.

34. HYDROCHLORIC ACID-d[93]

$$C_6H_5COCl + D_2O \longrightarrow C_6H_5COOD + DCl$$

$$C_6H_5COCl + C_6H_5COOD \longrightarrow (C_6H_5CO)_2O + DCl$$

A. Procedure

The apparatus shown in Fig. 8 is used. First 4.2 moles (475 ml, 1 pint) or 3.25 moles (375 ml, 1 pound) of benzoyl chloride are placed in the 1-liter reaction flask and the system

[92] Olah, G., and Kuhn, S., Z. anorg. allgem. Chem., 287, 282 (1956).

[93] Brown, H. C., and Groot, C., J. Am. Chem. Soc., 64, 2223 (1942).

flushed with dry nitrogen. The trap is then immersed in a dry ice-trichloroethylene bath. An equimolar amount (Note 1) of D_2O is placed in the dropping funnel and 250 to 350 ml of D_2O in the receiving vessel. The receiving vessel is immersed in an ice bath. About 25 or 30 ml of D_2O are added to the benzoyl chloride at room temperature, after which the temperature of the mixture is slowly raised to 120°. The remaining D_2O is added slowly to maintain a steady evolution of DCl gas. During each addition of D_2O the three-way stopcock should be open briefly to the atmosphere to adjust the pressure. When all the D_2O has been added, the temperature of the reaction flask is raised to 200°, and refluxing is continued until DCl evolution ceases. Generally this occurs in about 3 hours. The DCl solution is then transferred to an appropriate container (Note 2). Yields of DCl, on a benzoyl chloride basis, range from 90 to 100 per cent.

B. Other Methods

Numerous methods are available for the preparation of DCl. Brauer and Baudler[59] describe the preparation of DCl gas from NaCl and D_2SO_4[94, 95] and from $SiCl_4$ and D_2O.[96] The acid has also been prepared from $MgCl_2$ and D_2O at 600°,[97] PCl_5 and D_2O,[98, 99] $SOCl_3$ and D_2O,[100, 101] and $AlCl_3$ and D_2O.[102]

C. Notes

1. In the procedure outlined, excess D_2O is used so as to obtain the maximum yield per run. Excess benzoyl chloride may be used if deuterium must be conserved.

---

[94] Smits, A., Muller, G. J., and Kroger, F. A., Z. Physik. Chem. (Leipzig), 28B, 177 (1937).

[95] Frivold, O. E., Hassel, O., and Rustad, S., Physik. Z., 38, 191 (1937).

[96] Clusius, K., and Wolf, G., Z. Naturforsch., 2a, 495 (1947).

[97] Lewis, G. N., MacDonald, R. T., and Schutz, P. W., J. Am. Chem. Soc., 56, 494 (1936).

[98] Smits, A., and Muller, G. J., Nature, 139, 804 (1937).

[99] Ives, D. J. G., and Nettleton, M. R., J. Chem. Soc., 1948, 1085.

[100] Klit, A., and Langseth, A., Z. Physik. Chem. (Leipzig), 176A, 65 (1936).

[101] Nevell, T. P., De Salas, E., and Wilson, C. L., J. Chem. Soc., 1939, 1188.

[102] Post, B., and Hiskey, C. F., J. Am. Chem. Soc., 73, 161 (1951).

2. The reaction mixture should be disposed of by dumping into a pail of alkali before it cools. The equipment should then be soaked in water to which a detergent and alkali have been added.

35. HYDROBROMIC ACID-d

A. Procedure

Two methods are described in detail by Brauer and Baudler.[59] In the first, DBr is prepared directly from the elements.[103] D_2 gas is bubbled through Br_2 at 48° at a rate of about 2 liters per hour. The mixture of D_2 and Br_2 is then passed through a combustion tube filled with pieces of porcelain. The tube is wound with a nichrome-wire heating element in such a way that the entry portion can be maintained at 80°, and the remainder of the reactor at 700°. The exit gases are passed through a trap immersed in liquid ammonia and then through a column of copper turnings to remove the last traces of bromine. The DBr is then trapped out with liquid air (Note 1).

A second method[96] for preparing DBr employs the reaction between PBr_3 and D_2O. Ampoules of the reactants are broken in an evacuated 5-liter flask and are allowed to stand in the dark for 2 days with occasional shaking. The mixture should not be warmed, as D_3PO_3 will disproportionate to give PD_3. The reaction flask is then attached to a vacuum line and the DBr removed and condensed at liquid air temperature. The product is further purified by fractional distillation.

B. Notes

1. Goldblatt and Robinson[104] prepared DBr from the elements and found the density of the liquid from 0 to 25° to be given by the equation

$$d = 1.961 - 5.981 \times 10^{-3}t + 3.503 \times 10^{-8}t^2$$

36. HYDRIODIC ACID-d[59]
$$D_2 + I_2 \longrightarrow 2DI$$

A. Procedure

Deuterium gas and excess iodine are heated to 370° for 6

---

[103] Wilson, C. L., and Wylie, A. W., J. Chem. Soc., 1941, 596.

[104] Goldblatt, M., and Robinson, E. S., J. Phys. Chem., 60, 1588 (1956).

hours in a closed 5-liter bulb in the presence of a platinum
catalyst. The resulting DI is purified by distillation. [105, 106]

B. Other Methods

DI has also been prepared by reaction of phosphorus, iodine,
and heavy water, [96] and by reaction of D_2S and iodine. [107]

37. PERCHLORIC ACID-d[108]

$$D_2SO_4 + Ba(ClO_4)_2 \longrightarrow 2DClO_4 + BaSO_4$$

Anhydrous barium perchlorate is dissolved in D_2O, and the
solution is added slowly to concentrated D_2SO_4. When the reaction approaches completion, the $Ba(ClO_4)_2$ solution is added
dropwise, and the precipitated $BaSO_4$ is allowed to settle out
between drops so that the endpoint can be determined fairly
accurately. The reaction mixture is then carefully centrifuged,
and the resulting clear supernatant solution is distilled, preferably in a quartz still. All equipment should be clean and dry.
During the distillation, D_2O comes off first. There is a
large rise in temperature, to about 200°, and $DClO_4$ hydrate
then distills. Care must be taken to ensure that the still pot
does not go to dryness. The product will be about 70 per cent
perchloric acid (approximately 11.4 M). The precautions appropriate to work with perchlorates should be employed. [109]

38. MISCELLANEOUS COMPOUNDS

A variety of compounds have been prepared by simple exchange with heavy water. These compounds, along with literature
references are listed below:

---

[105] Rittenberg, D., and Urey, H. C., J. Am. Chem. Soc.,
56, 1885 (1934).
[106] Bates, J. R., Halford, J. O., and Anderson, L. C.,
J. Chem. Phys., 3, 415 (1935).
[107] Erlenmeyer, H., and Gartner, H., Helv. Chim. Acta,
19, 146 (1936).
[108] Sullivan, J., Cohen, D., and Hindman, J. C., J. Am.
Chem. Soc., 79, 3672 (1957).
[109] Smith, G. F., Perchloric Acid, G. F. Smith Chemical
Co., Columbus, Ohio.

D_3BO_3[110]

$ND_2OD \cdot DCl$[111]

$CuSO_4 \cdot 5D_2O$[112]

$SrCl_2 \cdot 6D_2O$[112]

KD_2PO_4[112]

$NaDSO_4$[112]

KD_2AsO_4[113]

$Ag_2D_3IO_6$[114]

$(ND_4)_2D_3IO_6$[115]

Metal ammines[116-118]

Sulfamic acid[119]

[110] Bethell, D. E., and Sheppard, N., Trans. Faraday Soc., 51, 9 (1955).

[111] Redlich, O., and Friedman, I. I., J. Am. Chem. Soc., 67, 893 (1945).

[112] Ubbelohde, A. R., Proc. Roy. Soc. (London), A173, 417 (1939).

[113] Dickson, D. H. W., and Ubbelohde, A. B., Acta Cryst., 3, 6 (1950).

[114] Herlach, F., Aboav, D., Granicher, H., and Petter, W., Helv. Phys. Acta, 30, 252 (1957).

[115] Aboav, D., Granicher, H., and Petter, W., Helv. Phys. Acta, 28, 299 (1955).

[116] Adamson, A. W., and Basolo, F., Acta Chem. Scand., 9, 1261 (1955).

[117] Barrow, G. M., Drueger, B. H., and Basolo, F., J. Inorg. & Nuclear Chem., 2, 340 (1956).

[118] Sheppard, N., and Powell, D. B., J. Chem. Soc., 1956, 3108.

[119] Vaugnat, A. M., and Wagner, E. L., J. Chem. Phys., 26, 77 (1957).

3

Syntheses with Tritium

F. S. ROWLAND
University of Kansas
Lawrence, Kansas

1. INTRODUCTION

A. Nuclear Characteristics

The only known radioactive isotope of hydrogen is the isotope of mass number 3, tritium, which is designated either by the usual chemical symbol H^3 or by the special symbol T. Tritium decays by pure-beta emission to stable He^3, with a half-life of 12.26 years,[1,2] long enough to be convenient for almost all experiments. Since the maximum beta energy is only 18.6 kev[3], and there are no associated gamma rays, counting techniques must be used in which the decaying atom is very close to, or within, the actual detection volume of the counter, as discussed in Sec. 2. At the same time, radiation shielding is made much easier, and the quantity of radioactivity that can be handled safely under given conditions is much greater than with most other isotopes.

B. Natural Occurrence of Tritium

Tritium occurs in nature in very small amounts as the result of nuclear reactions initiated by cosmic-ray interaction with the earth's atmosphere.[4,5] It is formed both by high-energy proton-spallation reactions[6] on oxygen and nitrogen and by the $N^{14}(n, T)C^{12}$

---

[1] Porter, F. T., Phys. Rev., 115, 450 (1959).

[2] The decay constant is 1.08×10^{-7} min[-1] or, for quick calculations, about 1 DPM for every 10^7 atoms of tritium.

[3] Jones, W. M., Phys. Rev., 100, 124 (1955).

[4] Faltings, V., and Harteck, P., Z. Naturforsch., 5a, 438 (1950); Nature, 166, 1109 (1950).

[5] Grosse, A. V., Johnston, W. H., Wolfgang, R. L., and Libby, W. F., Science, 113, 1 (1951).

[6] Fireman, E. L., and Rowland, F. S., Phys. Rev., 97, 780 (1955); Currie, L. A., Libby, W. F., and Wolfgang, R. L., Phys. Rev., 101, 1557 (1956).

reaction of energetic secondary neutrons.[7]

This tritium is found in the hydrogenic atmospheric components H_2O, H_2, CH_4 (?), etc., and has been used in tracer studies for meteorology and hydrology.[8]

The cosmic-ray tritium concentration in these atmospheric molecules is usually expressed in terms of the ratio of the number of tritium atoms to the number of hydrogen atoms (T/H), or in Tritium Units (1 T.U. corresponds to a T/H of 10^{-18}). The concentrations of tritium presently observed in atmospheric gases are much higher than the normal cosmic-ray level because artificially produced tritium is introduced into the atmosphere by nuclear testing. The highest observed T/H ratios in water, other than in the immediate nuclear test areas, have been about 3×10^{-15} and vary with the dates of the most recent nuclear tests and climatic conditions.[9] Atmospheric hydrogen and methane currently have T/H ratios of about 3 to 5×10^{-13} and 2×10^{-14}, respectively.[9-11] Even this artificially high background level of tritium in nature is completely negligible for all tracer experiments, except those involving activities at a very low level (T/H = 10^{-15} corresponds to about 10^{-2} DPM of tritium per mg H_2O).

C. Artificial Production of Tritium

Tritium is formed in many nuclear reactions, but only two reactions have cross sections large enough to be useful for the synthesis of tritium-labeled molecules. These two are the $Li^6(n,\alpha)T$ and $He^3(n,p)T$ reactions, which have thermal-neutron cross sections of 945 and 5400 barns, respectively, for the separated isotopes.[12] The lithium reaction is much the more important of the two and is the ultimate source of all the tritium, since the only good source of He^3 is the beta decay of tritium itself. The lithium reaction in hydrogen bombs is the main source of the artificial tritium in the atmosphere.

---

[7] Fireman, E. L., Phys. Rev., 91, 922 (1953).

[8] Bolin, B., Proc. Intern. Conf. Peaceful Uses Atomic Energy, Geneva, 18, 336 (1958).

[9] Begemann, F., and Friedman, I., Z. Naturforsch., 14a, 1024 (1959).

[10] Bishop, K. F., and Taylor, B. T., Nature, 185, 26 (1960); Bishop, K. F., Delafield, H. J., Egglestron, A. E. G., Peabody, C. O., and Taylor, B. T., Symposium on Detection and Use of Tritium in the Physical and Biological Sciences, I. A. E. A., Vienna, 1961, Paper No. TTS/79.

[11] Bainbridge, A. E., Suess, H. E., and Friedman, I., Nature, 192, 648 (1961).

[12] BNL-325, U. S. Government Printing Office, Washington, D. C.

2. MEASUREMENT OF THE RADIOACTIVITY OF TRITIUM

A. Introduction

The weak beta ray emitted by the decay of tritium is able to penetrate only a very short distance in matter (maximum range in aluminum is less than 0.6 mg per cm^2). Detection of this decay requires that the sensitive portion of the detector be no further than this from the site of decay, and usually the tritium atom is incorporated directly into the detection volume itself. The most popular methods for counting, at present, involve the placement of the tritium directly in the liquid scintillator for scintillation counting, or for complete conversion to a gas for assay in an ionization chamber or proportional counter. However, photographic-plate methods, which take advantage of the short range of the detected radiation to give unusually sharp radioautographs, as well as several other techniques, have been developed that have advantages for special circumstances. A detailed comparison of various counting methods has recently been published. [13]

The average energy released in tritium decay is approximately 5.7 kev, [14] and of course, ranges from 0 to the 18.6-kev maximum beta energy. In typical materials, the average beta will cause less than 200 ionizing events, and the low-energy tail will represent even fewer ionizations. One of the prime problems in any detector used for tritium arises from this small number of total ionizing events, and the necessity for distinguishing these from the noise background of the detector.

B. Scintillation Counting

A large part of the tritium assay work in the United States is presently being done by liquid scintillation counting. If the substance to be measured is compatible with a typical scintillator solution, such as p-terphenyl and POPOP in toluene, the material is simply added to it and assayed directly. The solution can be altered by the addition of dioxane to increase the solubility for water and permit direct assay of many aqueous solutions. [15-17]

---

[13] Christman, D., Nucleonics, 19 (5), 51 (1961).

[14] Gregory, D. P., and Landsman, D. A., Phys. Rev., 109, 2091 (1958); Pillinger, W., Hentges, J., and Blair, J., Phys. Rev., 121, 232 (1961).

[15] Hayes, F. N., Intern. J. Appl. Radiation and Isotopes, 1, 46 (1956).

[16] Haigh, C. P., Proc. Intern. Conf. Radioisotopes in Scientific Research, (UNESCO), 1, 663 (1958).

[17] Funt, B. L.,Can. J. Chem., 39, 711 (1961).

Many compounds, when present in too large a concentration, interfere with the scintillation process with a consequent decrease in efficiency of detection. Assurance that no quenching effect has occurred is frequently obtained by the further addition of a known amount of a standard sample for an immediate measurement of the counting efficiency. A very potent quenching agent, such as nitrobenzene, can reduce the counting efficiency by a factor of two, even at a concentration of 0.6 g per liter.[18]

The efficiency of detection from a scintillation solution is very dependent on the permissible background-count rate (or vice versa). The use of coincident detection by two photomultipliers in a refrigerated cabinet readily provides an efficiency of 12 per cent for toluene-soluble compounds, and 8 per cent for tritiated water (in dioxane-naphthalene solution), with a background of 100 CPM. A somewhat better performance can be obtained under some experimental conditions.[15, 19]

Scintillation counters can, of course, be operated using scintillation crystals or plastics, and will readily detect tritium either imbedded in, or adsorbed on, an uncoated surface. The necessity for incorporation in the scintillator usually makes this method less practical than liquid scintillation counting when samples are being analyzed on a regular basis.

Scintillation detectors have also been very useful in the detection of tritium present in a filter-paper strip, such as those obtained from paper chromatography or paper electrophoresis. A technique of spraying the strip with a scintillation solution of anthracene in benzene overcomes the difficulties arising from absorption of the weak beta, with a considerable increase in counting efficiency.[20]

C. Measurement of Tritium Activity in the Gas Phase

The decay of tritium in gaseous molecules can be conveniently detected with an ionization chamber, a proportional counter, or a Geiger counter. After deciding on a method for converting solid or liquid tritiated samples into a suitable gaseous form, any of the three detectors can be used satisfactorily. Almost all tritiated compounds can be converted successfully to a gaseous mixture of HT and CH_3T by combustion at 640 to 700°C[21] with a mixture

---

[18] Hayes, F. N., Intern. J. Appl. Radiation and Isotopes, 1, 284 (1956).

[19] Cameron, J. F., and Boyce, I. S., Intern. J. Appl. Radiation and Isotopes, 8, 228 (1960).

[20] Seliger, H. H., and Agranoff, B., Anal. Chem., 31, 1607 (1959).

[21] The combustion tube is made from Pyrex 1720 glass because of its mechanical strength at 700°C and its impermeability to tritium diffusion.

of zinc, nickelic oxide, and sufficient H_2O or paraffin. [22-25]

Many other gaseous conversion methods have been developed that provide a pure compound and, hence, a chemically reproducible gas. [26, 27] These methods normally require an additional step or more, and are most valuable with low-activity samples, for which it is desirable to get as much gas into the counter as convenient.

With more active samples, the tritiated gas is ordinarily supplemented in a counter with a much larger amount of a good filling gas in order to give reproducible counting characteristics. [28] Proportional-counter fillings give good plateaus for count rate vs. applied voltage despite the continuous low-energy beta spectrum.

Several pure hydrocarbons, or hydrocarbon-rare gas mixtures, are used in proportional-counter assays, and several per cent of most impurities can be tolerated without serious loss of accuracy in assay. Strongly electron-attaching gases, such as O_2 and CH_3I, will interfere with gas amplification, and will destroy the plateau when present in tenths of a per cent of total filling gas. A background-count rate of 60 CPM for a 100-ml counter surrounded by 2 inches of Pb is typical, with greater than 97 per cent efficiency for detection of decays within the active volume. Much lower backgrounds can be obtained with a low-level counting apparatus.

The ionization chamber will respond to all gaseous fillings very satisfactorily. However, the response is somewhat dependent on the actual gas composition and requires calibration for any important change in the macroscopic gas composition. The normal ionization-chamber sensitivity is not as low as the counter sensitivity, but it is also usually less affected in response by variations in gas composition.

―――――――
[22] Wilzbach, K. E., Kaplan, L., and Brown, W. G., Science, 118, 522 (1953); Wilzbach, K. E., van Dyken, A. R., and Kaplan, L., Anal. Chem., 26, 880 (1954).

[23] Rowland, F. S., Lee, J. K., and White, R. M., USAEC TID-7578, 1959, p. 39.

[24] Garnett, J. L., Hannan, W. K., and Law, S. W., Anal. Chim. Acta, 25, 170 (1961).

[25] Christman, D., and Paul, C., Anal. Chem., 32, 131 (1960).

[26] Simon, H., Daniel, H., and Klebe, J., Angew. Chem., 71, 303 (1959) describe conversion to HTO with $KClO_4$, counting as HT after reduction with Zn.

[27] References to many other gas-conversion procedures are given in Nucleonics, 16 (3), 63 (1958).

[28] In our laboratory, C. P.-grade propane is used as the normal filling gas. Commercially available counting-gas mixtures, such as helium-isobutane or argon-methane, can also be employed.

All the gas-phase detectors have been successfully operated
on the outlet end of flowing gas streams, especially for those
arising from gas-chromatographic separations.[29-32] Such counting techniques can be readily adapted to a variety of systems for
which continuous assay may be an advantage. For example, the
isotopic forms of hydrogen, HT, DT, and T_2, have been separated and analyzed by continuous assay of a gas-chromatographic
stream.[33] Labeled organometallics, silanes, etc., can be analyzed in a manner similar to that already applied extensively to
organic molecules.

Solid samples can also be counted directly if included inside the
counter. The short range of the beta makes the efficiency for
counting quite low except for extremely thin samples.[13]

D. Low-Level Measurement of Tritium

The interest in measurement of the tritium activity in the
natural environment has led to the design and operation of counting
facilities which routinely measure T/H ratios from 10^{-15} to
10^{-18}. Such counting facilities can also be utilized for measurement of extreme dilutions, in tracer experiments, for evidences of
very slow reactions, etc.[34]

Most of these facilities count tritium in the gas phase with a
large counter equipped with thick shielding and anticoincidence
counters. A complete description of a facility for low-level gas
counting of weak-beta emitters has been published,[35] and several
conversion methods have been used for getting suitable gas fillings.
The measurements of T/H ratios much smaller than 10^{-15}
require isotopic enrichment of the sample prior to counting.
Electrolysis of water, which leaves tritium behind preferentially,
is usually used for concentrating the heavier isotope in the residue.[36]

[29] Wolfgang, R., and Rowland, F. S., Anal. Chem., 30,
903 (1958).

[30] Wolfgang, R., and MacKay, C. F., Nucleonics, 16 (10),
69 (1958).

[31] Cacace, F., Nucleonics, 19 (5), 45 (1961).

[32] Lee, J. K., et al., Anal. Chem., in press.

[33] Gant, P., and Yang, K., Science, 129, 1548 (1959); Lee,
J. K., Musgrave, B., and Rowland, F. S., J. Chem. Phys., 32,
1266 (1960).

[34] Anderson, E. C., and Hayes, F. N., Ann. Rev. Nuclear
Sci., 6, 303 (1956).

[35] Libby, W. F., "Radiocarbon Dating," 2nd ed., Univ. of
Chicago Press, 1955.

[36] Kaufman, S., and Libby, W. F., Phys. Rev., 93, 1337
(1954); von Buttlar, H., and Libby, W. F., J. Inorg. & Nuclear
Chem., 1, 75 (1955).

Measurements of low T/H ratios by scintillation counting are
facilitated by inclusion of as much sample material in the scintillation solution as possible. Measurements can be made[37] down to
the $\mu\mu$curie per ml level, or T/H $\sim 10^{-15}$.

E. Autoradiography and Other Methods

The physical location of tritium radioactivity throughout thin
sections has been extensively used because of the sharp definition
obtained from the short-range beta. Successful application of this
method requires special preparation of the photographic plate to
permit intimate contact between the emulsion and the radioactive
material. The method is most widely used in biochemical and
biological studies, but adaptation to other systems is quite feasible.[38]

Tritium can be visibly detected in cloud chambers or in diffusion chambers in which its decay is characterized by its
extremely short ionization path.[39] The bremsstrahlung radiation
emitted in the deceleration of beta particles can also be used for
measurement of tritium in millicurie concentrations.[40]

3. CHEMICAL CHARACTERISTICS OF TRITIUM

A. Tritium-Exchange Reactions

The hydrogen atoms bonded to many elements undergo isotopic
exchange with other atoms similarly bonded with extreme rapidity,
often so rapidly that the isotopic composition of two components is
completely equilibrated before separation can be accomplished.

All O-H bonds, most N-H bonds, and generally all atom-
hydrogen bonds in which the atom has an unshared electron pair,
undergo very rapid exchange and do so even in the gas phase and
in inert solvents.[41,42] The rate constants for many of these

---

[37] Kaufman, W. J., Parks, G., Nir, A., and Hours, R. M.,
TID-7612, p. 239.

[38] Fitzgerald, P. J., Proc. Intern. Conf. Peaceful Uses
Atomic Energy, Geneva, 26, 208 (1958).

[39] Fireman, E. L., and Schwarzer, D., Phys. Rev., 94, 386
(1954).

[40] Westermark, T., Devell, L., and Ghanem, N. A., Nuclear
Instr. & Methods, 9, 141 (1960).

[41] Gold, V., and Satchell, D., Quart. Revs. (London), 9,
51 (1955).

[42] Roginsky, S., "Theoretical Principles of Isotope Methods
for Investigating Chemical Reactions," U.S.A.E.C. Translation
No. 2873.

reactions have recently been measured by NMR-relaxation techniques, and are as high as 10^{10} liter mole^{-1}sec^{-1} for H_2O + $H_3O^+ \longrightarrow H_3O^+ + H_2O$.[43] Hydrogen atoms bonded to nitrogen in ammonium salts, alkyl ammonium salts, and metal ammines are much less labile than the other N-H bonded atoms and have exchange times from minutes to hours under typical room-temperature conditions.[44-49]

The labeling of oxygen- and nitrogen-bonded hydrogen positions with tritium thus occurs very rapidly through isotopic exchange between any material containing labile tritium and the molecule whose labeling is desired. The exchange rates of the ammonium and metal ammine compounds, although slower than the above, are still rapid enough to make isotopic exchange by far the easiest synthetic route. Conversely, compounds with tritium bound into such labile positions can only be used as tracers under special circumstances in which this labile exchange with all other pools of labile hydrogen is either not important or can be satisfactorily handled.

Tritium atoms bonded to carbon are much less susceptible to exchange reactions with other hydrogen sources, and generally can be used quite satisfactorily as nonlabile tracers except under stringent conditions of strong acid or base, high temperature, etc. Isotopic exchange under these more drastic conditions is often a useful labeling method.

Less is known about the lability and the specific exchange rates of hydrogen atoms bonded to other central atoms. Sulfur- and phosphorus-bonded hydrogens exchange rapidly under some conditions, whereas the hydrogen bonds to silicon, tin, antimony, and germanium are often quite nonlabile.[41, 42] The possibility of isotopic exchange under each particular set of conditions should always be considered in tracer experiments with tritium.

---

[43] Meiboom, S., J. Chem. Phys., 34, 375 (1961) and earlier publications.

[44] Brodskii, A., and Sulima, L. Doklady Akad. Nauk. S.S.S.R., 74, 513 (1950).

[45] Kaplan, L., and Wilzbach, K., J. Am. Chem. Soc., 76, 2593 (1954).

[46] Swain, C. G., McKnight, J. T., Labes, M., and Kreiter, V. P., J. Am. Chem. Soc., 76, 4243 (1954).

[47] Swain, C. G., and Labes, M., J. Am. Chem. Soc., 79, 1084 (1957).

[48] Swain, C. G., McKnight, J. T., and Kreiter, V. P., J. Am. Chem. Soc., 79, 1088 (1957).

[49] Block, H., and Gold, V., J. Chem. Soc., 1959, 966; Anderson, J., Briscoe, H., and Spoor, N., J. Chem. Soc., 1943, 361.

B. Isotope Effects in Chemical Reactions and Equilibria

The mass ratio of tritium to protium is much greater than for any other pair of isotopes, with the consequence that the possible isotopic differences in reactions and in equilibria are extremely large, and easily measurable differences are quite frequent. The proper use of tritium as a tracer for protium requires careful consideration and evaluation of such isotopic differences, whereas quantitative measurement of their extent can provide much additional information about the course of a particular reaction.

The largest tritium-isotope effects are observed in kinetic studies, for reactions in which the tritium bond is intimately involved in the rate-determining step, as in its breakage in an oxidation reaction. Bigeleisen[50] has calculated that molecules with protium in such a position can react as much as 60 times more rapidly than the corresponding tritiated molecule at 25°C. In each system, the isotopic differences are enhanced as the temperature is lowered.

Even when the tritium bond is not directly involved in the chemical reaction, secondary isotope effects may also be observed. The limits for the ratio of reaction rates of the protium/tritium molecules have been calculated for some of these secondary effects, and range from 2.74 to 0.24 for hydrogen-oxygen bonds.[51] A ratio of less than one, corresponding to more rapid reaction of the tritiated molecule, is designated as an inverse-isotope effect. A large number of both normal- and inverse-isotope effects of varying magnitude have now been measured experimentally.[52] The secondary effects are not limited to atoms adjacent to those directly involved in the reaction, but are usually smaller the further away the label is from the position of chemical reaction in the molecule.

The theoretical basis for interpretation of hydrogen-isotope effects has been treated recently by several authors, and an extensive basis is available for their use in diagnostic measurements of the mechanism of chemical reaction.[51, 53-55]

Experiments in which the tracer molecule is used to follow the physical location of the entire molecule (i. e., those which do not involve bond rupture and/or formation in which the hydrogen atom is directly involved) will ordinarily be relatively free from isotopic differences.

---

[50] Bigeleisen, J., Science, 110, 14 (1949).

[51] Bigeleisen, J., and Wolfsberg, M., Advances in Chem. Phys., 1, 15 (1958).

[52] Weston, R., Ann. Revs. Nuclear Sci., 11, 439 (1961).

[53] Melander, L., "Isotope Effects on Reaction Rates," Ronald Press, New York, 1960.

[54] Westheimer, F., Chem. Revs., 61, 265 (1961).

[55] Bell, R. P., "The Proton in Chemistry," Methuen, London, 1959.

The equilibrium isotope effects are less than the kinetic isotope effects, but often are still readily measurable and important. As an example, the isotopic concentration of the tritium in saturated water vapor is less than that in the liquid phase in equilibrium with it, the ratio of concentrations varying from 0. 86 to 0. 97 between 0 and 90°C. [56]

Effects of similar magnitude will be widely observed in isotopic-exchange equilibria, etc., [42] and are largest for equilibria involving a strong and a weak bond for the exchanging hydrogen atoms.

4. GENERAL SYNTHETIC CONSIDERATIONS

A. Types of Labeled Molecules

The frequent occurrence of hydrogen atoms in several non-equivalent positions within a molecule makes it convenient to define three types of labeled molecule. A specifically labeled compound is one that contains all its radioactivity in only one of several nonequivalent hydrogen positions. A uniformly labeled molecule has radioactivity in all hydrogen positions, with the same ratio of T/H atoms in each position of the molecule. A compound is generally labeled if it is neither specific nor uniform, i. e., it has radioactivity in all or several positions of the molecule, with varying (or unknown) specific activities of tritium per position. The definition of uniform labeling is frequently relaxed to consider only the nonlabile positions in the molecule, or to ignore the variations in T/H ratios that arise from equilibrium isotopic effects.

The specifically labeled compound is preferable in most instances from the viewpoint of clarity of experimental results, since the source of the tritium can always be traced to a single molecular position. On the other hand, the compounds that are uniformly or generally labeled are often much more readily obtained. If the labeled group remains chemically intact throughout the experiment, all three types of labeled compounds are of about equal value.

B. Very High Specific-Activity Compounds

Protium-free tritiated molecules, or molecules with one pure tritium position in them, are very desirable for certain experiments, such as those in spectroscopy. The synthetic techniques usable for protium- and deuterium-free compounds or positions are much more limited in number than those available for high-specific-activity tracer syntheses, including only the direct chemical syntheses from a radioactive starting material.

---

[56] Sepall, O., and Mason, S. G., Can. J. Chem., 38, 2024 (1960).

Macroscopic quantities of tritium undiluted with protium are inevitably accompanied by a heavy flux of ionizing radiation from its own beta decay. An important consequence of this flux is the rapid introduction of radiation-induced chemical impurities in any freshly synthesized compound of very high specific activity. [57] Consequently, these syntheses will usually begin with the tritium present in a simple form, usually T_2 or T_2O, and both synthesis and experiment will be completed as quickly as possible.

The maximum isotopic purity of tritium available for such experiments is considerably greater than 90 per cent, and depends upon the freedom from protium of the whole production process. [58] An analysis of one recent commercial sample of T_2 showed HT (0.57 per cent), DT (0.25 per cent), and tritiated methane (0.22 percent) as radioactive impurities. [59]

C. General Synthetic Methods for Tritium Syntheses

Tritium has become very widely used in the last several years as a tracer material, especially in compounds of biochemical, biological, and organic chemical interest. [60] Several general types of synthesis have been available for many years for hydrogen-containing molecules, and some additional methods have been developed recently that are especially applicable to more complex molecules. The most important of these techniques[61] are: (a) direct chemical synthesis from at least one radioactive starting material; (b) isotopic exchange between a suitable radioactive material and the compound to be labeled; and (c) "energetic" syntheses in which tritium substitution occurs during chemical reactions initiated by tritium β-decay, gamma radiation, electric discharge, kinetic energy from nuclear recoil, etc.

The direct chemical synthesis usually offers the best control over the position of the label in the final product, and is therefore preferable when technically feasible. Syntheses involving protium-free tritium positions must be done in this manner. Such syntheses

---

[57] Approximately 1 per cent of the molecules in pure T_2 gas will be ionized every four hours from the direct interaction of emitted tritium betas. The exact value depends to some extent on the surface/volume ratio of the container, as well as on the sample density.

[58] The production of tritium from neutron-bombarded lithium has been described by Massey, B. J., U.S. Atomic Energy Commission, ORNL-2238.

[59] Yang, K., and Gant, P., J. Chem. Phys., 31, 1589 (1959).

[60] The current U.S.A.E.C. price of $2.00 per curie (plus handling charges) makes tritium the least-expensive isotope available.

[61] Biosynthesis from a radioactive environment is also useful for complex organic molecules.

can yield specifically or otherwise labeled compounds according to needs.

The isotopic-exchange syntheses offer a very convenient method of introducing tritium after the rest of the synthesis has been performed, or for the preparation of the desired labeled substance in a single step from available commercial materials. The only general requirement for such syntheses is that conditions must be found under which the isotopic exchange is more rapid than chemical deterioration of the compound from other reactions imposed by the exchange conditions. Isotopic-exchange syntheses very often lead to uniformly or generally labeled compounds, when more than one hydrogen position is present in the molecule.

The most widely used energetic synthesis is the self-irradiation of a mixture of T_2 and a target compound by the tritium betas to give isotopic substitution of the tritium for hydrogen in the target compound.[62] The greatest virtue of this method is that it requires a single chemical manipulation, the mixing of the two ingredients, for the synthesis. However, the molecules that are formed are generally labeled, and many other radioactive compounds are simultaneously created during the self-irradiation. This synthetic technique has been applied to hundreds of organic molecules to date, and has strong advantages only when the desired molecule is rather complex and cannot readily be made by direct syntheses or isotopic exchange. Syntheses of tritiated organometallics and molecules with organic ligands will certainly be performed by this techinque in the future. Specific radioactivities as high as 10^9 to 10^8 DPM per mg are typical. It is important to recognize that the Wilzbach technique requires subsequent radiochemical purification of the target material in all cases.

Some compounds, such as those containing olefinic groups, have proved rather difficult to label by the Wilzbach technique, and other energetic methods may be preferable in these instances.[63-65] Comparisons and reviews of several of these methods have been published.[66, 67]

------

[62] Wilzbach, K., J. Am. Chem. Soc., **79**, 1013 (1957); Wilzbach, K., Symposium on the Detection and Use of Tritium in the Physical and Biological Sciences, I. A. E. A., Vienna, 1961, Paper No. TTS/83.

[63] Dorfman, L., and Wilzbach, K., J. Phys. Chem., **63**, 799 (1959).

[64] Lemmon, R. M., Tolbert, B. M., Strohmeier, W., and Whittemore, I. M., Science, **129**, 1740 (1959).

[65] Ghanem, N. A., and Westermark, T., J. Am. Chem. Soc., **83**, 4432 (1960).

[66] Rowland, F. S., Proc. Intern. Conf. Peaceful Uses Atomic Energy, Geneva, **20**, 87 (1958).

[67] Wolf, A. P., Ann. Revs. Nuclear Sci., **10**, 259 (1960).

The Wilzbach self-irradiation technique is offered as a commercial service for a nominal fee by several companies. The T_2
gas itself is removed from the sample, and the purchaser need not
have the facilities required for handling curie quantities of tritium.
The most important subsequent requirement for such compounds is
that the purchaser needs to have the chemical capability for
removal of the other labeled compounds present, which are often
very similar in chemical structure to the target molecule. [62]
Through this method, a supply of the tritiated compound can frequently be obtained with a minimum of effort and cost, even though
the compound itself has not been listed as commercially available.

D. Tritium and Deuterium as Tracers

Essentially, every synthetic procedure listed in Chap. 2
(Deuterium) can be used almost intact for the preparation of the
corresponding tritium-labeled molecule. The tritium syntheses
must be performed with proper precautions for the radioactivity
involved, but the general equipment and conditions for synthesis
should be quite similar. If the tritium synthesis has not yet been
reported in the literature, the deuterium synthesis is very useful
as a guide.

The chief advantage that tritium has over deuterium as a tracer
is the much greater sensitivity with which it can be detected and,
in general, the lower cost of the analytical method. Moreover, at
typical tracer levels (10^3 to 10^6 DPM per mg compound), the
radiation effects accompanying the beta decay are negligible in
almost all systems. At higher levels of activity, of course, the
radiation can influence the system, and the behaviors of pure
deuterated and tritiated molecules are often not directly comparable for this reason. When tritium is being used as a tracer and
beta decay is suspected of perturbing the experimental system,
such effects can usually be tested for through parallel experiments
with tracers differing by a factor of ten in specific activity.

E. Equipment for Handling Tritium

The weak-beta particles emitted by tritium are effectively
absorbed by the walls of any laboratory vessel, making extra
shielding unnecessary even for multicurie-level operations. The
basic equipment for tritium handling and synthesis is therefore
the same as for the corresponding protium work, with modification
to prevent loss or escape of the tritiated material. In general,
experiments can be set up in moderate- to high-speed hoods as a
precautionary measure.

Tritiated hydrogen can be readily manipulated and recovered in
a standard-vacuum line with the addition of a uranium furnace.
Powdered uranium absorbs hydrogen and tritium very rapidly at
room temperature, forming $UH_3\text{-}\underline{t}$. The vapor pressure of

H_2-t (g) in equilibrium with the solid is so low that the hydrogen is, in effect, completely removed from the system as the hydride.[68] The gas is simply regenerated by heat.

A thorough description of a system for handling tritium gas is available in the literature.[69]

5. SPECIFIC SYNTHETIC METHODS

A. Nomenclature

The inorganic tritium syntheses summarized below are organized generally according to the system of "Inorganic Syntheses" (see ref. 85), in which the atom to which the hydrogen is bonded determines the group to which it belongs. Separate descriptions are given, first for the various isotopic molecular hydrogens, for water, and for some general techniques applicable to many compounds of varied characteristics. Syntheses intended to produce protium- and deuterium-free tritium in particular positions of the molecule are designated HT, TCl, etc. Syntheses that do not give this purity are designated as H_2-t, HCl-t, etc. However, these syntheses when performed with T_2 or T_2O often give specific activities almost as high as the same molecule with pure tritium in one position.

B. Wilzbach Synthesis[62]

This energetic synthesis utilizes the radiation accompanying T_2 to incorporate tritium into the target compound. The amount of sample and of tritium can be varied within wide limits, but quite satisfactory results have been obtained for solids with approximately 10 curies of tritium and 1 g of an organic target material sealed in glass tubes 1 cm in diameter and 10 cm long, and allowed to stand at room temperature for 1 to 2 weeks. The solid should be as finely divided as possible to facilitate intimate contact between the tritium gas and the material surface. Homogeneous gas-phase irradiations can be more conveniently carried out with larger bulbs,[62] in order to reduce the surface/volume ratio effect.

The experimental variations of this method, in which additional energy is provided to the system through electric discharge and ultraviolet light, have been described.[62-65]

---

[68] Spedding, F. H., et al., Nucleonics, 4 (1), 1 (1949); 4 (2), 17 (1949).

[69] Isbell, H., and Moyer, J. D., J. Research Natl. Bur. Standards, 63A, 177 (1959).

C. Tritiated Hydrogen

T_2. Most of the commercially produced tritium is isolated as very high specific activity T_2,[70] from neutron-irradiated lithium alloys. It contains varying amounts of H and D atoms, He^3-decay-product impurity, and small amounts of carbonaceous materials, mostly as methane. The He^3 and carbonaceous compounds can be eliminated by diffusion through hot palladium or nickel.[71] If necessary, the HT and DT impurities could be removed by gas-chromatographic separation.

The separation of T_2 into its ortho and para forms has not yet been reported, and will probably require lower gas-chromatographic column temperatures than those used in the separation of o-H_2 from p-H_2, and o-D_2 from p-D_2.

HT, free from H_2 and T_2.   The reaction of lithium aluminum hydride with water produces hydrogen molecules, almost all of which have one atom each from the hydride and the water.[72] Molecular HT, practically free from H_2 and T_2, can be produced by using either reactant in the protium-free tritiated form. Tritium hydride gas has been synthesized by the reaction of T_2O on an outgassed slurry of $LiAlH_4$ in n-butyl ether at 0°C. The detailed procedure of Wender and Orchin was followed with the omission of a carrier gas.[73] The final product contained 0.4 per cent T_2.

DT, free from D_2 and T_2.   This can be made following the procedure[72] for HT by using $LiAlD_4$ and T_2O.

H_2-t or D_2-t.   Freshly prepared mixtures of T_2 with H_2 (or D_2) can be equilibrated quickly by heating the mixing bulb or by discharging a Tesla coil to the bulb or to an electrode that passes into the bulb. If the T_2 is not greatly diluted by the inactive gas, radiation effects will rapidly cause equilibration.[74]

Reduction of tritiated H_2O or D_2O over zinc will also give the equilibrium mixture.

---

[70] The specific activity of T_2 is 2.63 curies/ml at NTP.

[71] Pratt, T., and Wolfgang, R., J. Am. Chem. Soc., 83, 10 (1961).

[72] Wender, I., Friedel, R. A., and Orchin, M., J. Am. Chem. Soc., 71, 1140 (1949); Orchin, M., and Wender, I., Anal. Chem., 21, 875 (1949).

[73] Wexler, S., J. Inorg. & Nuclear Chem., 10, 8 (1959).

[74] At ordinary temperatures, the equilibrium constant for $H_2 + T_2 \rightleftarrows 2HT$ is less than the statistical value of 4 because of isotopic effects. The equilibrium constant is given as 2.56 at 25°C by Urey, H. C., J. Chem. Soc., 1947, 562.

D. Water

T_2O. Tritium oxide nearly free from protium can be synthesized from T_2 by several oxidation methods. Once made, the water begins to undergo radiation decomposition to T_2 and T_2O_2. However, the radiolysis of water in closed systems quickly reaches a steady-state condition in which back-reactions resynthesize the water molecule just as rapidly as it is decomposed. [75]

T_2O has been synthesized by oxidation of T_2 over hot CuO. [76] In this procedure, if protium or deuterium is present in the T_2 gas, small amounts of HTO and DTO will be present either through co-production or exchange with T_2O.

H_2O-t. Tritiated water can be satisfactorily prepared from T_2 or H_2-t by many methods. Oxidation with platinic oxide in the presence of carrier water has been described. The specific activity depends upon the amount of carrier added and can presumably be carried out[79] with pure T_2 and dry platinic oxide to give T_2O. Very detailed directions for a similar procedure are also available. [69]

Tritium is formed by neutron irradiation of inorganic lithium salts and remains trapped in the crystal indefinitely at room temperatures. Dissolution of the crystal in a small amount of water (or other material containing labile hydrogen positions) introduces the tritium activity into the labile position. Distillation of the solvent then frees the active material from the inorganic salt. Irradiated $LiNO_3$ contains 4.0×10^7 DPM of tritium per mg after a 1-week exposure at 10^{12} neutrons per cm^2 sec. [78]

E. Group I

$LiH-t$. Tritiated lithium hydride has been prepared by heating 200-mesh LiH with tritium-containing hydrogen gas in a Pyrex flask at 350°C. The labeled lithium hydride so produced can be used to prepare HT by exchange with hydrogen gas at 200°C. This exchange goes to completion in about 24 hours.

F. Group II

CaH_2-t. Tritiated calcium hydride has been prepared for re-

[75] Allen, A. O., "The Radiation Chemistry of Water and Aqueous Solutions," Van Nostrand, Princeton, 1961.

[76] Staats, P., Morgan, H., and Goldstein, J. H., J. Chem. Phys., 24, 916 (1956).

[77] Swain, C. G., and Kresge, A. J., J. Am. Chem. Soc., 80, 5281 (1958).

[78] Hoff, W. J., Jr., and Rowland, F. S., J. Inorg. & Nuclear Chem., 5, 164 (1958).

[79] Wilzbach, K., and Kaplan, L., J. Am. Chem. Soc., 72, 5795 (1950).

action with organic compounds, especially alkyl halides. Finely divided calcium metal dispersed on fire brick was prepared by heating CaH_2 to decomposition while evacuating. The tritide was then synthesized by addition of tritiated hydrogen gas, giving a very finely divided CaH_2-t with high efficiency for reaction with organic vapors passed through the column. [80]

G. Group III

NaBH$_4$-t. The introduction of high-specific-activity tritium into particular compounds through the use of tritiated reducing agents offers many synthetic advantages. The important reagents in this category are all available commercially and can also be readily formed from tritiated hydrogen. A detailed description of apparatus for their preparation and handling during and after synthesis has been published (specifically for $LiBH_4$-t). [69]

The preparation of $NaBH_4$-t can be easily done through isotopic exchange between T_2 and the inactive $NaBH_4$. A recrystallized sample of the latter is placed in a 25-cc Pyrex tube lined with nickel foil to prevent decomposition of the borohydride by glass. The sample is then preheated for 1 hour with tank hydrogen at 350°C. The reaction vessel is then evacuated and filled with a tritiated-hydrogen mixture of the desired specific activity; after being heated to 350°C for 8 hours, the exchange of hydrogen between H_2 and $NaBH_4$ is essentially complete. The quantity of gas remains constant during the exchange experiment, although some increase in pressure may be observed during the preheating. The active hydrogen is then pumped off, usually to powdered uranium, and the $NaBH_4$-t is ready for subsequent use. [81]

LiBH$_4$-t. The exchange reaction between tritiated hydrogen and $LiBH_4$ is carried out as with the $NaBH_4$-t synthesis, except that the exchange proceeds at a convenient rate at 200°C. The preheating with hydrogen was then carried out at 200°C, also.

The tritiated lithium borohydride has also been converted to $LiB(OCH_3$-t$)_4$ by reduction with methyl formate in tetrahydrofuran solution. [82]

B$_2$H$_6$-t. Tritiated diborane has been prepared through the exchange reaction at 55°C of gaseous HT (and of DT) with B_2H_6. After exchange, hydrogen was pumped off while the B_2H_6-t was frozen with liquid nitrogen. [83]

---

[80] Stöcklin, G., Schmidt-Bleek, F., and Herr, W., Angew. Chem., 73, 220 (1961).

[81] Brown, W. G., Kaplan, L., and Wilzbach, K. E., J. Am. Chem. Soc., 74, 1343 (1952).

[82] Smith, N. H., Wilzbach, K., and Brown, W. G., J. Am. Chem. Soc., 77, 1033 (1955).

[83] Rigden, J. S., and Koski, W. S., J. Am. Chem. Soc., 83, 3037 (1961).

LiAlH₄-t. Lithium aluminum hydride-t has been prepared by the reaction of LiH-t and aluminum chloride in ether solution. [79]

H. Group IV

This group includes hundreds of organic compounds that have been labeled with tritium and a very rapidly increasing number that are available commercially. Most of the common organic ligands or functional groupings used in inorganic syntheses are already available, whereas those that are not can usually be synthesized easily by the Wilzbach method. [62, 79, 82]

TCN. Hydrogen cyanide with very little protium present has been synthesized by the direct reaction of T_2O vapor with solid $P(CN)_3$. [84] The T_2O was synthesized by oxidation of T_2 gas over hot CuO. The $P(CN)_3$ was prepared by the reaction of AgCN and PCl_3, followed by sublimation at 170°C. A very detailed description of the $P(CN)_3$ preparation has been published. [85]

The TCN gas is unstable because of the high radiation level, and reacts spontaneously. Eighty per cent of the gaseous compound polymerized in the first 12 hours.

(R)₃SiH-t. Tritiated triphenylsilane has been prepared by the reaction of LiAlH₄-t with triphenylchlorosilane, and purified by fractional distillation at reduced pressure. [86] Tri-n-propyl-silane-t was similarly obtained by the reduction of tri-n-propyl-chlorosilane. [86]

I. Group V

Hydrogen atoms bonded to elements of group V are all relatively labile, and most syntheses except protium-free preparations are performed by isotopic exchange.

NH₃-t. Ammonia has been labeled with tritium by liberating it from a solution of ammonium chloride in tritiated water. To avoid isotopic dilution, the aqueous solution can be treated with metallic sodium and the resultant ammonia-molecular hydrogen gas mixture purified by gas-phase preferential evaporation at liquid-nitrogen temperatures.

(Et)₃NHCl-t. Triethyl ammonium chloride-t was prepared by solution of the unlabeled salt in tritiated water. The water was removed under vacuum, and the salt was heated until it sublimed vigorously. The sample was then recrystallized twice from a

---

[84] Staats, P. A., Morgan, H. W., and Goldstein, J. H., J. Chem. Phys., 25, 582 (1956).

[85] J. C. Bailar, Jr. (ed.), "Inorganic Syntheses, "Vol. VI, McGraw-Hill, New York, 1960, p. 84.

[86] Kaplan, L., and Wilzbach, K., J. Am. Chem. Soc., 74, 6152 (1952); 77, 1297 (1955).

2:1 acetone-absolute ethanol mixture.[48]

NH_4NO_3-t; $(Et)_2NH_2Cl$-t; $(Me)_3NHCl$-t. All three salts have been tritiated by isotopic exchange between the inactive salt and tritiated butyl alcohol in chloroform solution. The half-times for exchange at 0°C with 0.1 $\underline{M}$ concentrations of salt and alcohol were 2 minutes for trimethyl ammonium chloride, 10 hours for diethyl ammonium chloride, and 3 minutes for ammonium nitrate.[45]

H_3PO_3-t. Hypophosphorous acid labeled with tritium in the P-H bonds has been prepared by isotope exchange between H_3PO_3 and H_2O-t in acid solution. The exchange proceeds with measurable speed, and is essentially complete in 1 day at 25°C. Washing with water removes the labile activity.[88]

J. Group VI

UH_3-t. Uranium hydride has been shown to undergo isotopic exchange very rapidly with hydrogen even at -80°C, and the tritiated hydride has been made both by exchange[89] and by addition of T_2 to powdered uranium (from the evacuation, during heating, of uranium hydride).[90,91]

K. Group VII

TCl. Tritium chloride was prepared by the reduction of AgCl with T_2 at about 700°C.[92] It has also been prepared by the action of ultraviolet light on a mixture of T_2 and Cl_2.[93]

TBr. Tritium bromide has been prepared by the reaction of T_2 and Br_2 at a hot filament,[92] and by the action of ultraviolet light on the same mixture.[93]

[87] Guttman, J. R., and Wolfsberg, M., J. Chem. Phys., 33, 1592 (1960).

[88] Jenkins, W. A., and Yost, D. M., J. Inorg. & Nuclear Chem., 11, 297 (1959).

[89] Bigeleisen, J., and Kant, A., J. Am. Chem. Soc., 76, 5957 (1954); this reference pertains to the UH_3-HD exchange only, but similar considerations are valid for the systems UH_3-HT or UH_3-T_2 with appropriate modification.

[90] Felter, R., and Currie, L., Symposium on the Detection and Use of Tritium in the Physical and Biological Sciences, Vienna, 1961, Paper No. TTS/21.

[91] Wenzel, M., Wollenberg, H., and Schulze, P., Symposium on the Detection and Use of Tritium in the Physical and Biological Sciences, Vienna, 1961, Paper No. TTS/66.

[92] Jones, L. H., and Robinson, E. S., J. Chem. Phys., 24, 1246 (1956).

[93] Burrus, C., Gordy, W., Benjamin, B., and Livingston, R., Phys. Rev., 97, 1661 (1955).

HCl-t. Tritium-labeled hydrogen chloride has been prepared by the distillation of tritiated water onto phosphorus pentachloride. The resulting tritiated hydrogen chloride was carefully dried by passage through an efficient, multiple freeze-out trap cooled in a dry ice-acetone mixture. [94] It has also been prepared by bubbling dry protium chloride through two successive, 1-ml portions of concentrated sufluric acid rich in tritium. [95]

Another preparation for HCl-t was carried out through the exchange reaction between T_2 and dry HCl over a hot platinum wire at about 860° C. [96]

L. Tritiated Metals in Nonstoichiometric Ratios

Metal foils capable of retaining tritium are desirable as targets and as radiation sources in some applications. These have been prepared by the reaction of T_2 gas with a metal surface of zirconium[97] or titanium. [98] The composition of these foils is not necessarily stoichiometric, although tritide formation does occur.

[94] Klein, F. , and Wolfsberg, M. , J. Chem. Phys. , 34, 1494 (1961).

[95] Satchell, D. P. N. , J. Chem. Soc. , 1960, 4388.

[96] Comyns, A. E. , Howald, R. , and Willard, J. E. , J. Am. Chem. Soc. , 78, 3989 (1956).

[97] Arrol, W. J. , Wilson, E. J. , and Evans, C. , AERE I/R 1135 (1953).

[98] Gow, J. D. , and Pollocks, H. C. , Rev. Sci. Instr. , 31, 235 (1960).

4

Nitrogen-15

W. SPINDEL

Rutgers, The State University

Newark, New Jersey

1. INTRODUCTION AND GENERAL LITERATURE SURVEY

In the three decades since the discovery by Naude[1] of a rarer heavy stable isotope of nitrogen in the band spectrum of nitric oxide, a very voluminous literature has developed concerning its concentration from naturally occurring material, as well as its use as a tracer in inorganic chemical systems and, even more significantly, in organic and biochemical systems. Chapman and Broida[2] have compiled a bibliography listing over 400 references to the literature appearing through 1952, including a few later references relating to the natural abundance of N^{15}, its physical properties, methods of concentration, methods of analysis for N^{15}/N^{14}, and the synthesis and uses of labeled compounds. Begun's[3] recent compilation of abstracts of unclassified literature on isotope separation and isotope exchange contains numerous references, through 1957, to work with N^{15}. These include both work reported in the published literature and in declassified laboratory documents. The paper by Stranks and Wilkins[4] on isotopic tracer investigations in inorganic chemistry serves as an excellent general review of the insights into reaction mechanisms and molecular structure, which have been obtained in inorganic systems by the applications of tracer techniques, and includes extensive tables that comprehensively cover the work with N^{15} through March 1957. Clusius[5] has written a review of the earlier portion of the prolific and careful studies that he and his co-workers have carried out on the reactions of N^{15} and the physical properties of its compounds; it should be useful to those

[1] Naude, S. M., Phys. Rev., 34, 1498 (1929); **36**, 333 (1930).

[2] Chapman, M. W., and Broida, H. P., Natl. Bur. Standards (U.S.) Circ. 575, Oct. 1, 1956.

[3] Begun, G. M., Isotope Separation and Isotope Exchange, ORNL-2852, 1959.

[4] Stranks, D. R., and Wilkins, G. W., Chem. Revs., 57, 743 (1957).

[5] Clusius, K., Angew. Chem., 66, 497 (1954).

working with this nuclide.

The recent book by Melander,[6] as well as the review by Bigeleisen and Wolfsberg[7] and the book by Roginsky[8] (available in an English translation), all review the underlying theory of isotope effects in chemical reactions. These references will be of interest to anyone using N^{15}-labeled compounds to study differences in the kinetic and equilibrium properties of isotopically substituted materials. Those employing N^{15}-labeled compounds merely as tracers for natural nitrogen need rarely be concerned about a significant error in such experiments, owing to the difference in reaction rates between the isotopes. Nonetheless, they may wish to consult the above references for a critical evaluation of the conditions under which an isotope effect may be observed and for an indication of its magnitude.

2. STABLE AND RADIOACTIVE NUCLIDES—PROPERTIES AND ABUNDANCES

Although several radioactive isotopes of the element nitrogen are well known, very few studies[9-12] have utilized these as tracers, in spite of the relative ease and sensitivity of radioactivity counting techniques. The known radionuclides of nitrogen are listed in Table 1, and it may be noted that their half-lives are all inconveniently short for chemical studies.

In addition to the common isotope of mass number 14, naturally occurring nitrogen also contains a heavier stable isotope of mass 15. The abundance of this isotope has been measured by numerous investigators since its discovery by Naude.[1] The most reliable value for the natural abundance is 0.365 atom per cent

[6] Melander, L., "Isotope Effects on Reaction Rates," Ronald Press, New York, 1960.

[7] Bigeleisen, J., and Wolfsberg, M., Theoretical and Experimental Aspects of Isotope Effects in Chemical Kinetics, in "Advances in Chemical Physics," Vol. I, Interscience, New York, 1958, Chap. II.

[8] Roginsky, S. Z., "Theoretical Principles of Isotope Methods for Investigating Chemical Reactions," Academy of Sciences USSR Press, Moscow, 1956. (Available in English translation from Office of Technical Services, Department of Commerce, Washington 25, D.C. as AEC-tr-2873.)

[9] Nishina, Y., Iimori, T., Kubo, H., and Nakayama, H., J. Chem. Phys., 9, 571 (1941).

[10] Norris, T. H., Ruben, S., and Kamen, M. D., J. Chem. Phys., 9, 726 (1941).

[11] Ogg, R. A., Jr., J. Chem. Phys., 15, 613 (1947).

[12] Meier, D., and Garner, C., J. Chem. Phys., 17, 1344 (1949).

Table 1
Properties of the Radioactive Nitrogen Nuclides[13]

Nuclide	Half-life	Decay mode	Energy, Mev
N^{12}	1.25×10^{-2} sec	β^+	16.6
N^{13}	10.05 min	β^+	1.24
N^{16}	7.38 sec	β^-	4.2, 10.3 (γ 6.13)
N^{17}	4.14 sec	β^-	3.7

as determined by Nier.[14] The abundance of N^{15} varies slightly in different naturally occurring sources of the element, as indeed do the isotopes of all the lighter elements.[15] Dole and co-workers[16] have measured the N^{15} abundance in air samples taken at elevations up to 50 km. Hoering[17] and Parwel et al.[18] have measured its abundance in a wide variety of naturally occurring substances of both mineral and biological origin. The largest variations in abundance found differed from the value reported by Nier[14] by about 1 per cent. Most workers agree that the deviations in isotopic abundance of nitrogen in different naturally occurring sources are less than the variations found for isotopes of other elements of similar mass (i.e., carbon and oxygen). In contrast to this constancy of N^{15} content for natural sources of nitrogen, Clusius[19] has recently reported a strikingly decreased N^{15} content in certain manufactured nitrate and nitrite salts, arising from isotopic fractionation in the manufacturing process. He found that the salts produced as by-products of nitric acid contained only 0.309 per cent N^{15}, whereas the acid produced contained approximately the normal atmospheric abundance of 0.365 per cent. These findings emphasize the need for caution in using such manufactured compounds as reference standards in isotopic analyses.

13 Hollander, J. M., Perlman, I., and Seaborg, G. T., Revs. Modern Phys., 25, 469 (1953).

14 Nier, A. O., Phys. Rev., 77, 789 (1950).

15 Urey, H. C., J. Chem. Soc., 1947, 567.

16 Dole, M., Lane, G. A., Rudd, D. P., and Zaukelies, D. A., Geochim. et Cosmochim. Acta, 6, 65 (1954).

17 Hoering, T., Natl. Acad. Sci. -Natl. Research Council, Publ. No. 400, 39 (1956).

18 Parwel, A., Rhyage, R., and Wickman, F. E., Geochim. et Cosmochim. Acta, 11, 165 (1957).

19 Clusius, K., and Piesbergen, U., Helv. Chim. Acta, 43, 1562 (1960).

3. CONCENTRATION OF N^{15}

Because of its usefulness for tracer and isotope-effect studies, a variety of methods has been explored for concentrating the heavy stable isotope of nitrogen in laboratory quantities. More recently, an added incentive for such studies has been the possibility that large quantities of highly enriched N^{15} may have nuclear reactor applications because of the low thermal neutron absorption cross section of N^{15} (2. 4 $\times$ 10^{-5} barns) as compared to ordinary nitrogen (1. 8 barns). Several approaches have successfully produced relatively high concentrations of the isotope, and in the last decade most of the research on this problem has been concerned with improving the efficiency of separation process, i. e. , to increase the N^{15} assay of the separated material, reduce the power consumption and size of apparatus required, and to achieve higher yields of highly concentrated isotope from simpler systems.

The Hertz[20] gaseous diffusion process was used by Kruger[21, 22] and by Wooldridge and co-workers[23, 24] to prepare milligram quantities of nitrogen gas enriched several times in N^{15}. Beams and Haynes, [25] used a gas centrifuge to partially fractionate the isotopes in gaseous nitrogen, and Hutchison[26] tried the electrolysis of an aqueous solution of ammonium chloride.

The techniques that have been most successful in preparing highly concentrated N^{15} have involved various modifications of either chemical exchange, thermal diffusion, or distillation.

Urey and co-workers[27] developed an isotope-separation process utilizing exchange between ammonia gas and a solution of

---

[20] Hertz, G. , Z. Physik, 91, 810 (1934).
[21] Kruger, H. , Naturwiss., 26, 445 (1938).
[22] Kruger, H. , Z. Physik, 111, 467 (1939).
[23] Wooldridge, D. E. , and Jenkins, F. A. , Phys. Rev. , 49, 704 (1936).
[24] Wooldridge, D. E. , and Smythe, W. R. , Phys. Rev. , 50, 233 (1936).
[25] Beames, T. W. , and Haynes, F. B. , Phys. Rev. , 50, 491 (1936).
[26] Hutchison, D. A. , Phys. Rev. , 75, 1303 (1949).
[27] Urey, H. C. , Huffman, J. R. , Thode, H. G. , and Fox, M. , J. Chem. Phys. , 5, 856 (1937); Thode, H. G. , and Urey, H. C. , ibid, 7, 34 (1939).

ammonium nitrate. This process has been used extensively[28-31] for the production of N^{15}.

Several modifications of this process have been described recently. Begun et al.[32] have suggested the use of ammonium carbonate in place of ammonium nitrate to reduce the cost of the chemicals consumed, and Spedding and co-workers[33] have used ion exchange resin columns instead of a packed distillation column to reduce the size of the apparatus required.

The exchange between nitric oxide gas and either an aqueous nitric acid solution or liquid N_2O_3 has been utilized by Taylor and co-workers,[34-37] to prepare highly concentrated N^{15}. The system using aqueous nitric acid is currently being used for the commercial preparation of laboratory quantities of the separated isotope.[38,38a]

Clusius[39] used nitrogen gas in a cascade of thermal diffusion columns to produce highly concentrated N^{15}, but the quantity of separated isotope obtained was very small, because of the low transport rates in the gaseous system.

Until recently, distillation, which has proved quite effective for concentrating isotopes of several of the lighter elements, was found not to be particularly effective for separating nitrogen

[28] Stewart, D. W., Nucleonics, 1, 25 (1947).

[29] Becker, E. W., and Baumgartel, H., Z. Naturforsch., 1, 514 (1946); Angew. Chem., A59, 88 (1947).

[30] Sugimoto, A., Nakane, R., and Watanabe T., Bull. Chem. Soc. Japan, 24, 153 (1951).

[31] Panchenkov, I. G. M., Semiokhin, I. A., Renzaeva, A. A., Molchanov, V. V., and Kalashnikov, O. P., Zhur. Fiz. Khim., 31, 1352 (1957).

[32] Begun, G. M., Palko, A. A., and Brown, L. L., J. Phys. Chem., 60, 48 (1956).

[33] Spedding, F. H., Powell, J. E., and Svec, H. J., J. Am. Chem. Soc., 77, 1393 (1955).

[34] Spindel, W., and Taylor, T. I., J. Chem. Phys., 23, 981 (1955); 24, 626 (1956); Trans. N. Y. Acad. Sci., 19, 3 (1956).

[35] Taylor, T. I., and Spindel, W., Proceedings of the International Symposium on Isotope Separation, North Holland Publishing Company, Amsterdam, 1958, p. 158.

[36] Monse, E. U., Spindel, W., Kauder, L. N., and Taylor, T. I., J. Chem. Phys. 32, 1557 (1960).

[37] Monse, E. U., Taylor, T. I., and Spindel, W., in press.

[38] Begun, G. M., Drury, J. S., and Joseph, E. F., Ind. Eng. Chem., 51, 1035 (1959).

[38a] Isomet Corp., Palisades Park, New Jersey.

[39] Clusius, K., Helv. Chim. Acta, 33, 2134 (1950).

isotopes. Attempts made with ammonia,[40] nitrogen,[41] and nitrogen tetroxide[42] have met with only limited success. Clusius and co-workers, however, in a series of recent papers[43-48] have found remarkably high vapor pressure ratios for isotopic nitric oxides in the region of the triple-point temperature, 110° K, and have demonstrated that distillation of nitric oxide provides a very effective method for simultaneously concentrating the rarer isotopes of nitrogen and oxygen.

4. METHODS OF ANALYSIS

The mass spectrometer has proved to be so universally useful an instrument for isotopic analysis, as to completely overshadow all other analytical techniques in this area. Nevertheless, a number of other instrumental methods has been used for N^{15} determinations, and should be mentioned here, not only for the sake of completeness, but because they require much less costly equipment, and some of the techniques are less sensitive to interfering impurities.

A gas density balance has been used by Clusius and co-workers[49,50] for the measurement of N^{15}, but the particular sensitivity of this method to traces of any foreign gas impurities causes inordinate difficulties in sample preparation. Workers at

---

[40] Wahl, M. H., Huffman, J. F., and Hipple, J. A., Jr., J. Chem. Phys., 3, 434 (1935).

[41] Krauss, A., German Pat. No. 632,071 (July 2, 1936).

[42] Begun, G. M., J. Chem. Phys., 25, 1279 (1956).

[43] Clusius, K., and Schleich, K., Helv. Chim. Acta, 41, 1342 (1958).

[44] Clusius, K., Vecchi, M., Fischer, A., and Piesbergen, U., Helv. Chim. Acta, 42, 1975 (1959).

[45] Clusius, K., Schleich, K., and Vecchi, M., Helv. Chim. Acta, 42, 2654 (1959).

[46] Clusius, K., and Schleich, K., Helv. Chim. Acta, 42, 232 (1959).

[47] Clusius, K., and Vecchi, M., Helv. Chim. Acta, 42, 1921 (1959).

[48] Clusius, K., Schleich, K., and Vecchi, M., Helv. Chim. Acta, 44, 343 (1961).

[49] Clusius, K., and Becker, E., Z. anorg. u. allgem. Chem., 251, 92 (1943).

[50] Schumacher, E., Mollet, H., and Clusius, K., Helv. Chim. Acta, 33, 2117 (1950).

the same laboratory have developed[51, 52] a band spectroscopic
micromethod for isotopic nitrogen analysis that requires only
20 to 50 g of nitrogen for an analysis, and in contrast to mass
spectrometry is quite insensitive to impurities such as CO, CO_2,
or NO in N_2 samples. The method uses the ultraviolet emission
spectrum of gaseous samples excited by means of an electrodeless
radiofrequency discharge. For $20-\mu g$ nitrogen samples having
an N^{15} concentration of less than 10 atom per cent, the authors
report an average deviation of ± 2 per cent.

Southern, and co-workers[53] reported an investigation on the
use of a microwave spectrograph for the analysis of N^{15} using
ammonia gas samples. N^{15} could be determined to approximately
± 3 per cent of its concentration in the range 0.38 to 4.5 per cent;
the minimum sample size required was about 3 mg of ammonia.

Kluyver et al.[54-57] have studied the analysis of isotope abundance
ratios by means of infrared analysis. They used an instrument of
the nondispersive-filter type containing a selective detector filled
with a concentrated sample of the component being measured. Thus,
in the analysis for C^{13}, the detector cell gas was filled with enriched
$C^{13}O_2$, whereas for N^{15} analysis it contained nitrous oxide enriched
to 64 per cent $N^{15}NO$. Using an instrument of the double-beam type,
in which the reference sample cell was filled with N_2O of natural
composition, they were able to measure the N^{15} content in a 6-mg
nitrous oxide sample in the region of the natural N^{15} abundance with
a precision of ± 0.015 atom per cent. They report that the sensitivity
decreases slightly for higher percentages, and the quantity of sample
may be reduced with a consequent loss of precision.

As already noted, the mass spectrometer is almost exclusively
the instrument chosen for N^{15} analysis. With present-day units

------

[51] Hoch, M., and Weisser, H. R., Helv. Chim. Acta, 33,
2128 (1950).

[52] Hürzeler, H., and Hostettler, H. U., Helv. Chim. Acta,
38, 1825 (1955).

[53] Southern, A. L., Morgan, H. W., Keilholtz, G. W., and
Smith, W. V., Phys. Rev., 78, 639 (1950); Anal. Chem., 23,
1000 (1951).

[54] Milatz, J. M. W., Kluyver, J. C., and Hardebol, J.,
J. Chem. Phys., 19, 887 (1951).

[55] Kluyver, J. C., and Milatz, J. M. W., Physica, 19, 401
(1953).

[56] Kluyver, J. C., and Blokhuis, E. W. M., Physica, 20,
427 (1954).

[57] Kluyver, J. C., Rec. trav. chim., 74, 322 (1955).

of the dual-collector type described by Nier[58] (McKinney et
al., [59] Dole, [60] and Wanless and Thode [61]) in which ion peaks at
adjacent masses are simultaneously compared, N^{15}-abundance
ratios can be routinely determined to a precision of ± 0.1 per cent
(i. e., 0.3650 ± 0.0003). By rapidly interchanging standard and
unknown samples in an inlet system similar to that first described
in the paper by McKinney et al., [59] differences in abundance ratios of
the order of ± 0.01 to 0.02 per cent can be detected. For a complete
isotopic analysis, a sample containing about 1 mg of nitrogen is
required. The flow of sample gas into the mass spectrometer is
only of the order of 1 standard cc (1.2 mg) per 24 hours; the 1-mg
sample is needed to fill the sample inlet system of the spectrometer
to a reasonable pressure (i. e., 2 to 5 cm Hg), and most of the gas
can be recovered after the analysis if desired. Where only very
small quantities of nitrogen are available for analysis, the quantity
of gas needed can probably be reduced tenfold by reducing the volume
of the inlet system. To avoid the possibility of air contamination in
small samples, high-vacuum metal valves can be used in place of
greased stopcocks.

Although other gaseous compounds such as NO or NO_2 have been
used, [62] nitrogen gas (N_2) itself has been found to be the most
satisfactory compound for mass-spectrometric isotope analysis. In
his excellent review, Rittenberg[63] has discussed the mass spectrometry of N_2 in detail, and has outlined equations for calculating the
per cent of N^{15} in a sample from a direct measurement of the ratio
of masses: $28:29$ ($N^{14}N^{14+}/N^{14}N^{15+}$) or the ratio of masses,
$30:29$ ($N^{15}N^{15+}/N^{15}N^{14+}$) in highly enriched samples.

Mixtures of nitrogen gas of different isotopic composition do not
exchange isotopes among the molecular species, $N^{14}N^{14}$, $N^{14}N^{15}$,
and $N^{15}N^{15}$ at ordinary temperatures. In fact, exchange is quite
slow, even at elevated temperatures in the absence of

---

[58] Nier, A. O., Rev. Sci. Instr., 18, 398 (1947).

[59] McKinney, C. R., McCrea, J. M., Epstein, S., Allen, H.
A., and Urey, H. C., Rev. Sci. Instr., 21, 724 (1950).

[60] Dole, M., Chem. Revs., 51, 263 (1952).

[61] Wanless, R. K., and Thode, H. G., J. Sci. Instr., 30,
395 (1953).

[62] Begun, G. M., J. Chem. Phys., 25, 1279 (1956); Begun,
G. M., and Melton, C. E., ibid., 25, 1292 (1956); Begun, G. M.,
personal communication.

[63] Rittenberg, D., Wilson, D. W., Nier, A. O., and Reimann,
S. P., in "Preparation and Measurement of Isotopic Tracers,"
J. W. Edwards, Ann Arbor, 1947.

82   INORGANIC ISOTOPIC SYNTHESES

suitable catalysts.[64] This can serve as a sensitive indication
of air contamination in gas samples, for samples contaminated
with atmospheric nitrogen will shown an abnormally high mass-28
($N^{14}N^{14+}$) peak, and the N^{15} per cent calculated from the in-
tensities of all three peaks (28, 29, 30) will differ from a value
calculated from either pair of peaks (28:29 or 30:29).

As a further check for air contamination, Rittenberg[63] suggests
examination of the spectrum for a peak at mass 32 (oxygen) or
mass 40 (argon), and outlines a procedure to correct for this
contamination in samples containing small quantities ($<$ 3 per
cent) of air. Holt and Hughes[65] point out that some oxygen
may be lost from an air-contaminated nitrogen sample if the
sample is passed over hot copper-copper oxide in a purification
step, and suggest that correction for air contamination can more
reliably be made from the magnitude of the mass-40 peak of argon.
More recently, Crable and Kerr[66] have shown that small quantities of oxidizing gases, such as O_2 or NO, in nitrogen samples
react with carbides on the mass spectrometer filament to produce
carbon monoxide in the ion source. In light of these results and
of observations in the author's own laboratory, it seems advisable
to avoid the presence of oxygen for the most precise analysis
and, preferably, to discard air-contaminated samples rather
than to correct for the presence of air.

In preparing nitrogen samples for mass spectrometric analysis, not only must air contamination be avoided in the conversion
procedure, but, in addition, the reactions used must yield N_2
gas, free of molecular species that produce interfering peaks in
the spectrum, such as hydrocarbons, amines, carbon monoxide
or carbon dioxide, and nitrogen oxides. Procedures for converting organic nitrogen compounds to N_2 gas have been described
in several textbooks[63, 67-69] on isotopic tracers. Rittenberg and
co-workers[63, 70, 71] have developed a modified micro-Kjeldahl

[64] Kummer, J. T., and Emmett, P. H., J. Chem. Phys.,
19, 289 (1951).
[65] Holt, B. F., and Hughes, B. P., J. Chem. Soc., 1955,
95.
[66] Crable, G. F., and Kerr, N. F., Anal. Chem., 29, 1281
(1957).
[67] Glascock, R. F., "Isotopic Gas Analysis for Biochemists,"
Academic, New York, 1954.
[68] Kamen, M. D., "Isotopic Tracers in Biology," 3rd ed.,
Academic, New York, 1957.
[69] Francis, G. E., Mulligan, W., and Wormall, A., "Isotopic
Tracers," 2nd ed., University of London Press, 1959.
[70] Rittenberg, D. Keston, A. S., Rosebury, F., and Schoenheimer, R., J. Biol. Chem., 127, 291 (1939).
[71] Schoenheimer, R., Ratner, S., and Rittenberg, D., J.
Biol. Chem., 130, 703 (1939).

procedure for converting organic substances into elemental
nitrogen. The first step in their procedure consists of a Kjeldahl
digestion for 12 to 18 hours of a sample large enough to yield
1 mg of nitrogen as ammonia. After complete digestion, the
mixture is made alkaline with 40 per cent NaOH, and the liberated ammonia is distilled into sulfuric acid in a slow stream of
NH_3-free air. The ammonia is then quantitatively oxidized to
N_2 by treatment with an alkaline hypobromite solution:

$$2NH_3 + 3NaOBr \longrightarrow N_2 + 3H_2O + 3NaBr$$

in an apparatus such as that shown in Fig. 1. The acidic ammonium sulfate solution and the hypobromite solution are placed
in the two limbs of the reaction vessel (V) and, after cooling,
evacuation, and outgassing, are allowed to mix and react. The
liberated nitrogen gas is passed through a trap, which is cooled
with a dry ice slush, and collected in the sample tube with the
aid of the Toepler pump shown.

Rittenberg[63] has indicated that the long digestion period is
necessary to avoid the formation of traces of methylamine that
may give rise to spurious peaks in the mass spectrum. Sprinson
and Rittenberg[72] have suggested that $HgSO_4$ be used in the digestion mixture (instead of a K_2SO_4-$CuSO_4$ mixture) since traces of
Cu^{2+} may cause liberation of O_2 gas from the hypobromite solution in the subsequent NH_3-oxidation step. They give details for
the preparation and handling of the hypobromite solution so as to
avoid the liberation of oxygen. Sims and Cocking[73] have pointed
out that addition of 0.1 per cent KI to the hypobromite solution
before use prevents the liberation of oxygen. Hoering[74] has found
that, even with prolonged digestion, remaining traces of amines
may yield erratic analyses, and suggests that, for the most precise analyses, the nitrogen gas should be passed over a Cu-CuO
mixture at 600 to 700° C and then cooled with liquid nitrogen to
remove final traces of organic compounds. Several authors[51, 64,75]
eliminate the hypobromite step completely and oxidize the ammonia
directly to N_2 gas by passing it over CuO at 600 to 700° C.

Holt and Hughes[76] have modified the apparatus used in the
standard micro-Dumas method for determining nitrogen so that
the 40 per cent KOH solution, over which the N_2 gas is collected,
can be freed of dissolved nitrogen before a sample is collected.
Their technique was originally developed to permit a study of the

[72] Sprinson, D., and Rittenberg, D., J. Biol. Chem., 180,
707 (1949).

[73] Sims, A. P., and Cocking, E. C., Nature, 181, 474 (1958).

[74] Hoering, T., Science, 122, 1233 (1955).

[75] Kirshenbaum, I., J. Chem. Phys., 9, 660 (1941).

[76] Holt, B. F., and Hughes, B. P., J. Chem. Soc., 1953,
1666.

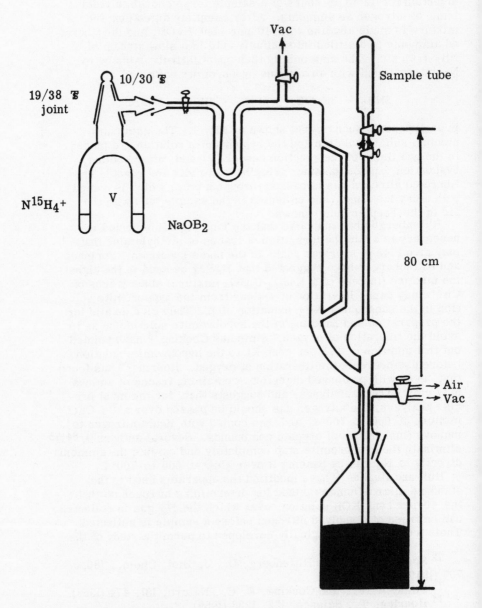

Fig. 1 Apparatus for preparing nitrogen gas from ammonia for
mass spectrometric analysis. (Based upon a design of
Rittenberg.[63])

thermal decomposition of N^{15}-labeled hydrazobenzene, since the Dumas procedure avoids the equilibration of the N_2^{14}, N_2^{15}, and $N^{14}N^{15}$ species that occur in the Rittenberg[63] procedure. The apparatus for the combustion and collection of gas samples is shown in Fig. 2. In a later publication,[77] the authors propose that the Dumas method is generally useful for converting organic nitrogen compounds to N_2, and is less likely to yield samples contaminated with oxides of nitrogen, CO, or hydrocarbons than the Kjeldahl procedure. They suggest the additional packing of iodine pentoxide at 130° C in the combustion train to oxidize traces of NO and CO to NO_2 and CO_2, and the substitution of NiO at 1050° C for CuO, to oxidize traces of CH_4 or other hydrocarbons. Ory et al.[78] report finding traces of NO in N_2 samples prepared by the Dumas procedure and suggest the use of an alkaline $KMnO_4$ solution to purify the gas.

For the conversion of inorganic nitrates to nitrogen, Clusius and Schumacher[79] use Devarda's alloy (50 per cent Cu, 45 per cent Al, 5 per cent Zn) to reduce the nitrate to NH_3 in an alkaline solution. The liberated NH_3 is then absorbed in hydrochloric acid, and the ammonium chloride formed is oxidized with hypobromite as in the Rittenberg[63] procedure. The N_2 gas is freed of traces of N_2O and water vapor by passing it through a trap cooled with liquid nitrogen before analysis. Others[80, 81] first reduce nitrates to nitric oxide by treatment with mercury and sulfuric acid,[82] and then reduce the nitric oxide gas to N_2 over a mixture of Cu and CuO at 750° C. The CuO serves to oxidize traces of CO to CO_2, which is then frozen out in a liquid-nitrogen-cooled trap. Taylor[83] has eliminated the reduction with Cu by subjecting the nitric oxide gas, confined in a sample tube, to an electric discharge that decomposes it into a mixture of N_2 and O_2. After exposure to the discharge, the sample tube is immersed in liquid nitrogen to freeze out remaining traces of nitrogen oxides, and the uncondensed gases are introduced into the spectrometer for iso-

[77] Holt, B. F., and Hughes, B. P., J. Chem. Soc., 1955, 95.

[78] Ory, R. L., Prescott, J. M., and Lyman, C. M., J. Am. Chem. Soc., **76**, 1449 (1954).

[79] Clusius, K., and Schumacher, H., Helv. Chim. Acta, **43**, 1562 (1960).

[80] Kauder, L. N., Taylor, T. I., and Spindel, W., J. Chem. Phys., **31**, 232 (1959).

[81] Stern, M. J., Kauder, L. N., and Spindel, W., J. Chem. Phys., **34**, 333 (1961).

[82] Friedel, R. A., Sharkey, A. G., Schultz, J. L., and Humbert, C. R., Anal. Chem. 25, 1314 (1953).

[83] Taylor, T. I., personal communication.

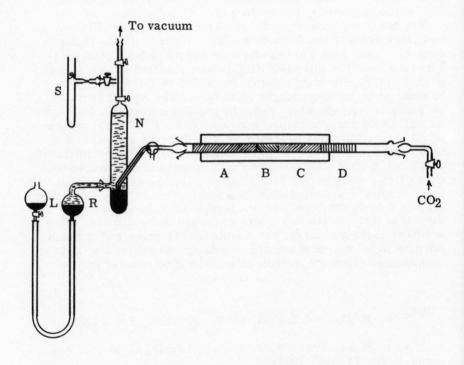

Fig. 2 Apparatus for preparing nitrogen gas for mass spectrometric analysis by the micro-Dumas method. A-D,
combustion tube filling; A, wire copper oxide (21 cm);
B, reduced copper wire (4 cm); C, wire copper oxide
(8 cm); D, copper oxide powder (7 cm); N, nitrometer;
R, mercury and alkali reservoir; L, leveling bulb; S,
sample tube. (Based on a design of Holt and Hughes[77];
reprinted from Glascock. [67])

topic analysis. This procedure is especially rapid and convenient for analysis of nitrogen oxide samples but should be used with caution when very precise results are required, because of the afore-mentioned possibility of forming interfering ions in the spectrometer source by reaction of carbides with O_2. Clusius[48] has recently reported using this procedure with satisfactory results.

One further gaseous nitrogen compound that has been used for mass spectrometric N^{15} analyses is nitrous oxide. Friedman and Bigeleisen[84] and Clusius and Schumacher[85] have found that N_2O formed by the thermal decomposition of NH_4NO_3 is not equilibrated with respect to the species: $N^{14}N^{14}O$, $N^{14}N^{15}O$, and $N^{15}N^{15}O$. Thus nitrous oxide prepared from $N^{15}H_4N^{14}O_3$ is predominantly $N^{15}N^{14}O$, whereas gas prepared from the nitrate-labeled salt will consist of the $N^{14}N^{15}O$ isomer. Since the mass spectra of fragments of the isotopic molecules are different, the labeling position in the molecule can be determined mass spectrometrically. Where the labeling position is of special interest, the use of N_2O gas may be advantageous.

5. SYNTHESIS OF COMPOUNDS

Although N^{15} is extremely useful as a tracer in biological and organic chemical systems, no attempt will be made in this article to review the literature dealing with the syntheses of organic nitrogen compounds. Instead, in keeping with the general scope of the present volume, the discussion will be limited essentially to the preparation of inorganic compounds labeled with N^{15}. Some of these compounds will be useful to organic chemists and biochemists as "key substances" for introducing N^{15} into a variety of organic nitrogen compounds. For further information on the synthesis of labeled organic nitrogen compounds, the review by Clusius,[5] the bibliography compiled by Chapman and Broida,[2] and the comprehensive text by Murray and Williams[86] should be consulted.

In considering the synthesis of a particular labeled compound, one is limited, in choosing a starting material, to one of the chemical forms in which the concentrated heavy isotope is obtained from a separation process. Table 2 summarizes the isotope-separation processes that have been used and the chemical form in which enriched N^{15} is obtained from each. It seems worthwhile, there-

[84] Friedman, L., and Bigeleisen, J., J. Chem. Phys., 18, 1325 (1950).

[85] Clusius, K., and Schumacher, H., Helv. Chim. Acta, 41, 2252 (1958).

[86] Murray, A., III, and Williams, D. L., "Organic Syntheses with Isotopes," Part II, Interscience, New York, 1958.

Table 2
Chemical Form of N^{15} from Various Separation Processes

Separation process	Chemical form obtained as product
Thermal diffusion[39]	N_2^*
Chemical exchange	
$NH_4^+ - NH_3$ [27-33]	$N^*H_4NO_3$, N^*H_3
$HNO_3 - NO$ [34, 35]	HN^*O_3, $N^*O + N^*O_2$
$N_2O_3 - NO$ [36, 37]	$N^*O + N^*O_2$
Distillation[46-48]	N^*O

fore, to consider first procedures for interconverting the various N^{15} compounds, N_2, NO, NO_2, HNO_3, and NH_3, and then to examine syntheses of other compounds starting with N^{15} in the most convenient chemical form. Reactions for interconverting various inorganic nitrogen compounds are also useful if one wishes to recover the enriched isotopic material for re-use in further experiments.

One unusual property of the element greatly simplifies the synthesis and handling of its labeled compounds. All compounds of nitrogen studied so far undergo negligible exchange with atmospheric nitrogen under any reasonable conditions.[5] This is in marked contrast to the properties of hydrogen, carbon, or oxygen, where exchange with atmospheric water vapor and CO_2 must be carefully avoided. Many oxygen compounds also undergo isotopic exchange with glass at moderately elevated temperatures, and this creates additional problems. Any labeled nitrogen compound may be exposed to air and stored indefinitely without any concern about having the heavy isotope diluted by exchange with atmospheric nitrogen. A gaseous compound, such as $N^{15}O_2$ or $N^{15}H_3$ that has become contaminated with air, can be repurified without isotope dilution by simply cooling it to an appropriate low temperature and pumping off the uncondensed gas.

Highly enriched N^{15} is commercially available in several chemical forms; the Isomet Corporation[38a] offers concentrations in excess of 95 atom per cent as nitric acid, alkali nitrate, ammonia, nitrogen, cyanide, urea, and glycine at prices ranging from \$350 to \$910 per gram of N^{15}. A French company, ONIA (Office Nationale Industriel de l'Azote), Usines a Toulouse, 143 route d'Espagne, has also advertised N^{15} for sale as a labeling tool. Further, the isotope-separation group, under J. S. Drury, at the Oak Ridge National Laboratory, Oak Ridge, Tennessee, has separated considerable quantities of N^{15} and may be contacted directly by scientists needing research quantities not available from commercial sources.

A. Ammonia

Preparation of anhydrous $N^{15}H_3$ from an ammonium salt. Pure dry $N^{15}H_3$ is readily prepared from an enriched ammonium salt, such as the chloride, nitrate, or sulfate, by the simple expedient of treating a solution of the salt with an excess of KOH and distilling off the ammonia through a drying column packed with KOH pellets. Clusius and Effenberger[87] have described a very simple convenient apparatus for carrying out this reaction on small quantities ($\sim$ 1 g) of salt in a quantitative manner. Their arrangement is illustrated in Fig. 3. Approximately 1 gm of the labeled ammonium salt dissolved in about 5 ml of water is introduced into the flask through tube A. About 4 g of KOH pellets is packed into the lower section of the column through the opening B, and an additional 8 gm of pellets is placed into the column above the condenser via opening C. Indentations in the glass tubing keep the pellets from falling into the reaction vessel. The inlet tubes, A, B, and C are sealed off, trap T_1 is cooled with liquid nitrogen, and the pressure in the system is reduced to about 450 mm. Stopcock H is then closed and is kept closed during the subsequent gas evolution to prevent any loss of $N^{15}H_3$. The reaction vessel is carefully heated with a micro burner; the salt dissolves, and the rising water vapors dissolve the KOH pellets in the neck of the vessel. Ammonia evolution begins as soon as the KOH solution enters the lower vessel. The evolved ammonia carries along sufficient water vapor to dissolve the KOH below the condenser completely, and the reaction continues with the flame removed. The cooling section is useful in removing some of the water vapor from the gas stream before it enters the drying tower. The apparatus tends to be self-regulating, for any excessive ammonia pressure is decreased by the resulting increased solubility of the gas in the liquid phase, especially in the condensed water in Z. The transfer of gas to trap T_1 is essentially complete in about 1/2 hour of boiling; finally, with the heat removed, the system is evacuated to about 30 mm. The traps are sealed off at point S, trap T_2 is cooled with liquid nitrogen, and the liquid-nitrogen bath surrounding T_1 is replaced with a dry ice-trichlorethylene slush. The remaining air is pumped away, and the ammonia is dried by trap-to-trap distillation from T_1 to T_2. The yield obtained

---

[87] Clusius, K. , and Effenberger, E. , Helv. Chim. Acta, **38**, 1834 (1955).

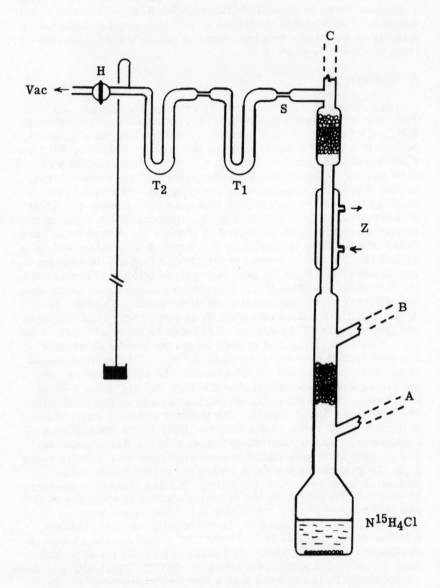

Fig. 3 Apparatus for the preparation of dry ammonia from N^{15}-
labeled ammonium salts. (Based upon design of Clusius
and Effenberger.[87])

approaches 100 per cent. Several authors[88, 89] have recommended condensing the $N^{15}H_3$ over metallic sodium for removing final traces of moisture; Thode[88] suggests a preliminary recrystallization of the ammonium salt from ethanol, to remove traces of amines that may have been concentrated in the isotope-separation process.

Preparation of $N^{15}H_3$ and ammonium salts from elementary nitrogen. Ammonia may conveniently be prepared from N_2 gas by decomposing a metallic nitride[5, 85] with water, as follows:

$$3Ca + N_2^{15} \longrightarrow CaN_2^{15}$$

$$Ca_3N_2^{15} + 6H_2O \longrightarrow 3Ca(OH)_2 + 2N^{15}H_3$$

Clusius[5] used a welded steel retort (illustrated in Fig. 4) for

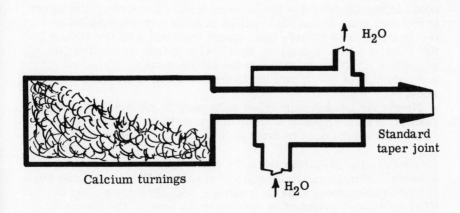

Fig. 4 Steel retort for the preparation of calcium nitride from N^{15}. (From Clusius.[5])

[88] Thode, H. G., J. Am. Chem. Soc., **62**, 581 (1940).
[89] Wiesendanger, H. V. D., Jones, W. H., and Garner, C. S., J. Chem. Phys., 27, 668 (1957).

nitriding the metal. The cooling jacket shown (or several spirals of copper tubing) serve to protect the greased joint when the body of the retort is heated. Several grams of coarse, bright calcium chips, which have been stored under ether, are introduced into the retort, and the ether is first removed by evacuation with an oil pump. The retort is then well evacuated with a diffusion pump, while maintained at the operating temperature of 200 to 300° C. Enriched N_2^{15} gas is introduced into the system and reacts rapidly with the hot calcium metal. In a few minutes the pressure drops to below 1 mm Hg. Dry $N^{15}H_3$ gas is then conveniently prepared by shaking the granular black reaction product into a large round bottom flask and carefully introducing into the flask about 95 per cent of the calculated quantity of water, contained in a sealed, thin-walled glass ampoule in which it was previously out-gassed. After evacuation, the flask is shaken to break the ampoule and to permit the contents to react. The liberated ammonia gas is removed only after several days, during which time the flask is occasionally shaken. In this way the $N^{15}H_3$ gas is thoroughly dried by contact with the $Ca(OH)_2$, and is finally transferred, by freezing it into a liquid-nitrogen-cooled trap, while any hydrogen gas formed from free calcium metal is pumped away.

Clusius[5] points out that this method is also a convenient one for preparing the doubly labeled $N^{15}D_3$, using D_2O to decompose the nitride instead of light water. He indicates, further, that possible contamination of the calcium metal by traces of atmospheric nitrogen must be guarded against to avoid isotopic dilution of the ammonia, and advises that, where ammonia with the highest N^{15} concentration is desired, it is best prepared by an alternate procedure involving oxidation of the nitrogen gas to nitrate ion, and reduction of the nitrate ion to ammonia with Devarda's alloy.[79]

Numerous labeled ammonium salts may be readily prepared by absorption of $N^{15}H_3$ into a dilute acid solution of the appropriate anion, and evaporating to dryness to obtain the desired salt.

Preparation of ammonium salts and $N^{15}H_3$ from nitrites or nitrates. Nitrate or nitrite salts labeled with N^{15} are readily converted to ammonium salts by treatment with Devarda's alloy in a KOH solution,[79] followed by distillation to remove the liberated ammonia. A standard Kjeldahl apparatus is suitable for carrying out the conversion, and labeled ammonium salts are obtained directly by absorbing the $N^{15}H_3$ gas in an acid solution of the corresponding cation. If anhydrous $N^{15}H_3$ is desired, the apparatus may be modified as in Fig. 3, in order to remove water vapor with KOH pellets, and the NH_3 gas collected in a cold trap. Quantitative evolution of ammonia may be effected by bubbling a slow stream of NH_3-free nitrogen gas through the alkaline solution.

Nitric oxide, nitrogen dioxide, or mixtures of these gases may be converted to ammonia after preliminary oxidation to nitrite and nitrate salts (see Sec. 4).

B. Elementary Nitrogen

Preparation of N_2^{15} from an ammonium salt (or from $N^{15}H_3$).
Clusius[5] has adapted the Rittenberg[63] procedure for converting
macro quantities of ammonium salts to nitrogen gas by oxidation with
alkaline hypobromite. Using an apparatus similar to that shown in
Fig. 5, Clusius and Bühler[90] converted 50 gm of ammonium nitrate,
containing 63 per cent N^{15} in the ammonium group, to elementary
nitrogen. The labeled salt was introduced into the evacuated round-
bottom reaction flask A as a concentrated solution, and the hypobromite solution (25 cm^3 of Br_2 to 1 liter of an ice-cold solution
containing 125 g KOH) was added slowly from the dropping funnel
B. As the hypobromite solution trickled down through the 20-cm
length column M, packed with glass beads, the counterflowing
stream of evolved nitrogen gas was freed of remaining traces of
ammonia. A 2.5-fold excess of the hypobromite solution was used
to insure complete oxidation of the ammonium ion. The nitrogen
gas evolved was passed through a liquid-nitrogen-cooled trap to
freeze out water vapor as well as N_2O. The latter gas is formed to
the extent of about 3 per cent as a side product of the reaction.[91]
To obtain nitrogen of the highest purity, it is advisable to pass the
gas over metallic Cu at 600° C to remove traces of oxygen. The
nitrogen gas is most conveniently transferred into an evacuated
storage flask by adsorption in a cooled charcoal trap or by condensation at liquid-hydrogen temperature. The yield by this procedure
is no larger than about 95 per cent because of the N_2O produced as
a side product and because 0.4 per cent of the ammonium ion is
oxidized completely to nitrate.[90] These N^{15} losses may be recovered by further treatment if desired.

An alternate procedure for oxidizing $N^{15}H_3$ gas to elemental
nitrogen, which has been used by a number of workers,[51, 64, 75, 92]
involves passing the gas over CuO at 500 to 600° C. Appreciable
quantities of ammonia can be conveniently converted in this way by
continuously circulating the gas over hot copper oxide and through a
dry-ice-cooled trap in series, with the aid of an automatic Toepler
pump such as that described by Urry.[93] This technique appears
simple and convenient and should yield a pure product directly.

Preparation of N_2^{15} from nitrates and nitrites or nitrogen oxides.
Elemental nitrogen may be prepared from nitrates, nitrites,

---

[90] Clusius, K., and Bühler, H. H., Helv. Chim. Acta, 37,
2361 (1954).

[91] Clusius, K., and Rechnitz, G., Helv. Chim. Acta, 36, 59
(1953).

[92] Nyman, C. J., Fung, S. C., and Dodgen, H. W., J. Am.
Chem. Soc., 72, 1033 (1950).

[93] Urry, G., and Urry, W. H., Rev. Sci. Instr., 27, 819
(1956).

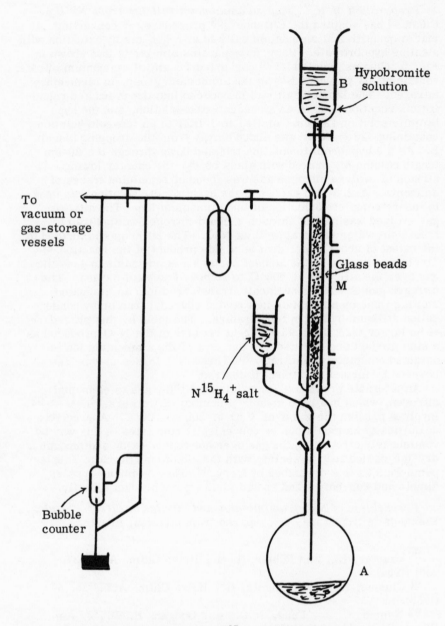

Fig. 5 Apparatus for converting N15-labeled ammonium salts to
elementary nitrogen. (Based upon design of Clusius.[5])

or mixtures of nitrogen oxides by first reducing these compounds to NH_4^+ and then oxidizing the NH_4^+ to N_2 as outlined
above. Alternately, nitrates and nitrites can be quantitatively reduced to NO by treatment with an excess of Hg and 90 per cent
H_2SO_4,[5,80-82,94] and the NO can be reduced to N_2 by circulating
over Cu at 750°C. The nitrate-reduction reaction with Hg starts
slowly but then proceeds quite vigorously. It is complete in 24
hours if the reaction vessel is shaken occasionally, or even more
rapidly if it is mounted on a shaking machine, so that a fresh Hg
surface is continuously exposed for reaction. This latter procedure
has been found completely satisfactory for preparing liter quantities
of N_2 containing 99+ per cent N^{15} with chemical yields of 95
per cent or higher based upon nitrate.[95]

Where quantities of higher nitrogen oxides are to be converted
to elemental nitrogen, the preliminary reduction to nitric oxide is
unnecessary, for these gases are reduced directly to N_2 by reaction with hot copper. Circulation of nitrogen dioxide by means
of a Toepler pump is unsatisfactory because the mercury is attack-
ed rapidly, but mixtures containing nitrogen dioxide can be conveniently circulated in a vacuum system with the aid of a stainless
steel micro-bellows pump.[96]

Kummer[97] has also reported the quantitative reduction of N_2O
to N_2 at room temperature over reduced Fe catalyst.

C. Nitrates

Preparation of alkali nitrites from elemental nitrogen. Clusius
and Hürzeler[94] have developed a very elegant procedure for synthesizing sodium nitrite-N^{15}, free of nitrate contamination, starting
with elemental N_2^{15}. Since nitrites are very useful as starting
reagents for introducing N^{15} into a variety of organic compounds,
such as diazo compounds, azides, and nitroso-amines, this synthesis
is of considerable interest to organic chemists as well as to inorganic chemists. Their procedure consists of first oxidizing
nitrogen to a mixture of nitrogen oxides in a high-voltage arc, reducing the higher oxides to nitric oxide with Hg and sulfuric acid,
and allowing nitric oxide and oxygen gas to react under carefully
controlled conditions with a sodium hydroxide solution.

These authors[94] have discussed the factors involved, and the
conditions which must be adjusted so that the equilibria in Eqs. (1-7)

$$N_2 + O_2 \rightleftharpoons 2NO \tag{1}$$

---

[94] Clusius, K., and Hürzeler, H., Helv. Chim. Acta, 35, 1103
(1952).

[95] Spindel, W., and Taylor, T. I., unpublished results.

[96] Research Appliance Co., Pittsburgh, Pa.

[97] Kummer, J. T., J. Am. Chem. Soc., 69, 2559 (1947).

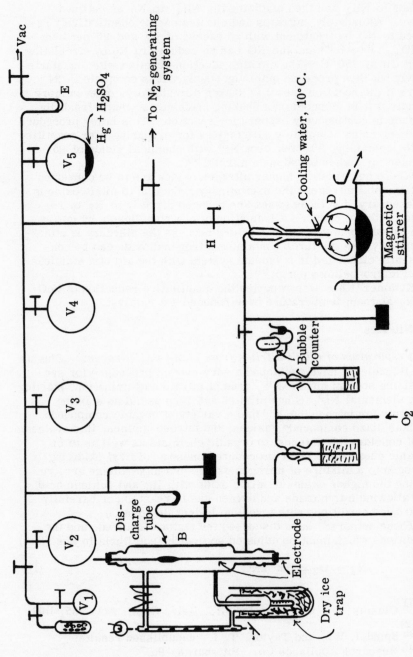

Fig. 6 System for the preparation of pure nitrite or nitrate from N_2^{15}. (Based upon a design of Clusius.[5])

$$2NO + O_2 \rightleftharpoons 2NO_2 \tag{2}$$

$$2NO_2 \rightleftharpoons N_2O_4 \tag{3}$$

$$NO + NO_2 \rightleftharpoons N_2O_3 \tag{4}$$

$$N_2O_3 + H_2O \rightleftharpoons 2HNO_2 \tag{5}$$

$$N_2O_4 + H_2O \rightleftharpoons HNO_3 + HNO_2 \tag{6}$$

$$3HNO_2 \rightleftharpoons HNO_3 + 2NO + H_2O \tag{7}$$

all operate to yield maximum nitrite and minimum nitrate formation. In brief, it is necessary to keep the NO_2 concentration as
low as possible, so as to shift equilibria (3), and thus (6), toward the left, thereby favoring reactions (4) and (5). This is
accomplished by reducing the nitrogen oxides completely to NO,
transferring the NO to a vessel containing a well-stirred solution
of NaOH, and only then admitting oxygen gas slowly so that the
NO_2 is converted to N_2O_3 and NO_2^- as rapidly as it is formed.
Further, it is necessary to keep the HNO_2 concentration as low
as possible, in order to drive reaction (5) toward completion and
to hinder the decomposition reaction, Eq. (7). This is accomplished by using a strongly alkaline solution. Finally, the reaction
solution should be kept cold to keep the vapor pressure of water at
a minimum, and thus minimize reaction (6) in the gas phase.

The system used for the preparation of nitrite is pictured in
Fig. 6. Enriched nitrogen gas from the storage vessels V_2-V_4,
or from the hypobromite generator shown in Fig. 5, was oxidized
with an excess of pure O_2 in the discharge vessel B, mainly to
N_2O_4. The discharge tube contained nickel electrodes 2mm in
diameter. The upper electrode was inserted into the tube through
a packed seal and had an insulated handle, so that the electrode
spacing could be adjusted after the arc was ignited. A transformer
with a 30-kv secondary mainitained a 12-cm-long vertical arc with
a current of 30 ma. About 2 per cent of the mixture reacted in
the arc, and the gas was circulated convectively through the simple
colorimeter K, which continually monitored the extent of the reaction. The N_2O_4 (together with a small amount of N_2O_3) was
frozen out in the trap. The freezing was accomplished with pure
dry ice without addition of any organic solvent, so that, in case of
a break in the trap, no explosive mixture with the molten N_2O_4
would form. Occasionally, the trap was allowed to warm, so that
the crystals of N_2O_4, which tend to impede convective flow, melted and dropped down into the lower, graduated portion of the trap
where the volume of N_2O_4 formed was measured. About 2 g of
N_2O_4 per hour were produced.

The oxygen used for this oxidation should be free of argon to avoid a buildup of inert gas pressure in the arcing vessel, which would eventually quench the arc. It should also be as free of N_2 as possible to avoid isotopic dilution of highly enriched N^{15} due to free radical reaction processes in the arc.

The N_2O_4 formed was transferred to vessel V_5, where it was reduced completely to NO with mercury and 90 per cent H_2SO_4, as outlined above, and the nitric oxide produced was stored in the now empty vessels V_2-V_4. Clusius[5] reported a yield of 31 liters of nitric oxide from 15.5 liters of nitrogen.

The nitric oxide was converted to nitrite in vessel D, shown in the lower right-hand portion of Fig. 6. The 1-liter round bottom flask contained 125 g of a carbonate-free saturated sodium hydroxide solution, diluted with 250 ml of ice water. The contents were stirred with a magnetic stirrer and kept cool by flowing 10°C water over the walls. After evacuation to a pressure of less than 30 mm, the vessel was filled with nitric oxide to a pressure of 650 mm, and pure oxygen was introduced slowly through the mercury bubble counter.

Puffs of brown nitrogen dioxide form in the region near the oxygen inlet tube, and, because the gases are heated by the exothermic reactions (2) and (3), the reaction products do not sink through the nitric oxide but, instead, rise and circulate as shown by the dashed lines in the gas space of vessel D. Thus, only very dilute N_2O_3 contacts the liquid surface, and only nitrite is formed.

The total pressure in D decreased continuously and was maintained at 600 to 650 mm by distilling in fresh nitric oxide from the U tube E, through stopcock H. Toward the end of the reaction, oxygen was introduced very slowly, and the process was stopped when the total pressure dropped to about 200 mm Hg. The remaining gas was frozen back into the small storage flask V. This gas was later oxidized to nitrate, so that none of the enriched N_2^{15} was lost. The entire conversion of nitric oxide required about 2 hours.

The alkaline nitrite solution was centrifuged to remove any precipitated silicic acid, and the solution was concentrated by evaporation in a platinum dish until sodium nitrite crystallized out. The crystals were washed with a small amount of ice water and finally dried in a desiccator over anhydrous calcium chloride. Starting with 15.5 liters of N_2, 95.5 g of dry sodium nitrite was obtained with a nitrite content of 99.9 per cent as determined by titration with permanganate solution.

The slightly alkaline mother liquor from the nitrite crystallization was combined with the remaining nitrogen oxides in V_1, acidified slightly with sulfuric acid, and the mixture allowed to stand for several days in a flask filled with 300 mm of oxygen. In this way, an additional 5.6 g of $NaN^{15}O_3$ was obtained. The total N^{15} yield was quantitative.

Preparation of nitrites from nitrates. Several authors[94,98-100] have prepared alkali metal nitrites by heating a nitrate with metallic lead:

$$NaNO_3 + Pb \longrightarrow NaNO_2 + PbO$$

Maimind and co-workers[100] have described detailed conditions for preparing either potassium or sodium nitrite from the corresponding nitrate, in relatively high yields. Typically, 0.01 to 0.05 mole of finely pulverized $KN^{15}O_3$ or $NaN^{15}O_3$ was thoroughly mixed with a 50 per cent excess of Pb dust and the mixture placed in a pyrex test tube. The tube was immersed in a bath of Wood's metal, the air displaced with a stream of nitrogen, and the bath quickly heated to 200°C to drive off traces of moisture. After about 20 minutes at 200° C, the bath was slowly raised to the required temperature. For preparation of $NaN^{15}O_2$, the salt mixture was maintained at 330°C for 2 hours; for $KN^{15}O_2$ it was maintained at 390°C for 1 hour. After cooling, the nitrite was extracted with 20 to 50 ml of water. Titration with permanganate indicated a conversion to nitrite of 91 to 93 per cent. The nitrite was purified of nitrate by recrystallization, and the unreacted nitrite was recovered and reprocessed along with a later batch of nitrate to avoid N^{15} loss.

This procedure is an extremely simple and rapid one, but, as Clusius[94] has pointed out, it always yields a product contaminated with nitrate and may involve some loss of N^{15} as $N^{15}O_2$. A purer product can be obtained by first reducing the nitrate to nitric oxide, and then preparing the nitrite salt as outlined above.

Preparation of nitrites from $N^{15}H_3$. Clusius[5,94] converted $N^{15}H_3$ and $N^{15}H_4^+$ to nitrite by first oxidizing the ammonia to nitrogen and then preparing the nitrite as outlined previously. Maimind et al.[100] converted ammonia directly to nitrate by a procedure described below and then reduced the nitrate to nitrite as discussed above. Maimind's procedure is much simpler and more direct for converting ammonia to nitrate, but the purest nitrite product is best obtained by first reducing the nitrate to nitric oxide, as suggested by Clusius.[94]

D. Nitrates

Preparation of $N^{15}O_3^-$ from N_2^{15}, or $N^{15}O_2$. The same

[98] Vaughan, W. R., McCane, D. I., and Sloan, G. J., J. Am. Chem. Soc., 73, 2298 (1951).

[99] Bothner-By, A. A., and Friedman, L., J. Am. Chem. Soc., 73, 5391 (1951).

[100] Maimind, V. I., Tokarev, B. V., Gomes, E., Vdovima, R. G., Ermolaev, K. M., and Shemyakim, M. M., J. Gen. Chem. U.S.S.R., 2187 (1956).

The same apparatus used by Clusius[5, 94] to prepare pure $NaN^{15}O_2$ (Fig. 6) is also useful for preparing either $HN^{15}O_3$ or $KN^{15}O_3$. Nitrogen gas is oxidized to N_2O_4 in the high-voltage discharge tube, and the N_2O_4 gas is directly introduced into the evacuated vessel D, which, in this case, contains a quantity of 2.5-$\underline{N}$ KOH solution not quite sufficient to completely neutralize the acidic oxides. If N^{15} is already available as NO, NO_2, or a mixture of these, the arcing step is omitted, and the oxides are introduced directly into the reaction flask containing the stirred KOH solution. External cooling of the reaction flask is unnecessary for the preparation of nitrate. The gas reacts with the solution

$$N_2^{15}O_4 + 2KOH \longrightarrow KN^{15}O_3 + KN^{15}O_2 + H_2O$$

and the nitrate-nitrite solution first formed disproportionates as it becomes acidic

$$3HN^{15}O_2 \longrightarrow HN^{15}O_3 + 2N^{15}O + H_2O$$

and is converted by an excess of oxygen at 50° C completely into nitrate within a few hours.

After a final neutralization, pure $KN^{15}O_3$ may be crystallized out or, alternatively, concentrated H_2SO_4 may be added and $HN^{15}O_3$ obtained by distillation.

Preparation of $N^{15}O_3$ from $N^{15}H_3$ Clusius[5, 94] prepared $N^{15}O_3^-$ from ammonia and ammonium compounds after a preliminary oxidation to elementary nitrogen. A much simpler method has been described by Maimind et al.[100] in which $N^{15}H_3$ is oxidized directly to $N^{15}O_3^-$ with $KMnO_4$. In this procedure, 0.82 mole of potassium permanganate and 0.15 mole of $N^{15}H_3$ dissolved in 750 ml of water are put into an autoclave, and the mixture is heated for 7 to 8 hours at 170 to 180° C. The excess of $KMnO_4$ decomposes completely to MnO_2 during the heating, and, after reaction is complete, the MnO_2 is filtered off, washed free of NO_3^-, and the filtrate and wash liquids are combined. At this point in the procedure, the $N^{15}O_3^-$ yield is 87 to 88 per cent. The solution is concentrated to a volume of 250 to 300 ml, neutralized with 20 per cent H_2SO_4, and evaporated to dryness. The salts are taken up in 70 ml of 9 $\underline{M}$ sulfuric acid, and the mixture is gradually heated to 230° C to distil off HNO_3. The distillate is diluted, exactly neutralized with NaOH, and evaporated to dryness on a water bath. The final yield of $NaN^{15}O_3$ is 82 to 84 per cent.

E. Nitric Oxide-N^{15}

$N^{15}O$ can be prepared readily either from $N^{15}O_2$ or from labeled nitrites or nitrates by treatment with Hg and H_2SO_4, as described earlier.[94] If the starting material is elemental nitrogen, the first step in the synthesis involves oxidation in an electric arc to $N_2^{15}O_4$. Any of these conversions may be readily carried out using appropriate sections of the apparatus shown in Fig. 6. For conversion of $N^{15}H_3$ to $N^{15}O$, either of the alternate procedures described previously for the preparation of nitrates may be used. Ammonia may be oxidized to N_2^{15} and the elemental nitrogen converted to $N^{15}O$, or the reaction described by Maimind et al.[100] may be used to prepare NO_3^- and the NO_3^- reduced to $N^{15}O$. The permanganate oxidation to NO_3^- requires much less special equipment and is therefore preferable.

F. Nitrogen Dioxide (di-Nitrogen Tetroxide) -N^{15}

Any of the procedures outlined above for the synthesis of nitric oxide can readily be modified to yield $N^{15}O_2$, since nitric oxide is rapidly and completely converted to NO_2 at room temperature in the presence of excess O_2. The NO_2 can be freed of oxygen by cooling with dry ice and pumping off the unreacted O_2.

Leifer[101] prepared $N^{15}O_2$ from $N^{15}H_3$ by catalytic oxidation over a single layer of 80-mesh Pt gauze in the presence of excess oxygen. The products of reaction were collected by condensation at liquid nitrogen temperature, after passing over a drying tube packed with P_2O_5. No estimate of the yield was given. It should be pointed out that, although this catalytic oxidation is the first step in the commercial process for manufacturing nitric acid, if the catalyst is not functioning properly, a considerable fraction of ammonia may be converted to elemental nitrogen, and this would constitute a loss of valuable N^{15}.

Ogg and co-workers[102] prepared $N^{15}O_2$ from $KN^{15}O_3$ by heating the dry salt together with PbO. No yield estimate was given. They also prepared $N^{15}O_5$ by ozonization of the enriched $N_2^{15}O_4$.

Amell and Daniels prepared $N^{15}O_2$ from $KN^{15}O_3$ by dissolving the salt in 85 per cent phosphoric acid and adding a coil of copper wire.[103] The evolved gases were collected in a liquid-nitrogen-cooled trap. After reaction ceased, the nitrogen oxides collected were vaporized and allowed to react with an excess of air to completely oxidize nitric oxide to nitrogen dioxide. The nitrogen dioxide was freed of excess oxygen and nitrogen by freezing with dry ice and subsequent pumping. A 90 per cent theoretical yield was obtained.

101 Leifer, E. ,J. Chem. Phys. , 8, 301 (1940).
102 Ogg, R. A., Jr., Richardson, W. S., and Wilson, M. K., J. Chem. Phys. , 18, 573 (1950).
103 Amell, A. R., and Daniels, F., J. Am. Chem. Soc., 74, 6209 (1952).

G. Nitrous Oxide

The various labeled isotopic isomers, $N^{15}N^{14}O$, $N^{14}N^{15}O$, and $N^{15}N^{15}O$ may be conveniently synthesized by the thermal decomposition of ammonium nitrate.[84,85,97,104] Friedman and Bigeleisen[84] studied the decomposition reaction in detail and showed that $N^{15}H_4NO_3$ yields exclusively the end-labeled molecule $N^{15}N^{14}O$ upon decomposition, whereas $N^{14}H_4N^{15}O_3$ yields only $N^{14}N^{15}O$. The doubly labeled species $N_2^{15}O$ is obtained from ammonium nitrate in which the ammonium and the nitrate ion are both labeled with N^{15}. They also found that a trace of water vapor was required to catalyze the reaction; no decomposition was evidenced when the thoroughly dried salt was heated up to 300° C. Their procedure consisted of drying the salt by evacuation at 150° C overnight, followed by a final heating to 300° C in vacuo. After cooling, a trace of H_2O vapor was added, and the salt was reheated; decomposition now commenced at 180° C and the generation of N_2O was completed by maintaining the salt at $220 \pm 20°$ C. The N_2O gas was dried by passage through a dry-ice-cooled trap, and subsequently condensed in a liquid-nitrogen-cooled trap. About 98 per cent of the gas not condensed at -80° C was N_2O; the remainder was N_2 plus some O_2.

Clusius and Schumacher[85] used the same procedure to prepare $N^{15}N^{14}O$ starting with 31 mmoles of elemental nitrogen containing 96 per cent N^{15}. The nitrogen was first oxidized to ammonia by reaction with calcium turnings, as described previously, and the $N^{15}H_3$ was absorbed in ordinary nitric acid to form $N^{15}H_4N^{14}O_3$. After purification of the $N^{15}N^{14}O$ by repeated distillation between dry ice and liquid-nitrogen traps to remove N_2 and traces of higher oxides, the final yield was 72.5 per cent of the theoretical, based upon N_2^{15}. They emphasize the importance of heating the salt carefully, and controlling the decomposition temperature at about 200° C, since appreciable amounts of N_2 and higher oxides form at temperatures above 250° C, and at 300° C the salt may decompose explosively.[105]

H. Hydrazine-N^{15}

Labeled hydrazine, and the related salt hydrazine sulfate, were prepared by Cahn and Powell[106] using a small-scale Raschig[107]

[104] Richardson, W. S., and Wilson, M. K., J. Chem. Phys., 18, 694 (1950).

[105] Keenan, A. G., J. Am. Chem. Soc., 77, 1379 (1955).

[106] Cahn, J. W., and Powell, R. E., J. Am. Chem. Soc., 76, 2568 (1954).

[107] Raschig, F., Z. anorg. Chem., 20, 2068 (1907).

synthesis. The $N^{15}H_3$ from 4 mmoles of $N^{15}H_4NO_3$ was liberated with sodium hydroxide and distilled in vacuo into a reaction
vessel containing 10 ml of water, 0.50 mmoles of NaOCl, and
200 mg of gelatin. The reaction mixture was heated for 10 minutes at 80° C, and hydrazine formed by reactions (8) and (9).

$$NH_3 + OCl^- \longrightarrow NH_2Cl + OH^- \qquad (8)$$

$$NH_2Cl + NH_3 + OH^- \longrightarrow N_2H_4 + Cl^- + H_2O \qquad (9)$$

One mmole of unlabeled N_2H_4 was added †as a carrier, and the
excess ammonia, plus N_2H_4, was distilled off in vacuo into a
solution of sulfuric acid. The hydrazine was recrystallized from
the sulfuric acid solution and used as the $N_2^{15}H_4 \cdot H_2SO_4$ salt. The
over-all yield was 11.5 per cent, based on the $N^{15}H_4$ consumed;
this is half the yield obtained from a large-scale synthesis.

The Raschig[107] procedure requires a large excess of NH_3 over
the limiting reagent, hypochlorite. This is particularly undesir-
able where labeled $N^{15}H_3$ is being used as a reactant. Unfortunately, the excess $N^{15}H_3$ is necessary, because a third reaction

$$2NH_2Cl + N_2H_4 + 2OH^- \longrightarrow$$
$$N_2 + 2NH_3 + 2Cl^- + 2H_2O \qquad (10)$$

reduces the yield of N_2H_4 and leads to loss of N^{15} as elemental
nitrogen. Cahn and Powell[106] point out that reaction (8) is rapid,
and reactions (9) and (10) are of comparable rates. To increase
the yield, reaction (9) may be favored and reaction (10) hindered
by a large excess of NH_3. The gelatin is added to complex traces
of Cu^{++}, which catalyze reaction (10). In the absence of gelatin
and with a Cu^{++} concentration of 10^{-6} moles liter^{-1}, no yield of
hydrazine was obtained. An excess of NaOH improves the yield
in the synthesis, since the copper-gelatin complex is unstable at
a pH of less than 11. To avoid loss of expensive N^{15}, the excess
unreacted $(N^{15}H_4)_2SO_4$ should be recovered from the sulfuric
acid solution after crystallization of the labeled hydrazine sulfate.

Rice and Scherber[108] used essentially the same procedure to
prepare predominantly singly labeled $H_2N^{14}N^{15}H_2$ by adding an
excess of unlabeled NH_3 to the hypochlorite-$N^{15}H_3$solution

---

†The authors mixed unlabeled $H_2N^{14}N^{14}H_2$ with the labeled
$H_2N^{15}N^{15}H_2$ so that they could determine whether nitrogen atoms
were randomized on oxidation of hydrazine. This dilution of the
labeled product with normal hydrazine must, of course, be
omitted ordinarily to avoid isotopic dilution.

[108] Rice, F. O., and Scherber, F., J. Am. Chem. Soc., 77,
291 (1955).

before heating. They obtained anhydrous hydrazine by shaking
dried, labeled hydrazine sulfate with ordinary liquid ammonia at
-45° C, filtering off ammonium sulfate, and evaporating the NH_3
solution from the filtrate.

Higginson and Sutton[109] report the synthesis of $N_2^{15}H_4$ from
labeled $N^{15}H_3$ using the Koenig and Brings[110] synthesis, which
involves passing a silent electric discharge through NH_3 gas, and
continuously condensing the ammonia along with any N_2H_4 formed. This procedure rapidly removes the products from the discharge zone. They used 0.9 g   of NH_3 containing 33.4 per
cent N^{15}. The final yield of hydrazine was 0.071 g   after about
25 per cent of the ammonia was decomposed to the elements. The
hydrazine was purified by absorbing it together with the undecom-
posed $N^{15}H_3$ into 0.1 $\underline{N}$ H_2SO_4 and crystallizing insoluble
$N_2^{15}H_4 \cdot H_2SO_4$. Unconverted $N^{15}H_3$ can be recovered from the
mother liquor.

Although the yield in this synthesis is about 34 per cent of the
$N^{15}H_3$ decomposed, the decomposition of a major fraction of the
ammonia to N_2^{15} is a disadvantage. The enriched N_2 gas could
be recovered from the exit gases, either by passing them through
a trap cooled with liquid hydrogen, or by absorbing the nitrogen
onto heated calcium metal.

I. Metal Amides

$NaN^{15}H_2$ was prepared by Clusius and Effenberger[87] by the reaction of heated sodium metal with $N^{15}H_3$ gas in the apparatus
shown in Fig. 7. The small iron boat S is attached to the standard taper joint T by means of a welded iron wire with a slotted
socket. In this way, the boat is suspended in the reaction tube so
that it does not touch the wall of the vessel. This prevents attack
of the glass by the molten reaction product, which has a great
tendency to creep along a surface. The cold end of the wire stem
keeps the amide from reaching the glass. The tube is surrounded
by an electrically heated furnace O, containing a thermocouple.
The boat is first filled with 10 cm (~ 10 mmoles) of Na wire,
inserted into the system by means of the tapered joint, and the
apparatus is evacuated through stopcock H. The furnace is heated
to 250 to 300° C, and, after closing the stopcock, $N^{15}H_3$ is introduced from the reservoir A. The reaction

$$2Na + 2NH_3 \longrightarrow 2NaNH_2 + H_2$$

[109] Higginson, W. C. E., and Sutton, D., J. Chem. Soc., 1953,
1402.

[110] Koenig, A., and Brings, T., Z. Physik. Chem. (Bodenstein
Festband), 541 (1931).

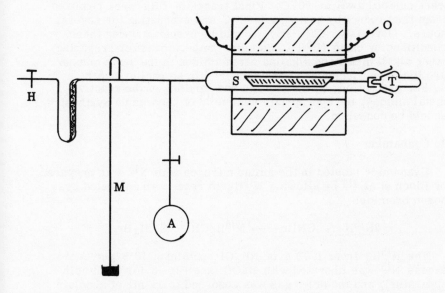

Fig. 7 Apparatus for preparing N^{15}-labeled amides. (From
      Clusius and Effenberger.[87])

proceeds rapidly at the start and later slows down. The rate of
reaction is conveniently followed by the pressure change indicated
on manometer M. From time to time the hydrogen gas formed is
pumped off through the glass-wool-packed U tube, which is cooled
to hold back any unreacted $N^{15}H_3$. Before pumping off hydrogen,
the furnace should be cooled below the melting point of the amide,
since the liquid amide will contain large quantities of dissolved
gas, and evacuation causes spattering of the liquid. The amide
formation is complete in approximately 24 hours, after three fillings of the system with $N^{15}H_3$; the completion of conversion is
observed by the absence of further pressure changes on the manometer. Residual gases are pumped off, and unreacted $N^{15}H_3$
can be recovered from the trap. Clusius and Effenberger[87] used
the product in situ without further treatment. No estimate of yield
was indicated.

Clusius and Schumacher[111] describe the preparation of unlabeled
$Ca(NH_2)_2$ using the same apparatus. Two grams of fresh Ca
turnings was put into an iron boat of 55 ml capacity. The calcium
metal expanded to about three times its volume on treatment with
dry NH_3. Calcium amide formed readily at temperatures of 20
to 60° C, and the amidization was accomplished by very slowly
raising the furnace temperature to 60° C. After reaction was
complete, most of the unreacted NH_3 and the hydrogen liberated
were pumped away at 60° C. Final traces of NH_3 were removed
from the product by heating to 100° C and evacuating for several
hours. Obviously, $Ca(N^{15}H_2)_2$ could be prepared under these
conditions by using $N^{15}H_3$. Suitable temperatures for preparing
other alkali metal and alkaline earth amides in the same manner
are listed by Clusius and Schumacher[112] in an earlier paper.

For precautions on the storage and handling of the reactive
metal amides, the appropriate volume[113] of "Inorganic Synthesis"
should be consulted.

J. Cyanamide

Cyanamide labeled in the amine nitrogen with N^{15} was prepared
by Bloch et al.[114] by allowing $N^{15}H_3$ to react with unlabeled cyanogen bromide:

$$2N^{15}H_3 + CNBr \longrightarrow N^{15}H_2CN + N^{15}H_4Br$$

The $N^{15}H_3$ from 1.07 g of NH_4Cl containing 10.5 per cent
excess N^{15} was liberated with NaOH (see Fig. 3 for a suitable
apparatus), and the dried gas was absorbed in 15 ml of absolute
methanol at -80° C. Any unabsorbed N^{15}-ammonia was recovered
in dilute sulfuric acid. To the alcoholic ammonia solution was
added 1.06 g of freshly prepared normal CNBr in 20 ml of absolute ether, and the mixture was kept for 12 hours at room temperature. The precipitated $N^{15}H_4Br$ formed was filtered off and
washed with ether. The filtrate and washings were combined and
evaporated to dryness in vacuo; the $N^{15}H_4Br$ precipitate and the
sulfuric acid solution were saved for recovery of N^{15}. The residue was extracted with dry ether, and the ether was finally removed with dry nitrogen gas. The final yield was 0.40 g of
crystalline cyanamide.

---

[111] Clusius, K., and Schumacher, H., Helv. Chim. Acta, 41,
2264 (1958).

[112] Clusius, K., and Schumacher, H., Helv. Chim. Acta, 41,
972 (1958).

[113] Fernelius, W. C., "Inorganic Synthesis," Vol. II, McGraw-
Hill, New York, 1946, p. 128.

[114] Bloch, K., Schoenheimer, R., and Rittenberg, D., J.
Biol. Chem., 138, 161 (1941).

The same synthesis was carried out on a larger scale by Bendich and co-workers[115] who started with 9 g of $N^{15}H_4NO_3$ containing 30 per cent N^{15} and collected the $N^{15}H_3$ in 65 ml of anhydrous ethanol at -70° C. To this solution was added 6.0 g of CNBr in 45 ml of dry ether, and the mixture was kept at room temperature for 16 hours. The cyanamide was separated from $N^{15}H_4Br$ and crystallized from ether in the manner described above. About 93 to 100 per cent of the $N^{15}H_4Br$ was recovered, and about 87 to 96 per cent of the theoretical yield of $N^{15}H_2CN$ was obtained. The pure crystals were stored in a refrigerator.

The above preparations yielded only an amine-labeled cyanamide because unlabeled CNBr was used as a reagent. A product with both nitrogen atoms marked could be prepared by carrying out the synthesis using $CN^{15}Br$. This reagent could be readily formed from $NaCN^{15}$ by using the procedure followed by Graff and co-workers[116] in preparing C^{14}-labeled cyanimide. They prepared $C^{14}NBr$ by treating an aqueous solution of $NaC^{14}N$ with bromine at 0° C and distilled the $BrC^{14}N$ formed into ice-cold ether. The freshly prepared ether solution of $BrC^{14}N$ was then added to a cold alcoholic ammonia solution, and the remainder of the synthesis of C^{14}-cyanamide was the same as for the N^{15} product described above. Substitution of $NaCN^{15}$ (see Sec. K) for the radiocarbon compound leads to the required $CN^{15}Br$.

An alternate route has been used by several workers[117] to prepare C^{14}-labeled cyanamide via barium cyanamide. When $BaC^{14}O_3$ is heated in a stream of dry ammonia for 3 hours at 850° C, quantitative conversion to BaNCN is obtained. Cyanamide was liberated by treating the barium salt with cold concentrated sulfuric acid. To adapt this procedure for the synthesis of N^{15}-labeled cyanamide, it would be necessary to circulate $N^{15}H_3$ over $BaCO_3$ in a closed system by means of a Toepler pump. It seems likely that under these conditions an appreciable fraction of the labeled ammonia would be decomposed to elemental nitrogen and hydrogen. The cold synthesis using $CN^{15}Br$ and $N^{15}H_3$ therefore appears preferable.

K. Cyanides

MacDiarmid and Hall[118] synthesized $NaCN^{15}$ by heating N^{15}-labeled potassium phthalimide with metallic sodium in a steel bomb. The bomb tube, made by drilling and threading a hole in a

---
[115] Bendich, A., Tinker, J. F., and Brown, G. B., J. Am. Chem. Soc., 70, 3109 (1948).

[116] Graff, S., Engelman, M., Gillespie, H. B., and Graff, A. M., Cancer Research, 11, 388 (1951).

[117] Ref. 86, Part I, p. 588.

[118] MacDiarmid, A. G., and Hall, N. J., J. Am. Chem. Soc., 75, 4580 (1953).

hexagonal steel bar, was charged with 0.3 g of potassium phthalimide-N^{15} and 1.5 g of sodium. The reactor was then capped with a steel bolt, using a soft-copper gasket to make the vessel gas tight, and heated in a furnace at 700° C in an upright position for about 20 minutes. After cooling, water was carefully added by drops to decompose any remaining sodium, and the charred mass was extracted from the bomb with hot water. The extract was treated with 5 ml of 0.1 $\underline{N}$ Ba(OH)$_2$ to precipitate BaCO$_3$, brought to boiling, and filtered to remove the BaCO$_3$ and carbon. The filtrate was acidified with 50 per cent sulfuric acid solution, and the HCN^{15} was distilled into 20 ml of 0.1 $\underline{N}$ NaOH solution. Yields of 97 to 100 per cent were obtained.

A number of microscale syntheses used to prepare KC^{14}N are listed in the text by Murray and Williams.[119] Of these, two seem readily adaptable for the preparation of N^{15}-labeled cyanides and offer the advantage of using readily available $N^{15}H_3$ as the starting compound. They also appear to be particularly convenient for preparing a cyanide in which both the carbon and nitrogen atoms are labeled.

The reduction of $C^{14}O_2$ gas with potassium and ammonia

$$4K + NH_3 + CO_2 \xrightarrow{\Delta} KCN + KH + 2KOH$$

was studied in detail by Loftfield,[120] and a modified procedure for synthesizing NaC^{14}N is outlined in the text by Calvin and coworkers,[121] who obtained yields of 90 to 96 per cent based on $C^{14}O_2$, and report that the yield is not sensitive to the NH$_3$ pressure. They used a Pyrex glass bomb tube (1 cm diameter × 40 cm long) and dropped into it 0.8 g of clean potassium metal after flushing the vessel with nitrogen. The tube was constricted about 5 cm from the open end, attached to a vacuum system by a length of plastic tubing, and evacuated to remove the solvent (petroleum ether) from the metal. The potassium metal was then dispersed as a mirror on the inner surface by clamping the evacuated tube in a horizontal position and heating the lower surface with a tiny flame while cooling the upper half of the cylinder with a wet towel. After forming a mirror over about 90 per cent of the tube surface, it was immersed in liquid nitrogen, and 1 mmole of CO$_2$ and 2 mmole of NH$_3$ were frozen in. The tube was sealed off at the constriction, placed in a steel protective jacket, and lowered into a furnace at 620° C. The total heating time was 12 minutes plus the time required to bring the tube and contents to the furnace

[119] Ref. 86, Part I, p. 563.

[120] Loftfield, R. B., Nucleonics, 1 (3), 54 (1947).

[121] Calvin, M., Heidelberger, C., Reid, S. C., Tolbert, B. M., and Yankwich, P. F., "Isotopic Carbon," Wiley, New York, 1949, p. 160.

temperature. (Bos,[122] in a similar procedure, reports a time
of 8 minutes to bring the contents to furnace temperature.) After
cooling, the glass bomb was again immersed in liquid nitrogen and
opened by heating the sealed tip with a small hot flame to release
the residual pressure. The hydrides and unreacted potassium
were decomposed by careful addition, by drops, of water or 50
per cent ethanol solution, and the mixture was evaporated in vacuo.
The cyanide was purified and recovered either by precipitation as
silver cyanide or by acidification of the mixture with formic acid
and distillation as HCN into a trap containing excess alkali.

All workers have reported high yields based on $C^{14}O_2$; Loftfield[120] reported a maximum yield of 96 per cent, and Bos[122] a
range of 89.2 to 92.7 per cent.

Sixma et al.[123] avoided the use of liquid nitrogen by carrying
out a similar micro-preparation of C^{14}-cyanide using $BaCO_3$,
NH_4Cl, and K metal. They added 1 to 2 g of clean potassium
metal to a mixture of 200 mg $BaCO_3$ and 100 mg NH_4Cl in a
Supremax tube (1.6 cm diameter, ~17 cm long) under a nitrogen
atmosphere. After evacuation and melting to remove solvent from
the metal, the tube was sealed, the metal remelted, and the contents thoroughly mixed by shaking. It was then heated in a furnace
at 640°C for 60 minutes plus the 9 minutes required to bring
the contents to furnace temperature. They found that a shorter
heating time reduced the yield appreciably. After cooling and
opening the tube, the excess potassium was destroyed with ethanol
or water. The contents were transferred to a distilling flask with
hot water, acidified with sulfuric acid, and the HCN was distilled
into excess sodium hydroxide solution. An average over-all yield
of 94 ± 1.5 per cent of $C^{14}N^-$ was obtained.

Although the latter two procedures seem well suited for the
preparation of N^{15}-labled cyanides, it should be realized that the
specific reaction conditions and reactant quantities were developed
to conserve $C^{14}O_2$. In modifying the procedures for N^{15} synthesis, some study is required to determine appropriate reagent
quantities for maximizing the yield, based on $N^{15}H_3$ or $N^{15}H_4^+$.

Micro procedures developed for preparing cuprous cyanide
labeled with C^{13} or C^{14} from alkali cyanides are suitable without
modification for preparing a nitrogen-labeled product. Reid and
Weaver[124] prepared 350 mg of $Cu_2(CN)_2$ from $NaC^{14}N$ in 100
per cent yield by addition of an alkaline solution, by drops, containing the labeled cyanide plus sodium bisulfite to a well-stirred
solution of cupric sulfate. The reduction of the cupric ion was
accomplished by the bisulphite ion instead of by cyanide ion, and

[122] Bos, J. A., Experientia, 7, 258 (1951).

[123] Sixma, F. L. J., Hendriks, H., Helle, K., Hollstein, U.,
and VanLing, R., Rec. trav. chim., 73, 161 (1954).

[124] Reid, J. C., and Weaver, J. C., Cancer Research, 11,
188 (1951).

no cyanide was lost as cyanogen. Other workers[125,126] have reported yields of 80 to 95 per cent for similar procedures. Preparation of cuprous cyanide by shaking cuprous chloride with a solution of alkali cyanide has also been reported.[127,128] Martin[128] obtained a 91 per cent yield by this procedure.

L. Thiocyanate

Tesar and Rittenberg[129] modified the procedure of Schulze[130] in order to conserve $N^{15}H_4NO_3$, and synthesized $NaCN^{15}S$

$$3N^{15}H_4NO_3 + 3CS_2 + 2Fe(OH)_3 + 6NaOH \longrightarrow$$

$$3NaCN^{15}S + 2FeS + S + 3NaNO_3 + 12H_2O$$

A mixture of 25 ml of CS_2, 17 g of $Fe(OH)_3$, 40 ml of methanol, and 10.8 g of $N^{15}H_4NO_3$ was placed in a glass-stoppered bottle, which was mounted on a mechanical shaker and continuously agitated. To the mixture were added 10 g of NaOH pellets in nine portions at 2-hour intervals, and the shaking was continued for an additional 24 hours after all the sodium hydroxide was added. The contents were then diluted with water and centrifuged. The deposit was washed several times by centrifugation, and the supernatants were all combined, saturated with H_2S, and filtered. The filtrate was acidified to litmus with HCl, heated to boiling, then cooled and neutralized by adding dilute NaOH in an amount equal to the HCl used for acidification. The solution was evaporated to dryness in vacuo, and the salts were extracted with several portions of absolute ethanol. The extract containing $NaCN^{15}S$ was again evaporated to dryness on a steam bath, and the residue was reextracted with 100 ml of absolute ethanol. When this final extract was evaporated to dryness, 9.8 g of sodium thiocyanate was obtained. The product was 99 per cent pure, as determined by a colorimetric assay against normal thiocyanate. The final yield was 90 per cent based upon $N^{15}H_4NO_3$.

---

[125] Dauben, W. G., Hiskey, C. F., and Muks, M. A., J. Am. Chem. Soc., 74, 2082 (1952).

[126] Vaughan, W. R., and McCane, D. I., J. Am. Chem. Soc., 76, 2504 (1954).

[127] Anker, H. S., J. Biol. Chem., 176, 1337 (1948).

[128] Martin, L., and Baker S. B., U.S. Atomic Energy Comm. Report NP-3177; U.S. Atomic Energy Comm. Nucl. Sci. Abstr., 5, 5157 (1951).

[129] Tesar, C., and Rittenberg, D., J. Biol. Chem., 170, 35 (1947).

[130] Schulze, J., J. Prakt. Chem., 27, 518 (1883).

A number of workers[131] have prepared C^{14}-labeled NaCNS by refluxing $NaC^{14}N$ with sulfur in either an ethanol or an acetone solution; Sprinson and Rittenberg[132] carried out the same preparation by heating a dry mixture of alkali cyanides, potassium hydroxide, and free sulfur for 15 minutes at 310° C under nitrogen. Although these procedures are also suitable for the preparation of N^{15}-labeled thiocyanate, N^{15}-labeled cyanide is usually less readily available than labeled ammonia, and therefore the synthesis starting with $N^{15}H_4NO_3$ seems advantageous.

M. Cyanate-N^{15}

Williams[133] prepared ammonium cyanate, labeled with N^{15} in the ammonium position only, by reacting $N^{15}H_4Cl$ with ordinary silver cyanate. A mixture of 153.5 mg of $N^{15}H_4Cl$ (2.87 mmoles), 610.5 mg of AgCNO (4.07 mmoles, 40 per cent excess), and 10 ml of distilled water were placed in a 40-ml centrifuge tube and stirred rapidly for 7 hours to keep the unreacted silver cyanate and the silver chloride produced in suspension. The mixture was filtered and the precipitate of silver chloride and silver cyanate washed with a total of 100 ml of absolute ethanol. The washings were combined with the filtrate. The ammonium cyanate was not further purified in this procedure, since Williams used the solution to prepare singly labeled N^{15}-urea. This was accomplished by heating the alcoholic $N^{15}H_4CNO$ solution in a tightly stoppered 250-ml flask for 16.5 hours at 55° C. The solution was then evaporated to dryness and the urea extracted with 40 ml of absolute methanol. This extract was evaporated to dryness in a vacuum sublimator, and the urea was purified by two sublimations over a 6-hour period at a bath temperature of 68 to 70° C and a pressure of 2 to 3 microns. The final product was removed from the sublimator with methanol and evaporated to dryness. The yield was 85.4 per cent.

The preparation of N^{15}-labeled potassium cyanate has not been described in the literature, but the procedure used[134,135] for preparing $KC^{14}NO$ from $KC^{14}N$ should serve this purpose.

---

[131] See Ref. 86, Part I, p. 574, for details and specific references.

[132] Sprinson, D. B., and Rittenberg, D., J. Biol. Chem., 198, 658 (1952).

[133] Williams, D. L., U.S. Atomic Energy Comm. Report, AECU-664; U.S. Atomic Energy Comm. Nucl. Sci. Abstr., 4, 227 (1950).

[134] Haley, E. E., and Lambooy, J. P., J. Am. Chem. Soc., 76, 2926 (1954).

[135] Smith, L. H., Jr., and Yates, P., Jr., J. Am. Chem. Soc., 76, 6080 (1954).

Haley and Lambooy[134] prepared a mixture of 328.4 mg (5 mmoles) of $KC^{14}N$, 650 mg (11.5 mmoles) of KOH, 2.5 ml of water, and cupric hydroxide catalyst freshly prepared from 487 mg (2 mmoles) of $CuSO_4 \cdot 5H_2O$. To the stirred mixture in a 50-ml centrifuge tube, a solution of 675 mg (4.3 mmoles) of potassium permanganate in 12 ml of water was gradually added. The mixture was heated to 50°C for 5 minutes, cooled, and the excess permanganate destroyed by slowly adding 1 ml of 3 per cent hydrogen peroxide. The precipitate was separated by centrifugation and washed with three portions of water. The combined filtrate and washings were partly neutralized by addition of 0.45 meq of 0.1-N H_2SO_4, and the solution was concentrated under reduced pressure. The yield was quantitative.

Haley and Lambooy[134] used this solution directly for the preparation of urea-C^{14}. Since simpler methods are available for synthesizing urea-N^{15}, the above synthesis is primarily useful for preparing N^{15}-cyanates. Silver cyanate-N^{15} could readily be prepared by neutralizing the $KCN^{15}O$ solution from the above procedure with nitric acid instead of sulfuric acid and treating with a slight excess of 10 per cent silver nitrate solution at 2 to 4°C as outlined by Williams and Ronzio.[136] The silver cyanate-N^{15} could by converted readily to a doubly labeled $N^{15}H_4CN^{15}O$ by treatment with $N^{15}H_4Cl$ as described above.

N. Phthalimide-N^{15}

Potassium phthalimide labeled with N^{15} has been useful as a "key" substance for synthesizing labeled cyanides[118] and as a starting reagent for synthesizing labeled amino acids.[137] For this reason, its synthesis is included among inorganic nitrogen compounds. Schoenheimer and Ratner[137] prepared the labeled phthalimide salt by the series of reactions shown in reaction (11).

A sodium hydroxide solution was slowly added to 0.40 moles of a labeled ammonium salt, and the $N^{15}H_3$ liberated was distilled into a suspension of 68 g of phthalic acid in 200 ml of H_2O with the aid of a stream of nitrogen gas. After passing through the phthalic acid solution, the gas stream bubbled through a gas-washing bottle containing sulfuric acid to collect any unabsorbed $N^{15}H_3$. The ammonium acid phthalate dissolved as it formed and, after all the $N^{15}H_3$ was absorbed, the solution was transferred to a 1-liter round-bottom flask with a neck 75 cm long and 1.6 cm in diameter. A 12-mm side arm was attached 10 cm below the top of the neck of the flask, and bent downward in a right angle 25 cm from the flask. The descending portion of the side arm was jacketed with a

---

136 Williams, D. L., and Ronzio, A. R., J. Am. Chem. Soc., 74, 2407 (1952).

137 Schoenheimer, R., and Ratner, S., J. Biol. Chem., 127, 301 (1939).

$$N^{15}H_3 + C_6H_4(COOH)_2 \longrightarrow \underset{}{\bigcirc}\underset{-COON^{15}H_4}{\overset{-COOH}{}}$$

$$\downarrow \Delta \qquad\qquad (11)$$

$$\underset{CO}{\overset{CO}{\bigcirc}}N^{15}K \xleftarrow{\text{KOH}} \underset{CO}{\overset{CO}{\bigcirc}}N^{15}H$$

cooling condenser, and the bottom of the condenser entered a filter flask, the side arm of which connected to a trap containing dilute sulfuric acid, to recover any $N^{15}H_3$ evolved. The flask was first heated at 100° C until most of the water was driven off. The temperature was then slowly raised to 200° C to complete the removal of water. Finally the temperature was increased to 300° C; this temperature was maintained until the vigorous reaction was complete. The flask was cooled, the neck cut off, and the phthalimide-N^{15} removed with cold absolute ethanol. The yield was 56.4 g (96 per cent).

Potassium phthalimide-N^{15} was prepared in 92 per cent yield by the method of Salzberg and Supniewski.[138] Isotopic $N^{15}H_3$ was recovered from the alcoholic mother liquors and the acid traps by treating the combined solutions with an excess of alkali and distilling the ammonia into dilute sulfuric acid.

More recently, Maimind and co-workers[100] have described a modification of the above procedure that differs mainly in the procedure for isolation and purification of the phthalimide-N^{15}, and which thereby increases the yield of the potassium salt to 98 to 99 per cent.

These authors[100] prepared phthalimide-N^{15} from $N^{15}H_4NO_3$ by charging 100 mmoles of the salt as a 30 to 50 per cent aqueous solution into a three-necked flask fitted with a Kjeldahl trap in one of the necks. A tube, which served as an air condenser, led from the Kjeldahl trap into a receiver containing 105 mmoles of chemically pure, finely crystalline phthalic acid (previously crystallized from acetic acid, decolorized with charcoal, and recrystallized from water) suspended in 40 ml of water. A slow stream of nitrogen bubbled into the flask through the second neck, and a small excess of 40 per cent sodium hydroxide solution was run in slowly from a dropping funnel in the third neck. The $N^{15}H_3$ was evolved by gentle heating and was completely absorbed by the phthalic acid in 3 to 4 hours. During this time, all the ammonia was evolved,

---

[138] Salzberg, P. L., and Supniewski, J. V., Org. Syntheses, Coll. 1, 119 (1941).

about half the water was distilled into the receiver, and the ammonium acid phthalate was formed, together with the excess phthalic acid dissolved in the receiver.

The solution from the receiver was transferred to a 300-ml pyrex Kjeldahl flask with an extended neck (35 to 40 cm long and 12 to 15 mm in diameter), and the water was slowly driven off by immersing the lower quarter of the flask in a bath of Wood's metal maintained at 140° C. During this operation and the succeeding dehydration, the vapors were passed through a sulfuric acid trap to recover $N^{15}H_3$; Maimind[100] recovered about 1 per cent of the $N^{15}H_3$ from the water driven off. After removal of the water, the bath temperature was gradually raised; at 180 to 190° C the residue in the flask crystallized, and the dehydration commenced at about 200° C. At 290 to 300° C all the phthalimide formed sublimed on the walls and neck of the flask. Dehydration and sublimation required about 3 hours. The phthalimide was removed from the flask with about 15 to 20 ml of water, transferred to a small mortar, and slurried with 5 per cent sodium carbonate solution, which was added by drops until the mixture became alkaline. The precipitate was filtered, washed with 50 ml of water, and dried in a vacuum desiccator. The phthalimide yield was 98 to 99 per cent.

The potassium salt was prepared by shaking 50 ml of a hot 2-$\underline{N}$ potassium ethoxide solution in anhydrous ethanol with a hot solution of 100 mmoles of phthalimide-N^{15} in 350 ml of anhydrous ethanol. After cooling, the precipitate was filtered, washed with anhydrous ethanol until the washings no longer showed an alkaline reaction, then washed with acetone, and dried in a vacuum desiccator. The alcoholic mother liquor was recovered and re-used, thereby making the yield of potassium phthalimide-N^{15} nearly quantitative.

O. Urea-N^{15}

The preparation of singly labeled N^{15}-urea by Wöhler's reaction of $N^{15}H_4CNO$ has already been described. It was used by Rose and Dekker[139] to prepare urea containing 14.75 per cent N^{15}. Williams and Ronzio[136] used the same reaction to prepare a product in which both the nitrogen and carbon atoms were isotopically labeled by the rearrangement of $N^{15}H_4C^{14}N^{14}O$. In general this procedure is less advisable for preparing N^{15}-labeled urea than the one described below, because a twofold dilution of the $N^{15}H_3$ results unless the cyanate ion is also N^{15}-labeled.

The most satisfactory procedure for preparing N^{15}-urea is by the ammonolysis of diphenyl carbonate. Bloch and Schoen-

---

[139] Rose, W. C., and Dekker, E. E., J. Biol. Chem., 223, 107 (1956).

heimer[140] first adapted the older method of Hentschel[141] for an isotopic synthesis, and introduced the use of Cu dust as a catalyst. The procedure has since been used by a number of workers[142-147] to prepare N^{15}-labeled urea.

The following procedure is essentially as described by Cavalieri et al.[142] A three-necked round-bottom flask equipped with a dropping funnel, reflux condenser, and inlet tube for nitrogen gas was used to generate labeled ammonia from 4.0 g of $N^{15}H_4NO_3$. A drying tower filled with potassium hydroxide pellets was attached to the top of the condenser, and a wide-bore tube from the top of the drying tower was connected into a glass bomb tube, 15 cm above the bottom of the bomb. An outlet from the top of the bomb tube led to an acid trap containing a known quantity of standard acid solution. The acid solution was used to recover and measure the quantity of uncondensed N^{15}-labeled ammonia.

The bomb tube was filled with an intimate mixture of about 5 g diphenyl carbonate and 130 mg copper powder , and the lower end was cooled with liquid nitrogen to condense and freeze the labeled ammonia. The entire system was flushed with a slow stream of oxygen-free nitrogen, and, while the nitrogen stream continued, potassium hydroxide solution was slowly added to the generating flask and the contents heated to boiling. The ammonia gas was generated, and condensed into the bomb tube over a 3-hour period. During this time, about 5 per cent $N^{15}H_3$ was collected in the acid trap. The ammonia gas must be liberated slowly to avoid plugging the inlet of the bomb with solid NH_3.

The bomb was sealed while immersed in dry ice, and then heated in a water bath at 90 to 100° C for 4 hours. After cooling and opening the bomb, the contents were dissolved in 50 ml of warm water, filtered to remove the copper dust, and the filtrate extracted with five 50-ml portions of chloroform. The aqueous phase was

[140] Bloch, K. , and Schoenheimer, R. , J. Biol. Chem. , 138, 167 (1941).

[141] Hentschel, W. , Ber. , 17, 1284 (1884).

[142] Cavalieri, L. F. , Blair, V. E. , and Brown, G. B. , J. Am. Chem. Soc. , 70, 1240 (1948).

[143] Benedict, J. D. , Forsham, P. H. , and Stetten, D. , Jr. , J. Biol. Chem. , 181, 183 (1949).

[144] Leitch, L. C. , and Davidson, W. M. , Can. J. Agr. Sci. , 29, 185 (1949).

[145] Kornberg, H. L. , and Davies, R. E. , Biochem. J. , 52, 345 (1952).

[146] San Pietro, A. , and Rittenberg, D. , J. Biol. Chem. , 201, 445 (1953).

[147] Walser, M. , George, J. , and Bodenlos, L. J. , J. Chem. Phys. , 22, 1146 (1954).

decolorized with charcoal and evaporated to dryness on a water
bath. The urea was recrystallized from acetone. The final yield
by this procedure was 57 per cent based on the ammonia condensed.

San Pietro and Rittenberg[146] modified the above procedure by
liberating ammonia from a dry mixture containing $N^{15}H_4Cl$, with
an excess of calcined CaO, and freezing the $N^{15}H_3$ into the bomb
tube with the remaining reactants. This simplification eliminates
the need for the ammonia-generating system and the nitrogen
stream and avoids the danger of explosion resulting from the condensation of liquid oxygen in the bomb tube because of impurities
in the tank nitrogen. The yield was not given, but it seems reasonable, by the handling of the dry reactants in a vacuum system, that
even small losses of enriched ammonia could feasibly be avoided.

P. Hyponitrite-N^{15}

Frear and Burrell[148] report the preparation of sodium hyponitrite by reduction of sodium nitrate containing 34.5 per cent N^{15},
with sodium amalgam. The procedure for the isotopic synthesis
was not described in detail but was reportedly the method first used
by Divers,[149] as modified by Partington and Shah[150] and Addison
et al.[151] The earlier workers[150, 151] used sodium nitrite as the
starting reagent and reported yields of up to 5 to 19 per cent of
anhydrous $Na_2N_2O_2$. The smaller-scale isotopic synthesis using
$NaN^{15}O_3$ as a starting reagent gave 90 per cent pure sodium
hyponitrite in a yield of about 9 per cent. Less than 0.1 per cent
of the impurities are reported to be nitrate or nitrite loans; the
major impurities were assumed to be sodium carbonate and sodium
hydroxide.

Q. Metal Azides

Clusius and co-workers have investigated extensively the
structure of azides and the mechanisms of bond formation and
cleavage in these compounds, using a variety of N^{15}-labeled com-

---

148 Frear, D. S., and Burrell, R. C., Plant Physiol., 33,
105 (1958).

149 Divers, E., J. Chem. Soc., 1899, 87, 95.

150 Partington, J. R., and Shah, C. C., J. Chem. Soc.,
1931, 2071.

151 Addison, C. C., Gamlin, G. A., and Thompson, R.,
J. Chem. Soc., 1952, 338.

pounds.[5, 87, 111, 112, 152-156] In the course of these studies, they found that no exchange took place between the central nitrogen atom and the end nitrogen atoms; thus synthesis of either type of labeled species was possible.

Potassium azide containing N^{15} in only the end atoms was prepared[153] by reacting ordinary hydrazine hydrate and labeled ethyl nitrite in the presence of potassium methylate, according to the method of Thiele-Stolle.[157]

Labeled ethyl nitrite required for the synthesis was prepared from $NaN^{15}O_2$ by dissolving 2.6 g   of sodium nitrite in 5.3 ml of water, and reacting the solution with 4.5 ml of ethanol and 3.2 ml of concentrated hydrochloric acid added by drops to the ice-cooled mixture. The ethyl nitrite formed was distilled through a tube filled with anhydrous potassium carbonate into an ice-cooled receiver. The yield obtained in this step was 2.8 ml of ethyl nitrite.

Potassium azide was prepared by dissolving 2.2 g of potassium metal in 14 ml of methanol in a vessel fitted with a reflux condenser. The ice-cooled solution was then treated with 28 ml of absolute ether, 2.8 ml of hydrazine hydrate, and 2.8 ml of the labeled ethyl nitrite obtained in the previous step. The mixture was allowed to stand, first at $0°C$, and finally at room temperature for 24 hours. The KN_3 that crystallized out was filtered and washed with a methanol-ether mixture and finally with pure ether. The over-all yield amounted to 2.2 g KN_3^{15} (72 per cent based upon $NaN^{15}O_2$).

Azides with only the central N atom labeled are most conveniently prepared by reaction of nitrous oxide and metal amides.[87, 111, 112, 155] The authors report[112] that the synthesis using calcium amide is much more convenient and less subject to losses of enriched material than a synthesis via organic nitrogen compounds used previously.[156] Calcium amide was used in preference to other amides for this synthesis because the reaction yields almost quantitatively a singly labeled reaction product.

Using $N^{15}NO$ containing approximately 96 per cent N^{15}, various centrally labeled metal azides were prepared.[111] Unlabeled calcium amide was synthesized in the apparatus shown in Fig. 7,

[152] Clusius, K. and Weisser, H. R., Helv. Chim. Acta, 35, 1548 (1952).

[153] Clusius, K., and Hürzeler, H., Helv. Chim. Acta, 36, 1326 (1953).

[154] Clusius, K., and Effenberger, E., Helv. Chim. Acta, 38, 1843 (1955).

[155] Clusius, K., and Knopf, H., Chem. Ber., 89, 681 (1956).

[156] Clusius, K., and Vecchi, M., Ann. Chem. Liebigs, 607, 16 (1957).

[157] Thiele, J., Ber., 41, 2681 (1908); Stolle, R., ibid., 41, 2811 (1908).

and any unreacted ammonia was removed by evacuation for several hours, with the amide maintained at 100°C. Then $N^{15}NO$ was introduced and allowed to react for several days with the amide at atmospheric pressure and at 95 to 100°C. The reaction rate was observed by following the pressure changes in the system; after several days the change amounted to only a few millimeters of Hg per day. From time to time, the oven was turned off, the gas was cooled with liquid N_2, traces of nitrogen and hydrogen formed were pumped off, and more $N_2^{15}O$ was added. The reaction product reacted very vigorously with water because it contained a large excess of amide; it was therefore allowed to stand in air for several days, and only after this was it decomposed with water. The hydrolysate was acidified with dilute sulfuric acid, and the hydrazoic acid liberated was distilled into a receiver containing a slight excess of KOH. The potassium azide solution was brought to dryness on a water bath, and the residue was recrystallized from water and ethanol. In this procedure, 1.57 g of pure $KNN^{15}N$ were obtained from two batches; the yield was 85 per cent based on the N_2O used.

Samples of labeled silver and lead azides were prepared[111] by precipitating these azides from aqueous solution, using 0.3 to 0.5 mmoles $KNN^{15}N$ and an equivalent amount of either silver nitrate solution or a saturated solution of lead or silver acetate. The azide precipitates formed were filtered, washed with alcohol and ether, and dried in air.

The heavy metal azides are of course very explosive. Clusius reports[111] explosion during the preparation of a batch of potassium azide, and suggests that the apparatus be isolated and suitably shielded.

Acknowledgments. The preparation of this chapter was facilitated by support from the U.S. Atomic Energy Commission, which the author acknowledges with thanks.

5

Oxygen-18

I. DOSTROVSKY and D. SAMUEL
Weizmann Institute of Science
Rehovoth, Israel

1. INTRODUCTION

There are seven isotopes of oxygen of which three, O^{16}, O^{17}, and O^{18}, are stable and occur in all natural oxygen-containing substances. The natural abundances of the stable isotopes of oxygen vary slightly in nature, and those shown in Table 1 are the best

Table 1
The Isotopes of Oxygen

Isotope	Half-life, sec		Abundance in air	Ref.
O^{14}	72	β^+, γ		6
O^{15}	112	β^+		6
O^{16}			99.759	7
O^{17}			0.0374	7
O^{18}			0.2039	7
O^{19}	29	β^-, γ		6
O^{20}	13.6	β^-, γ		5

values for air.

The radioactive isotopes are artificially prepared by various nuclear reactions. They are all too short-lived to be used as tracers in most chemical reactions. O^{15}, the longest-lived radio-isotope, has a half-life of about 2 minutes and has been used in a flow system in a number of physiological and chemical studies.[1-4]

O^{20}, an even-even nucleus and expected (on the basis of nuclear systematics) to be relatively long-lived, has recently been found to have a half-life of 13.6 sec[5] and thus to be of little value in tracer work.

In this chapter the syntheses of inorganic compounds labeled with O^{18} are described. These methods are equally valid for O^{17} labeling. A large number of organic syntheses with oxygen isotopes have already been described.[8] A review on methodology primarily intended for biochemists[9] has recently been published. A comprehensive bibliography of research, through 1957, involving stable isotopes of oxygen is available[10] with a supplement covering the research to the end of 1960.[11]

In each case the fullest details from the published literature or from private communication with those concerned are given. The authors are particularly indebted to Dr. M. Anbar, Dr. M. Halmann, and Dr. F. S. Klein for making available unpublished details of syntheses and to all members of the Isotope Department of the Weizmann Institute for help in the preparation of this chapter.

2. MATERIALS

In preparing many inorganic compounds enriched in one or more positions with O^{18}, simple exchange processes between the normal

[1] Dyson, N. A., Hugh-Jones, P., Newberry, G. R., and West, J. B., Proc. Second Intern. Conf. Peaceful Uses Atomic Energy, Geneva, 26, 103, (1958).

[2] Ter-Pogassian, M., and Powers, W. E., in R. C. Exterman (ed.), "Radioisotopes in Scientific Research," Vol. III, Pergamon, New York, 1957.

[3] Dollery, C. T., and West, J. B., Nature, 187, 1121 (1960).

[4] Amiel, S., and Samuel, D., private communication.

[5] Sharff-Goldhaber, G., Goodman, A., and Silbert, M. G., Phys. Rev. Letters, 4, 25 (1960).

[6] Strominger, D., Hollander, J. M., and Seaborg, G. T., Revs. Modern Phys. 30, 582, (1958).

[7] Nier, A. O., Phys. Rev., 77, 789 (1950).

[8] Murray, A., and Williams, D. L., "Organic Syntheses with Isotopes," Part II, Chap. 18, Interscience, New York, 1958.

[9] Samuel, D., Methodology of Oxygen Isotopes, in O. Hayaishi (ed.), "Oxygenases," Academic, New York, 1962.

[10] Samuel, D., and Steckel, F., "Bibliography of Oxygen Isotopes (O^{17} and O^{18})," Pergamon, New York, 1959.

[11] Samuel, D., and Steckel, F., Intern. J. Appl. Radiation and Isotopes, 11, 190 (1961).

compound and O^{18}-enriched water can be used to introduce a label. However, when highly enriched samples are required, repeated exchange steps are necessary. This process has the disadvantage of needing relatively large amounts of O^{18}-enriched water and also of reducing its enrichment. For this reason, wherever possible, techniques are described for direct syntheses rather than for exchange procedures.

The two starting compounds available commercially for the syntheses of inorganic compounds are O^{18}-enriched water and O^{18}-enriched gas.

A. Water

Water of enrichments from 1.5 to 97 atom per cent O^{18} and from 1.0 to 6.0 atom per cent O^{17} is available commercially.[12]

Water depleted in O^{18} (containing ca. 0.1 atom per cent O^{18}) is also available and is of use in certain cases. At present, all O^{18}-enriched water is prepared[13,14] by fractional distillation of ordinary water and is highly enriched in deuterium. The exact concentration of deuterium for each O^{18} concentration depends to a large extent on the design of the separation plant. In most cases this water is quite satisfactory for syntheses, but where hydrogen atoms are required in the final product (i. e., H_2SO_4, NaOH, or KH_2PO_4) for nuclear or biological work, or wherever hydrogen-isotope effects may be important, the deuterium-containing water used in the synthesis must first be "normalized" and the deuterium concentration reduced to its natural abundance. In some cases, this normalization can be done on the final product (i. e., KH_2PO_4) if the rate of hydrogen-isotope exchange with water is very much faster than the rate of oxygen exchange.

B. Oxygen

O^{18}-enriched gas of high isotopic enrichments (99 atom per cent O^{18} or 10 atom per cent O^{17}) is available commercially.[12]

For syntheses not requiring such high enrichments, O^{18}-or O^{17}-enriched gas can be prepared by the following methods:

1. For large quantities of oxygen gas, the best method is the electrolysis of alkaline O^{18}-enriched water. An investment of several milliliters of water is needed for hold-up of the electroly-

---

[12] Yeda Research & Development Corp., P.O. Box 26, Rehovoth, Israel.

[13] Dostrovsky, I., and Raviv, A., in J. Kistemaker, J. Biegeleisen, and A. O. Nier, (eds.), Proc. Amsterdam Conf. on Isotope Separation, North Holland Publishing Co., Amsterdam, 1957, Chap. 26, pp. 336-349.

[14] Thurkauf, M., Narten, A., and Kuhn, W., Helv. Chim. Acta, **43**, 989 (1960).

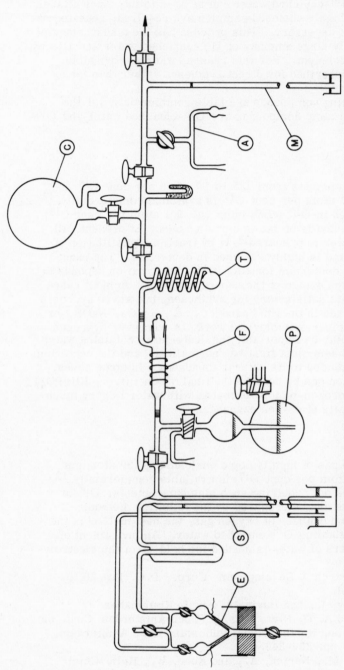

Fig. 2 Vacuum line for work with oxygen isotopes (not to scale); A, ampule-filling manifold; C, carbon dioxide-storage vessel; E, electrolyzer; F, furnace; M, manometer;
P, Toepler pump; and S, T, trap.

sis cell. To minimize this, cells have been designed with small
hold-ups consistent with reasonable rates of oxygen evolution. One
simple design is shown in Fig. 1. Since gas must often be fed to a
vacuum line from such cells, some special method has to be used
that allows the cell to operate at atmospheric pressure irrespective of
of the pressure conditions in the line. The arrangement that has

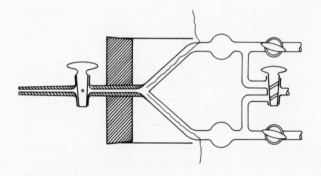

Fig. 1   Electrolytic cell for the preparation of O^{18}-labeled oxygen
gas (with water jacket).

been used for this purpose[15] is shown in Fig. 2. With the dimensions shown in Fig. 1, the cell can be operated at a current of 0.5
amp. The electrolyte is made by dissolving pure metallic sodium
in O^{18}-enriched water (see Sec. 5-A) to give a 4-$\underline{M}$ solution of
$NaO^{18}H$.

The oxygen evolved is dried by passage through a dry ice-
acetone-cooled trap and can either be stored in glass bulbs or used
directly in the synthesis of oxides. The vacuum line that permits
both storage of O_2 and various syntheses is shown in Fig. 2.

Microelectrolytic cells for the preparation of O^{18} gas have also

---
[15] Gat, J., private communication.

been described by Wiberg,[16] by Hunt et al,[17] by Bentley,[18] and by Millen and Pannel.[18a]

2. When small amounts of oxygen are required (a few ml) and the amount of O^{18}-enriched water available is small (1 ml), the simple microelectrolyzer shown in Fig. 3 may be used.[19] The

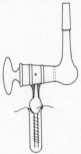

Fig. 3 Microelectrolyzer for the preparation of O^{18} gas.

electrolyzer is made from a vacuum stopcock with a standard ground joint at one end. By means of this joint, the electrolyzer is connected to a vacuum line, and small amounts of wet oxygen are bled into the system.

3. Small amounts of oxygen gas may be made from O^{18}-enriched water by the procedure described by Anbar[20] for the isotopic analysis of water. According to this procedure, about 10 to 20 mg of sodium and 1 to 3 mg of cobalt oxide are added to 200 mg of enriched water. The mixture is cooled in a seal-off tube fitted with a break-seal, the air is pumped out, a small amount of bromine is then condensed into the mixture, and the tube sealed off. Upon warming, the hypobromite formed decomposes catalytically with the evolution of oxygen. The sealed tube may be broken open in a vacuum line and the oxygen purified and used.

4. Two very convenient sources of small amounts of pure oxygen gas are either mercuric oxide-O^{18} (see Sec. 5-D) or silver oxide-O^{18} (see Sec. 5-C). A small amount of the oxide is placed in a tube, fixed to a vacuum line, and pumped out. Upon heating, small quantities of pure oxygen are evolved. The amount and rate of evolution are easily controlled by regulating the heating. If the oxides are available, this is the best way of making small amounts of pure oxygen. If the oxide has to be made, a relatively large

[16] Wiberg, K. B., J. Am. Chem. Soc., 75, 2665 (1953).

[17] Hunt, A. L., Hughes, D. E., and Lowenstein, J. M., Biochem. J., 69, 170 (1958).

[18] Bentley, R., Biochem. J., 45, 591 (1949).

[18a] Millen, D. J., and Pannel, J., J. Chem. Soc., 1961, 1322.

[19] Dostrovsky, I., and Klein, F. S., private communication.

[20] Anbar, M., Intern. J. Appl. Radiation and Isotopes, 3, 131 (1958).

amount of water must be on hand, but the water not used can be fully recovered in an almost undiluted state.

4. METHODS OF ISOTOPIC ANALYSIS

A. Mass Spectrometry

The isotopic composition of oxygen in various materials is usually determined mass spectrometrically. Only rarely is it possible or convenient to introduce the compound to be analyzed into the mass spectrometer. The few cases where this can be done occur when the substances are simple gaseous molecules. Thus, carbon dioxide, carbon monoxide, oxygen, and nitrous oxide are suitable molecules for the mass-spectrometric determination of oxygen. In most other cases, it is necessary to transfer all or part of the oxygen in the substance to be analyzed into one of the above gases. In general, this is not an easy thing to do, and much ingenuity has been used to arrive at simple and accurate procedures. In the following paragraph the various lines of approach will be outlined; the reader is referred to the original references for experimental details.

Attempts have been made, from time to time, to introduce more complicated molecules into the mass spectrometer, but these procedures usually suffer from considerable "memory" effects (the contamination of a sample by the remains of a previous sample) and the need to carry out extensive checks and calibration for each material. The analysis for O^{17} presents some additional complications. If the usual gases (CO_2, CO, or N_2O) are used for the analysis, the mass peaks due to O^{17}-labeled molecules are super-imposed on those of C^{13}- and N^{15}-labeled entities. In the dilute region (with respect to O^{17}), this means that one has to measure small differences between fairly large mass peaks, a factor that limits the precision. Thus when carbon dioxide is the analyzed gas, mass-peak 45 will be due to $C^{13}O^{16}O^{16}$ and to $C^{12}O^{17}O^{16}$. The intensity of the 45 peak due to C^{13} will be 1.11 per cent of the 44 peak $C^{12}O^{16}O^{16}$, so that the contribution of O^{17} derived from a material of twice the natural abundance will be only about 10 per cent of the total peak. A similar situation exists with CO and N_2O. Because of this, it is preferable to analyze for O^{17} in the form of O_2 gas. This limits the freedom of choice of techniques for analysis of O^{17} in complex oxygen-containing compounds.

In addition to the gases mentioned above, both nitric oxide[21] and sulfur dioxide[22] have been analyzed by direct introduction into the

[21] Spindel, W., and Stern, M. J., J. Chem. Phys., 32, 1579 (1960).

[22] Grigg, E. C. M., and Lauder, I., Trans. Faraday Soc., 46, 1039 (1950).

mass spectrometer, although these gases are fairly corrosive to the inlet system (especially in the presence of moisture); in addition, corrections are required for the natural abundance of S^{34} and N^{15}.

Water is rarely analyzed by direct methods, owing to the pronounced memory effect, but is usually equilibrated with CO_2 either at room temperature[23] or on a hot filament at 1000° for a few minutes.[24] The carbon dioxide is then analyzed mass spectrometrically in the usual way. Alternative methods involving the electrolytic or catalytic[20] decomposition of water to oxygen gas have been used and are applicable to the isotopic analysis of O^{17}, as well as of O^{18}.

Inorganic compounds are usually converted to either oxygen, carbon monoxide, or carbon dioxide for isotopic analysis. Thus the isotopic composition of oxygen in the following compounds has been determined by pyrolysis to oxygen gas: silver oxide, mercuric oxide, chromium trioxide, lead dioxide, silver phosphate, silver sulfate, sodium and lead chlorate, potassium chlorate, potassium perchlorate, potassium and silver bromate, potassium, silver, and barium iodate, potassium permanganate, and barium manganate.

Phosphate (in shells, etc.) has been very accurately analyzed[25] for its oxygen isotopic content by evolution of oxygen through the treatment of bismuth phosphate (30 to 40 mg) in a nickel and plastic apparatus with BrF_3 for 30 minutes at 90 to 100°. This method is free of isotopic fractionation or exchange, is accurate to ± 0.015 per cent, and may be used for the precise isotopic analysis of other oxy-anions. Similarly, oxygen gas has been evolved from alumina by treatment[26] with $KBrF_4$ at 500°.

Silicate has been analyzed following reaction with carbon in a high-vacuum resistance furnace (2000°) to form carbon monoxide.[27] Barium sulfate (washed and dried) has been analyzed[28] by incorporating the oxygen into carbon dioxide by heating with a three- to sixfold excess of powdered carbon (from spectroscopic rods), either in a platinum boat in an induction furnace for

[23] Cohn, M., and Urey, H. C., J. Am. Chem. Soc., 60, 659 (1938).

[24] Dostrovsky, I., and Klein, F. S., Anal. Chem., 24, 414 (1952).

[25] Tudge, A. P., Geochim. et Cosmochim. Acta, 18, 81 (1960).

[26] Wei, Y. K., and Bernstein, R. B., J. Phys. Chem., 63, 738 (1959).

[27] Baertschi, P., and Schwander, H., Helv. Chim. Acta, 35, 1748 (1952).

[28] Halperin, J., and Taube, H., J. Am. Chem. Soc., 74, 374 (1952).

35 to 45 minutes at 1000°, or by passing a current through the mixture in a molybdenum foil clamped between tungsten rods. On passing an electric current through the leads, the foil is heated to 1100° forming[29] carbon dioxide (and carbon monoxide, which is not analyzed). The accuracy of this method, in spite of rigorous degassing, is about ± 0.3 per cent, owing to the oxygen absorbed in the carbon. The lack of precision may also possibly be a result of isotopic fractionation in the process of reduction.

Potassium dihydrogen phosphate[30] and sulfur dioxide[30a] have also been reduced to carbon monoxide for analysis in a similar manner. Phosphate has been dehydrated by heating, and the water formed then equilibrated[31] with carbon dioxide or heated with mercuric cyanide in a sealed tube[32] for one hour at 250° to convert it to carbon dioxide.

Potassium carbonate has been analyzed after its pyrolysis[33] to carbon dioxide. Barium carbonate has been treated[34] with 100 per cent phosphoric acid to form CO_2, which does not exchange with the acid.

The oxygen in a large variety of inorganic compounds can be converted[35] to carbon dioxide by heating the substance in question with a mixture of mercuric chloride and mercuric cyanide for 2 hours at 400°. The carbon dioxide is purified by treatment with zinc amalgam at 200°. Compounds that have been analyzed in this way are mercuric, cupric, ferric, and cobaltous oxides; manganese and lead dioxides; barium sulfate, phosphate, and arsenate; and uranyl ferrocyanide. This method appears to be of very wide application and is reproducible to about 2 per cent.

Nitrous acid and nitrite ion in solution have been analyzed[36] by adding sodium azide at pH 2.5 and analyzing the N_2O evolved. N_2O does not exchange its oxygen with water under these conditions and may be purified by passing it over solid KOH and concentrated H_2SO_4. Nitrate has been analyzed[36] by converting it to the

[29] Hoering, T. C., and Kennedy, J. W., J. Am. Chem. Soc., 79, 56 (1957).

[30] Cohn, M., and Drysdale, G. B., J. Biol. Chem., 216, 831 (1955).

[30a] Clusius, K., Schleich, K., and Bernstein, R. B., Helv. Chim. Acta, 45, 252 (1962).

[31] Cohn, M., J. Biol. Chem., 201, 735 (1953).

[32] Williams, R. F., and Hager, L. P., Science, 128, 1434 (1958).

[33] Dole, M., and Slobod, R. C., J. Am. Chem. Soc., 62, 471 (1940).

[34] Rottenberg, M., and Baertschi, P., Helv. Chim. Acta, 39, 1973 (1956).

[35] Anbar, M., and Guttmann, S., Intern. J. Appl. Radiation and Isotopes, 4, 233 (1959).

[36] Anbar, M., and Taube, H., J. Am. Chem. Soc., 76, 6243 (1955).

ammonium salt, which is dried and pyrolyzed to N_2O at 300° in
a platinum crucible. Alternatively, a mixture of barium nitrate
and ammonium chloride can be heated in a sealed tube for 45 minutes at 400°.

Sulfur dioxide has been analyzed[37] after reduction to water by
heating it overnight at 350° with a slight excess of H_2S, using a
trace of water as catalyst. The water is then analyzed by equilibration with carbon dioxide.

B. Infrared and NMR Spectroscopy

Recently, a number of alternate methods of isotopic analysis
have been reported, such as infrared and nuclear magnetic reson-
ance spectroscopy. Barium sulfate has been analyzed[38] for O^{18}
by means of the isotopic shift in the infrared spectrum of the S-O
bond. Similar isotopic shifts have been found for potassium nitrite
and nitrate[39] and for a large number of organic compounds. [40]

The chemical shift of O^{17} in the NMR spectrum of various inorganic compounds, including hydrogen peroxide, sodium nitrate
and nitrite, liquid sulfur dioxide, [41] and various cobaltic complexes, [42] has been observed but, as yet, has not been used for isotopic analysis.

C. Activation Analysis

Activation analysis has been used for the oxygen-isotopic analysis in a limited number of inorganic compounds. The O^{17} content
of oxygen gas has been determined[43] by the deuteron bombardment
of a nickel oxide target. Similarly, potassium phosphate has been
analyzed[44] by proton bombardment in a cyclotron, with subsequent
measurement of the 112-minute isotope F^{18}, a positron emitter,

---

[37] Brown, L. L., and Drury, J. S., J. Phys. Chem., 63,
1885 (1959).

[38] Spencer, B., Biochem. J., 73, 442 (1959).

[39] Anbar, M., Halmann, M., and Pinchas, S., J. Chem. Soc.,
1960, 1242.

[40] Pinchas, S., Samuel, D., and Weiss-Broday, M., J. Chem.
Soc., 1961, 1688, 2382, 2666, 3063.

[41] Weaver, H. E., Tolbert, B. M., and La Force, R. C.,
J. Chem. Phys., 23, 1956 (1955).

[42] Jackson, J. A., Lemons, J. F., and Taube, H., J. Chem.
Phys., 32, 553 (1960).

[43] Welles, S. B., Phys. Rev., 69, 586 (1956).

[44] Fleckenstein, A., Gerlach, E., Janke, I., and Marmier, P.,
Pflüger's Arch. ges. Physiol., 271, 75 (1960); see also Fogel-
stroem-Finemann, I., et al., Intern. J. Appl. Radiation and Isotopes, 2, 280 (1957).

which is formed.   This method should be applicable to any nonvolatile compound containing O^{18}.

5. SYNTHESES

In the following pages, the syntheses of all inorganic compounds reported in the literature to the end of 1960 are listed. The experimental details from the original papers are given together with notes of other syntheses or of general interest. In certain circumstances the experience of the authors or of their colleagues with these syntheses have been added as private communications.

The syntheses have been grouped according to the periodic table. This method has previously been used in "Inorganic Syntheses" and refers to the central atom to which the oxygen is bound. Thus $NaO^{18}H$ is in Group I, CO_2^{18} in Group IV, $AgNO_3^{18}$ in Group V, and $ReO_3^{18}F$ in Group VII.

Group I

A. Sodium Hydroxide Solutions
$$2Na + 2H_2O^* \longrightarrow 2NaO^*H \text{ (aq)} + H_2$$

Concentrated solutions of sodium hydroxide-O^{18} in O^{18}-enriched water can be prepared without isotopic dilution by dissolving the required amount of metallic sodium, held either in capillaries[45] or in the form of a 3 to 5 per cent amalgam, in the water.

B. Cupric Oxide
$$2Cu + O_2^* \longrightarrow 2CuO^*$$

Cupric oxide-O^{18} can be prepared by the direct oxidation of copper at 350° with oxygen. It is best to use copper formed from microanalytical-grade cupric oxide previously reduced in situ by a stream of hydrogen.

$$CuCl_2 + 2NaO^*H \text{ (aq)} \longrightarrow Cu(O^*H)_2 \longrightarrow CuO^*$$

Cupric oxide-O^{18} can also be prepared[35, 46] by adding a slight excess of NaOH in O^{18}-enriched water to cupric chloride in O^{18}-enriched water. The hydroxide formed is centrifuged and washed repeatedly with O^{18}-enriched water until it becomes free of sodium hydroxide and chloride, and is then heated in a furnace to 600° thus converting it to the oxide.

[45] Dostrovsky, I., and Llewellyn, D. R., J. Soc. Chem. Ind. (London), 68, 208 (1949).

[46] Anbar, M., private communication.

C. Silver Oxide

$$2AgNO_3 + 2KO^*H(aq) \longrightarrow Ag_2O^* + 2KNO_3 + H_2O$$

Silver oxide-O^{18} can be prepared[47] by precipitation from a saturated solution of silver nitrate in O^{18}-enriched water on addition of a concentrated solution of KOH in O^{18}-enriched water. The precipitate is washed 10 times with ordinary water (20 ml), vacuum dried, and then left in a drying oven for 3 days at 105°.

Note: Ag_2O^{18} can be used as a source of O^{18}-labeled oxygen gas.[47]

Group II

A. Calcium Oxide--Hydration and Exchange

Calcium oxide-O^{18} can be prepared[48] by shaking pure CaO with O^{18}-enriched water. The $Ca(OH)_2$ is then dehydrated by heating for several hours to give CaO^{18}.

B. Zinc Oxide

$$ZnCl_2 + H_2O^* + 2NH_3 \longrightarrow ZnO^* + 2NH_4Cl$$

Zinc oxide-O^{18} can be prepared[49] by dissolving anhydrous zinc chloride (11 g) in O^{18}-enriched water (20 ml) at room temperature. A saturated solution of ammonia gas in O^{18}-enriched water is added drop by drop with stirring (about 5 ml required) until a flocculent precipitate is obtained, which is removed by filtration and dried in vacuo with heating. The excess O^{18}-enriched water is collected in a liquid-nitrogen-cooled trap.

Note 1. Excess ammonia is to be avoided, as it will redissolve the precipitate.

Note 2. The oxide was used in subsequent syntheses without further purification.

C. Mercuric Oxide

$$HgCl_2 + 2NaO^*H(aq) \longrightarrow HgO^* + 2NaCl$$

Mercuric oxide-O^{18} can be prepared[50] from mercuric chloride. A solution of O^{18}-enriched sodium hydroxide is prepared by dissolving sodium (2 g) in O^{18}-enriched water (20 ml). This solution is added drop by drop with stirring to a solution of mercuric chloride (10 g) previously dried in vacuo and dissolved in O^{18}-enriched

---

[47] Wang, J. H., and Fleischer, E. G., J. Am. Chem. Soc., 80, 3874 (1955).

[48] Magee, E. M., J. Phys. Chem., 61, 1671 (1957).

[49] Samuel, D., and Weiss-Broday, M., private communication.

[50] Halmann, M., private communication.

water (20 ml). A yellow precipitate of mercuric oxide is formed
and is left to stand overnight; it is then separated by centrifugation and washed with 3 portions of O^{18}-enriched water (5 ml) and
dried in vacuo. The water is subsequently collected in a liquid-
nitrogen-cooled trap.

Note 1. This oxide can be used for the preparation of small
quantities of O^{18} gas.

Note 2. The synthesis should be performed in a dry box to prevent isotopic dilution.

Note 3. The sodium should be added either as small pieces or
in glass capillaries. Sodium hydroxide prepared from an amalgam
gives an impure product. [49]

Group III

A. Aluminum Oxide

$$2Al + 3H_2O^* \longrightarrow Al_2O_3^* + 3H_2$$

Aluminum oxide-O^{18} can be prepared[49] from aluminum foil,
which is cut into strips, cleaned with acetone, dried, and dipped
for a few seconds into a dilute solution of mercuric chloride. The
strips are well washed with water, dried, wiped free of oxide, and
immediately placed in a flask containing O^{18}-enriched water, and
closed with a drying tube. After a number of days, with inter-
mittent gentle heating, the solution is decanted from the foil resi-
dues and the water removed by vacuum distillation. The hydroxide
is then heated in a platinum crucible in an induction furnace to ca.
1000° to form the oxide.

Note 1. The water formed in the final conversion to oxide is
used for isotopic-oxygen analysis.

Note 2. The above method gives a purer product than the
hydrolysis of aluminum chloride or sulfate by which basic salts
and condensed compounds are also formed.

Note 3. Aluminum oxide films can also be made by the electrolytic oxidation of aluminum foil in O^{18}-enriched water, [51] using
citrate as the electrolyte.

Note 4. Boehmite [AlO(OH)] has been prepared[26] by the reaction of aluminum with O^{18}-enriched water at 350° for ca. 15
hours.

Group IV

A. Carbon Monoxide and Carbon Dioxide

$$3C + 2O_2^* \longrightarrow CO_2^* + 2CO^*$$

Both carbon monoxide-O^{18} and carbon dioxide-O^{18} can be pre-

---

[51] Amsel, G., and Samuel, D., private communication.

pared[52] simultaneously using the apparatus shown in Fig. 2. Granulated charcoal (about 1 to 2 g; 8 mesh) is placed in a quartz boat in the furnace F. The system is pumped out and the pumping continued with the furnace heated to about 1000° until gas evolution ceases. The temperature is then dropped somewhat to bright-red heat (800 to 900°), and the trap T is cooled with liquid air. The main stopcock to the pumping line is turned off and the evacuated storage bulb connected by opening its stopcock. A stream of O^{18} direct from the electrolyzer E or from the Toepler pump P is then passed over the carbon, whereupon the material gradually burns up, starting with that at the end nearest the electrolyzer. When all the oxygen has been passed through, it will be found that a certain amount of permanent gas (i. e., noncondensible in liquid nitrogen) has been formed as shown by the pressure on manometer (M). To purify this carbon monoxide-O^{18} further, it is passed backward and forward over the remaining hot carbon, using the Toepler pump, and finally sealed in a storage bulb. Trap T contains carbon dioxide-O^{18}. If this material is needed, it can be stored in another storage bulb after pumping off the CO. Alternatively, the CO_2 can be converted to CO by allowing the trap to warm and by passing the gas back and forth over the hot charcoal using the Toepler pump. Trap T is cooled again, and the remaining CO_2 is frozen out. The CO can then be stored in a bulb.

Note 1. If only CO_2 is needed, the carbon can be maintained at a lower temperature (ca. 300°) after the initial bake-out. The proportion of CO formed is then much smaller.

Note 2. Carbon dioxide-O^{18} has also been prepared by exchange or by the reaction between a spectroscopically pure carbon[53] rod and O^{18} gas in a closed system. A cold finger speeds conversion.

Note 3. Carbon dioxide can be purified by repeated sublimation from a trap cooled with dry ice-acetone to another at liquid-nitrogen temperature.

B. Potassium Carbonate Exchange

Potassium carbonate-O^{18} can be prepared[49] by exchange. Polyethylene or metal containers should be used to avoid contamination of the product by silica.

———
[52] Dostrovsky, I., private communication.
[53] Eggers, D. F., Jr., and Arends, C. B., J. Chem. Phys., 27, 1405 (1957).

C. Carbon Oxysulfide
$$CO^* + S \longrightarrow CO^*S$$

Carbon oxysulfide-O^{18} can be prepared[54] by introducing CO^{18} prepared as described above at about 500 mm Hg into an evacuated tube fitted with a break-seal containing the required amount of sulfur. The tube is sealed and heated for 24 hours at 300°. The tube is then opened with a magnetic hammer, the excess CO pumped off, and the COS distilled into a receiver cooled with liquid air. The yield is 80 to 90 per cent.

D. Lead Dioxide
$$Pb(NO_3)_2 \xrightarrow[\text{in } H_2O^*]{O} PbO_2^*$$

Lead dioxide-O^{18} can be prepared[46] by the anodic oxidation of lead perchlorate in an O^{18} enriched perchloric acid solution.

Group V

A. Nitrous Oxide
$$HN_3^*(aq) + HNO_2^*(aq) \longrightarrow N_2O^* + N_2 + H_2O$$

Nitrous oxide-O^{18} can be prepared[55] by adding a solution of sodium azide in O^{18}-enriched water to a solution of nitrite-O^{18} (see page 134) in O^{18}-enriched water at pH 2.5 (phosphate buffer or dilute HCl).

$$NH_2OH(aq) + HNO_2^*(aq) \longrightarrow N_2O^* + 2H_2O$$

Nitrous oxide-O^{18} can also be prepared[56] by the reaction of hydroxylamine hydrochloride and nitrous acid made by bubbling dry HCl through sodium nitrite (0.25 g) in O^{18}-enriched water (2 ml) to pH 1 . Water containing 1.5 atom per cent O^{18} yielded N_2O^{18} with 0.975 atom per cent O^{18}.

Note 1. N_2O^{18} is dried and purified of acidic products (CO_2) and other oxides of nitrogen by storing it over pellets of NaOH and then over concentrated H_2SO_4.

Note 2. N_2O^{18} has also been prepared[55] by the pyrolysis of ammonium nitrate-O^{18} (300°) prepared from ammonium chloride and nitrate-O^{18} (see page 135).

---

[54] Matlock, G. M., Ferguson, R. E., Haskin, J. F., and Glockler, G., Proc. Iowa Acad. Sci., 59, 202 (1952); see also Geschwind, S., Gunther-Mohr, G. R., and Silvey, G., Phys. Rev., 85, 474 (1952).

[55] Anbar, M., and Taube, H., J. Am. Chem. Soc., 76, 6243 (1954).

[56] Bothner-By, A., and Friedman, L., J. Chem. Phys., 20, 459 (1952).

B. Nitric Oxide

$$N_2 + O_2^* \longrightarrow 2NO^*$$

Nitric oxide-O^{18} can be prepared[57] by passing a mixture of O_2^{18} gas (200 ml; 99.5 per cent O^{18}) with pure nitrogen (ca. 120 ml) through a high-tension arc to form a mixture of $N_2O_3^{18}$ and $N_2O_4^{18}$. The oxides of nitrogen are carefully purified of all traces of inert gases and sealed into a tube containing powdered selenium (10 g) and fitted with a break-seal. Both oxides are reduced to NO^{18} in the course of a few days at room temperature. The NO^{18} may be purified by sublimation. The yield is 180 ml (90 per cent).

Note 1. Half the O^{18} gas is lost as SeO_2^{18} in this synthesis.

Note 2. Mercury can be used for reduction in place of selenium.

Note 3. NO^{18} is blue when pure, but slowly turns green on standing because of impurities. It can be repurified by fractional sublimation.

Note 4. NO^{18} can also be prepared[46] from iodide and HNO_2^{18} in O^{18}-labeled water and by the pyrolysis of $AgNO_2^{18}$ (see page 135).

Note 5. The vapor pressure of NO^{18} at low temperatures has been measured.[57]

Note 6. NO^{18} has been used[46] to prepare $N_2O_3^{18}$ by the reaction with NO_2^{18} (see following synthesis).

C. Nitrogen Dioxide

$$PbNO_3^* \longrightarrow PbO^* + NO_2^*$$

Nitrogen dioxide-O^{18} can be prepared by heating the lead dioxide-O^{18} that is formed from lead chloride and KNO_3^{18} (see page 135).

Note 1. NO_2^{18} can also be prepared[46] by reacting nitric oxide and O^{18}-labeled oxygen gas. The isotopic enrichment is halved unless NO^{18} is used (see Synthesis B, above).

D. Sodium and Silver Nitrite Exchange

Sodium nitrite-O^{18} can be prepared[39] by dissolving dry sodium nitrite (6.9 g) in O^{18}-enriched water (25 ml) and acidifying it with 70 per cent perchloric acid (0.5 ml) with vigorous stirring. The solution (pH 4.9) is stored overnight, and a neutralized solution of anhydrous silver perchlorate (18.5 g) in O^{18}-enriched water (15 ml) is then added to it slowly with stirring, the resulting precipitate being centrifuged after each portion. The silver nitrite (10.5 g) is well washed with normal distilled water, centrifuged, and dried at 70° in vacuo.

---

[57] Clusius, K., and Schleich, K., Helv. Chim. Acta, 41, 1342 (1958).

Note 1. $AgNO_2^{18}$ containing over 60 atom per cent O^{18} was prepared from water of 90 atom per cent O^{18}.

Note 2. The infrared spectrum of $AgNO_2^{18}$ has been measured.[39]

Note 3. $NaNO_2^{18}$ has also been prepared[58] by exchange in the presence of HNO_3.

E. Potassium Nitrate Exchange

Potassium nitrate-O^{18} can be prepared[39] from nitric acid-O^{18} by keeping a mixture of nitric acid (5 ml; d = 1.48) and O^{18}-enriched water (15 ml) in a glass-stoppered flask at room temperature for 4 days. The acid is then exactly neutralized with a solution of KOH in O^{18}-enriched water. The bulk of the water is removed by distillation at normal pressure. The KNO_3^{18} crystallizes on cooling, is filtered off by suction, and is dried in vacuo (yield, 8 g). Further enrichment in O^{18} is achieved by sealing some of the above KNO_3(1 g) in a tube with O^{18}-enriched water (4 ml) and fuming nitric acid (0.1 ml). The tube is heated in an oven at 70° for 38 hours. Upon opening the tube, the water is recovered by distilling it in vacuo into a trap cooled with liquid nitrogen, leaving the nitrate behind.

Note 1. By using water of 90 atom per cent O^{18} enrichment, KNO_3^{18} containing 42.6 atom per cent O^{18} was obtained in the first stage, and 84.2 atom per cent O^{18} in the second.

Note 2. The infrared spectrum of KNO_3^{18} has been measured.[39]

Note 3. The self-diffusion of nitrate in $NaNO_3^{18}$ (no details of preparation given) has been measured.[59]

F. Phosphorous Acid
$$PCl_3 + 3H_2O^* \longrightarrow H_3PO_3^* + 3HCl$$

Phosphorous acid-O^{18} can be prepared[60] by the hydrolysis of phosphorus trichloride in O^{18}-enriched water. The water and hydrogen chloride are removed in vacuo leaving a colorless crystalline product (m.p., 71 to 73°).

Note 1. The water used should be "normalized" first if a deuterium-free product is required.

---

[58] Bunton, C. A., Llewellyn, D. R., and Stedman, G., J. Chem. Soc., 1959, 568.

[59] Van Artsdalen, E. R., Brown, D., Dworkin, A. S., and Muller, F. J., J. Am. Chem. Soc., 78, 1772 (1956).

[60] Petreanu, E., and Samuel, D., private communication.

G. Potassium Dihydrogen Phosphate Exchange

$$P_2O_5 + H_2O^* \xrightarrow{\text{KOH}} 2KH_2PO_4^*$$

Potassium dihydrogen phosphate-O^{18} can be prepared[61] by adding P_2O_5 to O^{18}-enriched water to a final concentration of approximately 0.5 M. The solution is adjusted to pH 4.5 with solid KOH (or KOH dissolved in O^{18}-enriched water) and heated in a sealed tube for 72 hours at 100° . The tube is opened and the water removed in vacuo.

Note 1. Water containing 1.4 atom per cent O^{18} produced phosphate containing 1.23 atom per cent O^{18}.

Note 2. Phosphoric acid-O^{18} has also been prepared[62] by the action of chlorine on white phosphorus in O^{18}-enriched water.

Note 3. Potassium dihydrogen phosphate-O^{18} has also been prepared[63] by adding O^{18}-enriched water to P_2O_5, adjusting the pH to 4.4 with 2 N KOH added to the cooled solution, and precipitating with 2 volumes of ethanol. The filtered precipitate is washed with ethanol and ether and dried in vacuo at 100° for 1 hour. Water containing 1.5 atom per cent O^{18} yielded $KH_2PO_4^{18}$ containing 0.7 atom per cent O^{18}.

Note 4. $KH_2PO_4^{18}$ has been prepared[64] by heating a 2.8-M solution of KH_2PO_4 in a sealed tube with O^{18}-enriched water at 120° for 8 days. The water is then removed by distillation in vacuo.

H. Barium Phosphate

$$PCl_3 + 3H_2O^* \longrightarrow H_3PO_3^* + 3HCl$$

$$3BaCl_2 + 2H_3PO_3^* \xrightarrow[\text{Br}_2 \text{ in } H_2O^*]{[O]} Ba_3(PO_4^*)_2 + 6HCl$$

Barium phosphate-O^{18} can be prepared[35] by the hydrolysis of phosphorus trichloride in O^{18}-enriched water. The product is oxidized without isolation by adding bromine slowly, with occasional warming, until a faint reddish color remains. The solution is neutralized by adding metallic sodium; the barium phosphate is then precipitated by adding $BaCl_2$. The free acid can be obtained by ion exchange (with Dowex 50) or by adding the exact amount of sulfuric acid, centrifuging off the precipitated barium sulfate, and removing the water in vacuo.

---

[61] Slocum, D. H., and Varner, J. E., J. Biol. Chem., 235, 492 (1960)

[62] Rittenberg, D., private communication.

[63] Cohn, M., J. Biol. Chem., 180, 771 (1949).

[64] Cohn, M., and Drysdale, G. R., J. Biol. Chem., 216, 831 (1955).

I. Potassium Dihydrogen Arsenate

$$As_2O_5 + H_2O^* \longrightarrow H_3AsO_4^* \xrightarrow{\text{KOH}} KH_2AsO_4^*$$

Potassium dihydrogen arsenate-O^{18} can be prepared[65] by adding As_2O_5 to O^{18}-enriched water, adjusting the pH to 3.5 with KOH, and removing the water by distillation in vacuo.

Note 1. Equilibration at an elevated temperature is not necessary. Water containing 1.4 atom per cent O^{18} yields KH_2AsO^{18} containing 1.38 atom per cent O^{18}.

Note 2. Barium arsenate-O^{18} has been obtained[35] by reacting $AsCl_3$ with O^{18}-enriched water followed by oxidation with bromine, as described for $KH_2PO_4^{18}$.

Group VI

A. Hydrogen Peroxide

$$2H_2O^* \xrightarrow{\substack{\text{electric} \\ \text{discharge}}} H_2O_2^* + H_2$$

Hydrogen peroxide-O^{18} can be prepared[66] by passing O^{18}-enriched water vapor through an electric discharge and trapping the product on a liquid-nitrogen-cooled surface. The apparatus consists of aluminum electrodes spaced 2 m apart in a Pyrex glass tube (28 mm i.d.). The electric field strength is 10 v cm^{-1} maintained by a neon-sign transformer. Two U tubes (13 mm i.d.) cooled by liquid nitrogen are used as traps. The first U tube is sealed directly to the discharge tube about 10 cm in front of the down-stream electrode. The second U tube is 50 cm downstream from the first and serves to prevent the diffusion of pump vapors into the discharge system. The system is evacuated by a mechanical oil pump with a capacity of about 0.4 liter sec^{-1} at 0.2 to 0.4 mm. Water vapor is admitted (80 to 200 mg) through a capillary (0.3 mm diameter, 5 cm long). A capillary of this size permits convenient control of the flow rate of water vapor by regulating the temperature (25 to 45°) of the tube used to introduce the water. The product $H_2O_2^{18}$ is pumped out of the first trap and collected in a small U trap connected to the system by a 10/30 joint and stopcock situated between the two larger traps.

In a typical run, water (96 mg; 10 atom per cent O^{18}) gave $H_2O_2^{18}$ (33 mg) 35 per cent conversion in 25 minutes, containing 1 mole per cent of doubly labeled $H_2O_2^{18,18}$.

Hydrogen peroxide-O^{18} can be prepared by introducing excess O^{18}-enriched oxygen gas to a glass bulb, the internal surface

---

[65] Varner, J. F., Slocum, D. H., and Webster, G. C., Arch. Biochem. Biophys., 73, 508 (1958).

[66] Jarnagin, R. C., and Wang, J. H., J. Am. Chem. Soc., 80, 786 (1958).

of which is coated with a sodium mirror formed by vacuum evaporation. [67] The vessel is then heated to 200° to ensure that all the

$$2Na + O_2^* \longrightarrow Na_2O_2^* \xrightarrow{H_2SO_4(aq)} H_2O_2^*(aq)$$

sodium has reacted to form $Na_2SO_2^{18}$. The bulb is opened and washed with an ice-cold solution of H_2SO_4 (1 M) in ordinary water. The $H_2O_2^{18}$ can be distilled in vacuo with water. Under these conditions no isotopic exchange of oxygen takes place.

Note 1. $H_2O_2^{18}$ has also been prepared by passing O^{18}-enriched water vapor through a glow discharge[68] (details not given) at low pressure, by passing a spark discharge[46] (Tesla coil) through O^{18}-enriched water, or by bubbling O^{18}-enriched water (dilute H_2SO_4 as electrolyte).

B. Sulfur Dioxide
$$S + O_2^* \longrightarrow SO_2^*$$

Sulfur dioxide-O^{18} can be prepared[22] by subliming pure sulfur into a bulb of 1-liter capacity. Pure O^{18} gas is introduced into the evacuated bulb to a pressure of 38 cm Hg. After heating for 50 hours at 285°, conversion is nearly complete. The SO_2 is freed from any trace of oxygen and transferred to a storage bulb. The authors claim that the SO_2 prepared in this way is quite free from SO_3.

Note 1. SO_2^{18} can be purified of SO_3 by shaking with mercury.

Note 2. Very pure, highly enriched SO_2^{18} has been prepared[30a] by the reaction of excess S with O_2^{18} in an all-glass apparatus.

C. Thionyl Chloride Exchange
$$SO_2^* + PCl_5 \longrightarrow SO^*Cl_2 + PO^*Cl_3$$

Thionyl chloride-O^{18} can be prepared[69] by bubbling SO_2 into O^{18}-enriched water to give an aqueous solution of SO_2^{18}. This is heated and the dried SO_2^{18} passed into PCl_5. The mixture is fractionated to give $SO^{18}Cl_2$ (b. p., 78°).

Note 1. SO_2^{18} prepared as above can also be used. The phosphoryl chloride will also be isotopically labeled in this procedure.

[67] Anbar, M., J. Am. Chem. Soc., 83, 2031 (1961).

[68] Halpern, J., and Taube, H., J. Am. Chem. Soc., 74, 380 (1952).

[69] Bunton, C. A., de la Mare, P. B. D., Greaseley, P. M., Llewelln, D. R., Pratt, N. H., and Tillet, J. G., J. Chem. Soc., 1958, 4751.

D. Sulfuric Acid

$$S + 4H_2O^* + 3Br_2 \longrightarrow H_2SO_4^* + 6HBr$$

Sulfuric acid-O^{18} can be prepared[70] in the following manner: Bromine (300 g) is added from a dropping funnel to a mixture of O^{18}-enriched water (80 ml) and analytical grade sulfur (32 g) in a three-necked flask fitted with a reflux condenser and a stirrer.

The bromine is added (with vigorous stirring) as fast as its color disappears. Toward the end of the reaction it is necessary to heat the mixture. When all the sulfur has dissolved, the mixture is distilled until the temperature of the residue reaches 130°. After addition of a few drops of nitric acid to oxidize impurities, the pressure is reduced and the distillation continued until the temperature reaches 220° (at 100 mm Hg). The residue consists of $H_2SO_4^{18}$ with an acid concentration of 99 per cent.

E. Chromium Trioxide Exchange

Chromium trioxide-O^{18} can be prepared[49] by placing chromium trioxide (10 g), which has been dried in vacuo at 80°, in O^{18}-enriched water (10 ml) and heating for a few minutes. The water is distilled off in vacuo and the oxide dried by heating to 100° for several hours.

Note 1. The oxide is analyzed for O^{18} content by heating to 500° in a sealed tube and analyzing the oxygen evolved.

F. Uranium Dioxide

$$U + O_2^* \longrightarrow UO_2^*$$

Uranium dioxide-O^{18} can be prepared[71] by the high-pressure oxidation of uranium metal with O^{18}-enriched water at 2200 psi and 340°C.

Group VII

A. Potassium Chlorate

$$3Cl_2 + 6KO^*H \longrightarrow KClO_3^* + 5KCl + 3H_2O$$

Potassium chlorate-O^{18} can be prepared[72] by the disproportionation of chlorine in a hot solution of KOH in O^{18}-enriched water,[72] or by anodic oxidation.[56]

---

[70] Anbar, M., and Dostrovsky, I., J. Chem. Soc., 1954, 1094.

[71] Auskern, A. B., and Belle, J., J. Chem. Phys., 28, 171 (1958).

[72] Hoering, T. C., Ishimori, E. T., and McDonald, H. O., J. Am. Chem. Soc., 80, 3876 (1958).

Note 1. $KClO_3^{18}$ can also be prepared by exchange.

B. Potassium Perchlorate

$$KCl \xrightarrow[\text{electrolysis in } H_2O^*]{[O]} KClO_4^*$$

Potassium perchlorate-O^{18} can be prepared[73] by electrolyzing a solution of lithium chloride in O^{18}-enriched water (4 M) in a semimicro electrolysis cell (4 ml capacity) with stationary platinum electrodes (electrodes are 1 cm^2). The cell is kept at 20° by a water jacket, and the solution is stirred constantly with a magnetic stirrer. The electrolysis is carried out at a current density of 1 amp cm^{-2}. A total of 16 ml of 4-M solution is electrolyzed over a period of 30 to 36 hours. A long period of electrolysis is required because the water is decomposed simultaneously. After electrolysis, the O^{18}-enriched water is distilled off[46] in vacuo and replaced by a fivefold volume of ordinary water.

A concentrated KNO_3 solution is then added to precipitate the $KClO_4$. The precipitate is separated by centrifugation and digested with concentrated HCl to eliminate any $KClO_3$ present. The HCl is then boiled off and the $KClO_4^{18}$ recrystallized from boiling water. The yield is 92 to 94 per cent.

Note 1. The method described was actually used for the preparation of $KCl^{36}O_4^{18}$.

Note 2. A certain amount of ozone is formed during the electrolysis.

Note 3. Perchlorate-O^{18} does not exchange its oxygen during the work-up.

Note 4. Water containing 45 atom per cent O^{18} yielded perchlorate containing 44.3 atom per cent O^{18}.

C. Potassium Bromate

$$KBr \xrightarrow[\text{in } H_2O^*]{\text{electrolysis}} KBrO_3^*$$

Potassium bromate-O^{18} can be prepared[74] by electrolytic oxidation[75] of KBr in O^{18}-enriched water.

Note 1. Potassium iodate-O^{18} can be prepared in an analogous manner[74] from KI, or by exchange.[74]

[73] Anbar, M., Guttmann, S., and Lewitus, Z., Intern. J. Appl. Radiation and Isotopes, 7, 87 (1959).

[74] Hoering, T. C., Butler, R. C., and McDonald, H. O., J. Am. Chem. Soc., 78, 4829 (1956).

[75] Elbs, K., "Electrolytic Preparations," E. Arnold & Co., London, 1903.

D. Manganese Dioxide
$$MnSO_4 + HO^*Br + H_2O^* \longrightarrow MnO_2^* + H_2SO_4 + HBr$$

Manganese dioxide-O^{18} can be prepared[46] by the oxidation of manganous sulfate with hypobromous acid-O^{18} (prepared from bromine and O^{18}-enriched water).

E. Potassium Manganate
$$KMnO_4 + KO^*H \longrightarrow K_2MnO_4^*$$

Potassium manganate-O^{18} can be prepared[76] by heating potassium permanganate with potassium hydroxide in O^{18}-enriched water. The excess permanganate is removed by washing with pyridine.

F. Potassium Permanganate.
This compound can be prepared by exchange.[76]

G. Permanganyl Fluoride
$$KMnO_4^* + 2SO_3HF \longrightarrow MnO_3^*F + KSO_3F + H_2SO_4$$

Permanganyl fluoride-O^{18} can be prepared[77, 78] by adding potassium permanganate-O^{18} (1 g) very slowly to SO_3HF (1 ml) in a copper flask cooled with dry ice. The flask is attached to a special copper vacuum line and allowed to warm to room temperature slowly in vacuo. The green gaseous $MnO_3^{18}F$ is condensed in Kel-F traps cooled with dry ice. The final traces of SO_3HF and HF are removed by repeated distillation with excess $KMnO_4^{18}$.

Note 1. The microwave absorption spectra of $MnO_3^{18}F$ has been measured.[73]

Note 2. Perrhenyl fluoride-O^{18} has also been prepared[79] by the reaction[80] of HF on perrhenic chloride-O^{18}. Its microwave absorption specrum has been measured.[79]

Group VIII

A. Ferric Oxide
$$FeCl_3 + 3NH_4O^*H \longrightarrow Fe(O^*H)_3 \longrightarrow Fe_2O_3^*$$

Ferric oxide-O^{18} can be prepared[50] by dissolving ferric

[76] Wiberg, K. B., and Stewart, R., J. Am. Chem. Soc., 77, 1786 (1955).

[77] Javan, A., and Engelbrecht, A., Phys. Rev., 96, 649 (1954).

[78] Engelbrecht, A., and Grosse, A. V., J. Am. Chem. Soc., 76, 2042 (1954).

[79] Lotspeich, J. F., Javan, A., and Engelbrecht, A., J. Chem. Phys., 31, 633 (1959).

[80] Bruckl, A., and Zuegler, K., Ber., 65, 916 (1932).

chloride hexahydrate (25.4 g) in O^{18}-enriched water (15 ml) and adding a saturated solution of ammonia in O^{18}-enriched water (30 ml). After warming gently, the precipitate is centrifuged, washed with O^{18}-enriched water, and dried in vacuo. After dehydrating at 250°, a reddish-brown nonmagnetic powder is obtained (6 g).

Note 1. If anhydrous ferric chloride is used, an impure product is obtained that contains some Fe_3O_4 (magnetite).

Note 2. Cobaltic oxide-O^{18} has been prepared[35] in a similar manner.

B. Nickel Oxide

$$2Ni + O_2^* \longrightarrow 2NiO^*$$

Nickel oxide-O^{18} can be prepared[52] by placing a weighed amount of finely powdered nickel (1 g; 200 mesh) in a boat in the furnace tube F (see Fig. 2). After pumping and baking out (ca. 900°), oxygen is slowly passed through tube F from the Toepler pump, with the main stopcock to the pump line closed. When no more reaction is evident, the oxygen pressure in the furnace is brought to atmospheric pressure, and heating is continued for 30 minutes at 600°. Upon cooling, the greenish-grey mass is weighed and powdered. The increase in weight gives the extent of reaction, which should be over 95 per cent.

Note 1. Traces of free metal are occluded in the oxide grains and are difficult to oxidize, even upon prolonged heating.

Note 2. A purer product can also be obtained[60] by precipitating nickelous carbonate-O_3^{18} from a solution of $NiCl_2$ with $K_2CO_3^{18}$. The $NiCO_3^{18}$ is then heated to give NiO^{18} and CO_2^{18}, which is used for isotopic analysis.

6

Radiophosphorus

L. LINDNER
Institut voor Kernphysisch Onderzoek
Amsterdam

1. INTRODUCTION

A. Nuclear Data

The element phosphorus has only one stable isotope, P^{31}, with 15 protons and 16 neutrons per nuclide. Thus far, six radioisotopes of this element have been reported[1,2] (see Fig. 1). The three neutron-deficient nuclides, P^{28}, P^{29}, and P^{30}, are positron emitters and have half-lives too short (0.28s, 4.45m, and 2.6m, respectively) to be of interest for use in isotopic syntheses. This also applies to P^{34}, a negatron emitter with a half-life of 12.4s.

The two other known neutron-rich isotopes, P^{32} and P^{33}, on the other hand, are both extremely useful for labeling purposes. This may be seen from their properties, listed in Table 1.

Table 1
Physical Properties of the Nuclides P^{32} and P^{33}

Nuclide	Half-life, τ[1,2]	Type of radiation	Maximum β energy[1,2]	β-Particle range,[3] R in mg Al/cm^2
P^{32}	14.3d	β^-, no γ	1.71 Mev	ca. 800
P^{33}	25d	β^-, no γ	0.25 Mev	ca. 60

[1] Nuclear Data Group, Nuclear Data Sheets USA-National Research Council, U.S. Government Printing Office, Washington, D.C.

[2] Strominger, D., Hollander, J. M., and Seaborg, G. T., Revs. Modern Phys., 30, 585 (1958).

[3] Friedlander, G., and Kennedy, J. W., "Nuclear and Radiochemistry," Wiley, New York, 1955, 0. 202.

Fig. 1 Chart of nuclides for 13 < Z < 17. The shading shows the stable (nonradioactive) species; the unshaded portion indicates the radioactive nuclides. Abundances are given in per cent.

Cl³² 0.3s β⁺ γ	Cl³³ 2.8s β⁺ γ	Cl³⁴ 32.4m 1.6s β⁺ | β⁺ γ	Cl³⁵ 75.53	Cl³⁶ 2.5 x 10⁵y β⁻ no γ	Cl³⁷ 24.47	Cl³⁸ 37.7m 1.5s β⁻ γ | γ	Cl³⁹ 56m β⁻ γ
S³¹ 2.7s β⁺ γ	S³² 95.0	S³³ 0.76	S³⁴ 4.22	S³⁵ 87d β⁻ no γ	S³⁶ 0.014	S³⁷ 5.1m β⁻ γ	S³⁸ 2.87h β⁻ γ
P³⁰ 2.6m β⁺	P³¹ 100	P³² 14.3d β⁻ no γ	P³³ 25d β⁻ no γ	P³⁴ 12.4s β⁻ γ			
P²⁹ 4.2s β⁺ γ	Si²⁸ 92.17	Si²⁹ 4.71	Si³⁰ 3.12	Si³¹ 2.64h β⁻ γ	Si³² 700y β⁻ γ		
P²⁸ 0.28s β⁺ γ	Si²⁷ 4.2s β⁺ γ	Al²⁷ 100	Al²⁸ 2.3m β⁻ γ	Al²⁹ 6.5m β⁻ γ			
Si²⁶ 2s β⁺ γ	Al²⁶ 6.5s 7.4 x 10⁵y β⁺ | β⁺ γ no γ						
Al²⁴ 2.1s β⁺ γ	Al²⁵ 7.2s β⁺ γ						

144

B. Counting Techniques

The β radiations from both P^{32} and P^{33} are sufficiently hard to allow the use of any standard thin end-window Geiger-Müller or proportional counter for their detection. Since thin end-window counters have window thicknesses of 1 to 2 mg per cm^2 or less, absorption in the windows is virtually negligible for the P^{32} radiation, and amounts to less than 10 to 20 per cent for the P^{33} radiation. For the same reason, self-absorption in samples of P^{32} is, in general, very low; even for P^{33} it is seldom a serious problem. In this connection, one should bear in mind the approximate relationship between range (R) and half-thickness $(d_{1/2})$ for β-particle absorption: $1/10R \approx d_{1/2}$. The range R is, in turn, related to the maximum beta energy (E_{max}) by the equation

$$R = 412E_{max} \ \exp(1.265 - 0.0954 \ln E_{max})$$

for $E_{max} < 2.5$ Mev.

A rather convenient and moderately efficient way of counting P^{32} is by assaying it in the form of liquid samples using so-called thin (< 30 mg per cm^2) glass-wall β-liquid counters, such as those manufactured by Philips, Mullard, 20th Century Electronics, and others.

Laboratories equipped with more elaborate apparatus for counting the soft β radiation of C^{14} and H^3 (tritium) by means of liquid scintillators can also utilize these instruments for measurements on P^{32} and P^{33}. Although more expensive, the efficiency of the method is close to 100 per cent for P^{32} and ca. 90 per cent for P^{33}.

In special cases in which P^{32} or P^{33} are incorporated in gaseous compounds, no difficulties should be encountered in employing gas (flow) counters such as those used in gas-chromatographic work.

Herber[4] reports the use of a thin-walled aluminum G. M. tube sealed into an annular jacket for the purpose of detecting the radioactivity of volatile compounds labeled with P^{32} and other β emitters of more than 0.15 Mev energy.

Rosen et al.[5] have developed techniques for β counting corrosive gases containing P^{32} (e.g., $P^{32}F_5$) using standard end-window G. M. counters by confining the labeled materials in a separate gas-cell having a thin-aluminum window and body.

Autoradiography with P^{32} has been shown to be useful in the

[4] Herber, R. H., Rev. Sci. Instr., 28, 1049 (1957).
[5] Rosen, F. D., and Davies, W., Jr., Rev. Sci. Instr., 24, 349 (1953).

study of biological materials, [6, 7] especially in conjunction with paper electrophoresis[8] and paper chromatography techniques. [9]

It is interesting to note in this connection the work of Mayr, [10] who attempted to apply autoradiography to the quantitative determination of the P^{33} present in samples of P^{32}. The experimental method is based on counting the numbers of the densely ionized terminal parts of the β-ray tracks in 200-μ-thick nuclear emulsions. Westermark et al. [11] have pointed out that the lower β energy of P^{33}, as compared with P^{32}, gives higher photographic sensitivity and better autoradiographic resolution.

This difference in maximum β energy also makes possible the detection and assay of P^{32} and P^{33} in the presence of each other, if the activity ratio for the two nuclides is not too extreme. When using end-window counters, an absorber of about 60 mg Al per cm^2 completely cuts out the P^{33} radiation, whereas at least 50 per cent of the P^{32} radiation is still transmitted. In the case of liquid-scintillation counting, the discriminator setting can play the role of the absorber. If one also takes into consideration the longer half-life of P^{33} as compared to P^{32}, it is seen that double-labeling with radiophosphorus is a potentially useful technique under appropriate conditions.

As both P^{32} and P^{33} are useful for labeling purposes from the standpoint of detection, one might wonder why, since P^{32} is so extremely well known and exploited, P^{33} is seldom employed in tracer experiments. The reason for this difference lies in the relative difficulties encountered in the production of P^{33} as compared to P^{32}.

C. Methods of Production

Phosphorus-P^{32}. All commercially available P^{32} is produced in nuclear reactors according to one of the nuclear reactions shown in Eqs. (1) and (2). Reaction (1) requires thermal neutrons in

$$P^{31} (n, \gamma) \ P^{32} \tag{1}$$

$$S^{32} (n, p) \ P^{32} \tag{2}$$

---

[6] Odeblad, E., Exptl. Cell Research, 2, 574 (1951).

[7] Rothenberg, S. F., Jaffe, H. L., Putnam, T. J., and Sinkin, B., Arch. Neur. Psychiatry, 23, 193 (1955).

[8] Sato, T. R., Anal. Chem., 31, 841 (1959).

[9] Grunze, H., Silikat Tech., 7, 134 (1956).

[10] Mayr, J., Experientia, 11, 21 (1955).

[11] Westermark, E. G. T., Fogelström-Fineman, I. G. A., and Forberg, S. R., Proc. Intern. Conf. Radioisotopes in Scientific Research, 1957, Vol. I, p. 19.

order to obtain highest yields. The thermal-neutron cross section is given[12] as about 190 mb. In general, the target material used is red phosphorus. No interfering activities are present if one allows a few short-lived periods, which might be formed (Si^{31}, Al^{28}; see Fig. 1), to decay. The fact that, in principle, no further chemical treatment is required, explains why P^{32} (as red phosphorus) is often the starting material in many procedures for labeling with radiophosphorus. A serious drawback to the activation of elementary phosphorus, however, is the relatively low specific activity that can be acquired; the highest specific activity of P^{32}, readily available as red phosphorus, is given[13] as 550 mc per g = 0.55 μc per μg. This value is about 1.4×10^{-2} of the highest-specific-activity P^{32} commercially available in the United States.[14]

The second mode of producing P^{32}, on the contrary, gives an essentially carrier-free product with specific activities as high as 1 to 5 mc per μg.[13] The (n, p) reaction on S^{32} is endothermic and has a threshold of about 0.9 Mev. Activations, therefore, are performed in or near the core of the reactor where the fast-neutron flux is highest. The cross section for the reaction has been investigated[15] with precision for neutron energies of 2 to 10 Mev (σ = 20 to 250 mb) and of about 14 Mev (σ = 250 mb). Activation cross sections for the average reactor-neutron spectrum range from 20 to 65 mb[16] depending on the type of reactor and the irradiation position utilized.

Some nuclear data pertinent to the production of P^{32} (as well as P^{33}) are compiled in Table 2.

In most cases, the target material used is elementary sulfur. The P^{32} produced will finally be isolated in the form of orthophosphate in a weakly acid solution. Except for very little P^{33} (1 to 2 per cent[11]) the product is very pure radiochemically. Although during the fast-neutron irradiation of sulfur, other radio-

---

[12] Hughes, D. J., and Harvey, J. A., Neutron Cross-Sections, B. N. L. 325; also published as "Selected Reference Material on Atomic Energy," Vol. 5, Geneva, 1955; for sale by the U.S. Government Printing Office, Washington 25, D. C.

[13] "International Directory of Radioisotopes," Vienna, 1959; Vol. 1: Unprocessed and processed radioisotope preparations, and special radiation sources; Vol. II: Compounds of C^{14}, H^3, I^{131}, P^{32}, and S^{35}.

[14] Catalogue, Radioisotopes, Oak Ridge National Laboratory, Oak Ridge, Tennessee.

[15] Liskien, H., and Paulsen, A., "Cross Sections for Neutron Threshold Reactions," Euratom Bur. Nucl. Meas., 1961.

[16] Passel, T. O., and Heath, R. L., Nuclear Sci. and Eng., 10, 308 (1961).

Table 2
Nuclear Data for the Production of P^{32} and P^{33} by Neutron
Irradiation

Target nuclide		Nuclear	Product	Cross section as a function of n energy		
Isotope	Abundance, %	reaction	nuclide	σ, mb	Ref.	$E_{neutron}$
P^{31}	100	(n,γ)	P^{32}	190	12	Thermal
S^{32}	95	(n, p)	P^{32}	0		Thermal
				20-65	16	Average reactor spectrum
				20-250	15	2-10 Mev
				250	15	About 14 Mev
S^{33}	0.75	(n, p)	P^{33}	2.3	22	Thermal
				30	22	Average reactor spectrum
Cl^{35}	75.4	(n, α)	P^{32}	10-60	12	3-4 Mev
				140	12	14.3 Mev

active species are also formed (Si^{31}, P^{34}, S^{35}, S^{37}; see Fig. 1),
only S^{35} with a half-life of 87 days remains after a short cooling
period, since the other isotopes have half-lives too short to
interfere.

Various methods are used to isolate carrier-free P^{32} from
the sulfur target. One possibility is to extract the radiophosphorus as orthophosphate from molten sulfur by treatment with hot
concentrated nitric acid at 135 to 138°C.[17]

Extraction with water at a temperature of 100°C has also been
reported.[18] At that temperature the sulfur is still in the solid
state, but the transition at 95.5°C from the rhombic to the mono-
clinic form apparently liberates the radiophosphorus, which is
initially trapped in the rhombic lattice.

The third and most efficacious method consists of distilling

[17] Rupp, A. F., Proc. Intern Conf. Peaceful Uses Atomic
Energy, Geneva, 1955, Vol. 14, p. 68
[18] Samsahl, K., Atompraxis, 4, 14 (1958).

the sulfur at $500\,°C$ so that the radiophosphorus remains be-hind. [19-21]

In the first procedure mentioned, a necessary purification step is the precipitation of lanthanum (or ferric) hydroxide, which quantitatively carries the P^{32} present as phosphate and leaves behind any S^{35} which is present in the form of sulfate (from oxidation of sulfur), as well as other anionic impurities. Subsequently, the precipitated La^{+3} (and other cationic impurities) is removed by passage through a cation-exchange column. If the sulfur is rigorously purified prior to irradiation, the second and third procedures seldom require additional purification steps.

Phosphorus-P^{33}. This isotope of phosphorus is not (yet) available commercially, in sharp contrast to P^{32} which is sold in more than sixty[14] different chemical forms (organic and inorganic). Accordingly, the literature on P^{33} is rather limited. Westermark et al., in a series of articles, [11, 22-26] have made important studies in connection with the difficulties encountered in an economic production of P^{33}, and have summarized much of the published data on P^{33} to date. The only method of several, to be considered briefly is pile-irradiation of S^{33} by the reaction $S^{33}(n, p)P^{33}$.

Whereas the nuclear reaction $S^{32}(n, p)P^{32}$ requires fast neutrons, the (n, p) reaction on S^{33} has no threshold and consequently proceeds with thermal neutrons. The thermal-neutron cross section, however, is rather small (2.3 mb). This, as well as the low abundance (0.75 per cent) of the target isotope S^{33}, results in low yields. The main difficulty, however, is the

[19] Geithoff, D., Kernforschungszentrum Karlsruhe, K. F. K. -Rep. 62 (1961).

[20] Evans, C. C., and Stevenson, J., Brit. Pat. No. 765,489; C.A., 51, 7896 (1957).

[21] Oak Ridge National Laboratory, Isotopes Division Annual Report 1957, ORNL-2492.

[22] Westermark, E. G. T., Phys. Rev., 88, 573 (1952).

[23] Fogelström-Fineman, I. G. A., and Westermark, E. G. T., Nucleonics, 14 (2), 62 (1956).

[24] Forberg, S. R., Barnevik, W., Fogelström-Fineman, I. G. A., Westermark, E. G. T., and Ubisch, H., Proc. Intern. Symp. Isotope Separation, Amsterdam, 1957, p. 243; published by North-Holland Publishing Co., Amsterdam.

[25] Forberg, S. R., and Westermark, E. G. T., Proc. I.A.E.A. Conf. Use of Radioisotopes in Physical Sciences and Industry, Copenhagen, 1960, preprint RICC/78.

[26] Westermark, E. G. T., Svensk Kem. Tidskr., 73, 153 (1961).

simultaneous, and therefore, interfering production of P^{32} resulting from the high abundance of S^{32} (95 per cent). Thus, notwithstanding the 0.9-Mev threshold for the reaction $S^{32}(n, p)P^{32}$, one indeed needs a highly thermalized (and consequently reduced) neutron flux in order to depress (ideally to exclude) the production of P^{32}. Westermark and co-workers, therefore, investigated methods to decrease the S^{32}/S^{33} ratio by using an isotope-enrichment procedure for S^{33} by means of anion exchange.[24, 25] Target material highly enriched in S^{33} does not need to be irradiated in well-thermalized neutron fluxes, since the average reactor-neutron cross sections for both (n, p) reactions are similar (see Table 2).

In this connection, it should be stressed that, in the author's opinion, the chemical purity of the target material (sulfur or one of its compounds) is of great importance, especially with respect to phosphorus and chlorine. For example, phosphorus present in concentrations of the order of 10^{-2} per cent in natural sulfur irradiated in a thermal neutron flux results in a P^{32} production from the reaction $P^{31}(n, \gamma)P^{32}$, comparable to that of P^{33} from the reaction $S^{33}(n, p)P^{33}$.

Chlorine impurities may also interfere as a result of the nuclear reaction $Cl^{35}(n, \alpha)P^{32}$, although the cross section is considerable only in the Mev region, and thus not of significance in well-thermalized fluxes.

The data given by Westermark et al.[23] for P^{32}/P^{33} yield ratios, as a function of irradiation position inside a nuclear reactor, may be open to some uncertainty because of the afore-mentioned purity considerations.[27]

Other reported efforts to enrich P^{33} over P^{32} appear to be unsuccessful. Nilsson[28] has examined the distribution of both P^{33}- and P^{32}-recoil atoms (produced in sulfur by neutron irradiation), among various possible oxidation states. Notwithstanding the difference in initial mean-average recoil energy (about 16 kev and 50 kev, respectively), no significant difference in the chemical behavior of the two isotopes could be observed.

The author[29] bombarded sulfates and sulfites (very pure with respect to phosphorus and chlorine contaminants) at dry-ice temperatures in a well-thermalized neutron flux. Within the experimental accuracy, no differences could be observed in the chemical properties of the P^{32}- and P^{33}-recoil atoms formed.

Because of the above-cited critical parameters, it is difficult to give a generally applicable prescription with respect to the irradiation conditions for the production of P^{33}. By trial and error, however, it is fairly simple to find suitable conditions for each irradiation facility (nuclear reactor) under consideration. The chemical separation of the P^{33} will depend on the chemical

---

[27] Lindner, L., unpublished results.

[28] Nilsson, G., Acta Chem. Scand., 10, 94 (1956).

[29] Lindner, L., to be published.

form of the irradiated target but will, in general, be similar to techniques developed for the recovery of P^{32}. Table 2 gives some nuclear data pertinent to the production of P^{33}.

D. Commercially Available Phosphorus-P^{32} Compounds

An up-to-date list of unprocessed and processed radioisotope preparations has been compiled[13] by the International Atomic Energy Agency. This directory "contains information on all radioisotopes that are for sale or distribution by the major suppliers in the world."

With respect to phosphorus, the two unprocessed forms available are red phosphorus-P^{32} and $KH_2P^{32}O_4$.

The synthesis of most inorganic-P^{32} compounds listed in Volume II of the directory are discussed in the present chapter. Exceptions are $P^{32}Br_5$, $P_2^{32}O_5$, $P^{32}Br_3$, and $K_3P^{32}O_4$, the synthesis of which, to our knowledge, has not been described in the open literature.

2. SYNTHETIC PROCEDURES FOR RADIOPHOSPHORUS COMPOUNDS

The labeling of inorganic compounds with radiophosphorus can often be achieved by following two entirely different paths.

One possibility is by normal chemical synthesis, according to "classical" methods, but modified to meet the typical requirements dictated by the radioisotope under consideration. Often important is the fact that the particular isotope is available only in a rather limited number of chemical forms. In the case of phosphorus, as already pointed out, the two common starting materials are red phosphorus-P^{32} and aqueous solutions of carrier-free phosphate-P^{32}.

The other possibility is the so-called method of recoil labeling. Here, one takes advantage of the (often rather highly specific) chemical reactivity of the nuclide, induced at the moment of its creation by chemical consequences of the nuclear transformation. Most nuclear reactions, for instance, impart to the new nuclide that is formed, kinetic ("recoil") energies that are very large compared to the excitation energies encountered in "classical" chemistry at moderate temperatures. It is beyond the scope of this book to give extensive details of this method, but the interested reader is referred to information on this subject summarized in recent publications. [30, 31]

Of primary importance in the consideration of recoil labeling
is the experimental evidence that, initially, the original chemical
bond(s) of the new nuclide is (are) ruptured in most, if not all,
the cases. Recoil particles can then lose their excess energy by
elastic and inelastic collisions with the atoms of the surrounding
medium and, finally, achieve a new state of chemical stability.
That fraction of the recoil particles that is ultimately stabilized,
in a chemical form identical to the material irradiated (parent
compound), is generally referred to as retention. The recoil
particles that combine to give chemical forms different from the
parent are present in essentially a carrier-free form.

Although potentially an extremely powerful method for the
labeling of compounds, applications of recoil methods to radiochemical syntheses have been limited. One reason is the difficulty
encountered in finding reliable analytical procedures for the
chemical separation of the complex mixtures of the labeled compounds that are often formed. A further proliferation of products
is due to the secondary reactions (annealing processes) that
take place during or after the actual irradiation, and that compli-
cate the ultimate chemical purification of the desired product.

Schematic diagrams for both the chemical and recoil syntheses
to be considered in this chapter are given, respectively, in Fig.
2 and Fig. 4. All synthesis reactions are denoted in the text by a
number (in brackets [5]), which also appears in the diagrams.
Reactions (procedures) that are advantageous and/or preferable
for some reason over alternate methods are indicated by bold-
face numbers.

CHEMICAL SYNTHESES

The starting materials for the chemical synthesis of P^{32}-
labeled compounds are invariably either red phosphorus-P^{32} or
(carrier-free) aqueous solutions of orthophosphate-P^{32}. Although
these forms of P^{32} are commercially available in high radiochemical purity, it is worth pointing out that this does not necessarily imply that the chemical state of the P^{32} is unambiguous.
For instance, Süe et al. [32] have demonstrated that about 6 per
cent of the total P^{32} activity in neutron-irradiated red phosphorus
can be extracted with water. The specific activity of this in-
organic-P^{32} fraction was twice that of the red phosphorus and

[30] Harbottle, G., Proc. I. A. E. A. Conf. Radioisotopes in
Physical Sciences and Industry, Copenhagen, 1960, preprint
RICC/290.

[31] Proc. I. A. E. A. Conf. Chem. Effects of Nuclear Transformations, Prague 1960; published by I. A. E. A., Vienna, 1961.

[32] Süe, P., and Merinis, J., Bull. soc. chim. France, 1959,
735.

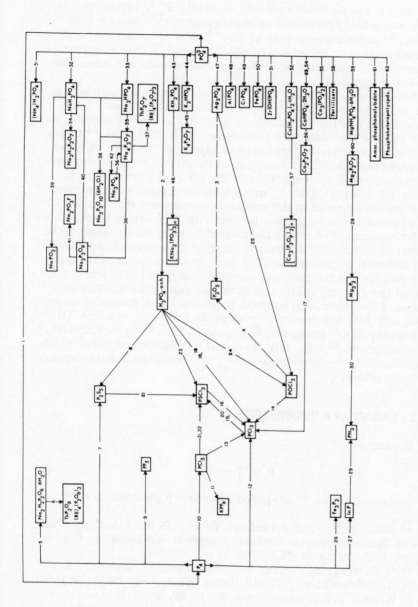

Fig. 2 Diagram of chemical syntheses.

153

contained, among other species, phosphite-P^{32}, hypophosphite-P^{32}, and small amounts of orthophosphate-P^{32}. Sato,[8] Dahl et al.,[33] as well as Babický et al.,[34] have demonstrated that commercial carrier-free orthophosphoric-P^{32} acid may contain considerable quantities of P^{32} as pyrophosphate and other condensed phosphates.

According to Babický et al.,[34] a brief treatment with boiling 1 N HCl converts all P^{32} to the orthophosphate form. Sato[8] showed that heating carrier-free $H_3P^{32}O_4$ solutions leads to the formation of the condensed phosphates-P^{32}; Dahl et al.[33] indicated that these products form even on standing. Dahl et al. also observed considerable adsorption of carrier-free P^{32} on glassware upon standing, especially in the pH range from 5 to 8. In the pH interval 2 to 3, much less adsorption was observed.

It should be noted in the synthesis procedures that follow, when solutions of orthophosphates labeled with P^{32} are to be used, the orthophosphate-P^{32} under consideration need not necessarily be prepared separately; addition of carrier-free orthophosphate-P^{32} or carrier-free phosphoric-P^{32} acid to the solution of the particular salt serves the purpose. In this connection is is worth pointing out the general absence of exchange among the various oxyanions of phosphorus in aqueous solutions. For example, no exchange of P^{32} has been observed in the following systems: (1) orthophosphate—phosphite,[35] hypophosphite,[36] pyrophosphate,[37] hypophosphate,[38] tri-, trimeta-, and tetrametaphosphate[33]; (2) pyrophosphate——hypophosphate[38]; (3) trimetaphosphate—hexametaphosphate.[39]

3. ELEMENTARY PHOSPHORUS

A. Procedure

$$P^*O_4^{-3} \longrightarrow P^* \qquad\qquad [1]$$

Oosterbaan et al.[40] prepared elementary phosphorus-P^{32}

---

[33] Dahl, J. B., and Birkelund, O. R., Proc. I.A.E.A. Conf. Use of Radioisotopes in Physical Scieneces and Industry, Copenhagen, 1960, preprint RICC/262.

[34](*) Babický, A., Bass, A., Chaloupka, J., and Zak, R., Physiol. Bohemoslov., 7, 112 (1958); C.A., 52, 16961 (1958).

[35] Wilson, J., J. Am. Chem. Soc., 60, 2697 (1938).

[36] Lindner, L., Thesis, University of Amsterdam, 1958.

[37] Hull, D. E., J. Am. Chem. Soc., 63, 1269 (1941).

[38] Moeller, T., and Quinty, G. H., J. Am. Chem. Soc., 74, 6122 (1952).

[39] Vogel, R. C., and Podall, H., J. Am. Chem. Soc., 72, 1420 (1950).

[40] Oosterbaan, R. A., and van Rotterdam, J., J. Am. Chem. Soc., 78, 5641 (1956).

starting with 3 ml of an aqueous solution of carrier-free
$H_3P^{32}O_4$. To this was added 150 mg of inactive H_3PO_4. This
mixture was dropped into a porcelain boat holding 1 g of carbo
adsorbens (activated charcoal). After each addition of a 1-ml
portion, the material was dried by infrared heating. The
porcelain boat was placed in a quartz tube and heated in an electric
furnace to 400° for 15 hours, while flushing with dry, oxygen-free
nitrogen gas (10 ml per min). The temperature was then raised to
900°C within 4 hours, and condensed water was continuously removed by local heating with a flame. At the moment the phosphorus production started (at 900°C), the nitrogen stream was reduced
to 2 ml per min, and the quartz tube was connected to a trapping
system cooled to -75°C with a methylene dichloride-dry ice
mixture. The red phosphorus-P^{32} produced sublimed just beyond
the hot zone, whereas the white phosphorus-P^{32} condensed in the
cooler parts of the quartz tube. After 8 to 9 hours at 950°,
the reduction was complete. After cooling to 200°C, the trap
refrigerant was removed. A yield of 60 to 70 per cent was reported.

Kafalas et al.[41] and Bocquet,[42] in a similar procedure, obtained elementary phosphorus-P^{32} starting with $Ca_3(P^{32}O_4)_2$ [55]
by reduction, respectively, with charcoal and SiO_2 at 1300°C,
and by reduction only with charcoal at 1050 to 1200°C.

B. Discussion

The potential importance of this procedure is the possibility of
obtaining elementary phosphorus-P^{32} with much higher specific
activities than red phosphorus-P^{32} produced by radiative-neutron
capture in a reactor (see Sec. 1-C). This is often extremely
advantageous if preparations of the highest possible specific activity are desired for syntheses that start from elementary phosphorus.

4. ANHYDROUS PHOSPHORIC ACID

A. Procedures

$$H_3P^*O_4 \text{ (aq)} \xrightarrow{\text{-}H_2O} H_3P^*O_4 \text{ (anh)} \qquad\qquad [2]$$

An aqueous solution of $H_3P^*O_4$ (carrier-free or not) can yield
anhydrous $H_3P^{32}O_4$ (with less than 0.005 per cent loss) by
gradually heating the aqueous system to 180°C in an oil bath while

---

[41] Kafalas, J. A., Gatos, H. C., and Button, M. J., J. Am.
Chem. Soc., 79, 4260 (1957).
[42] Bocquet, J. R., Ann. Soc. Roy. Sci. Med. Nat. Bruxelles,
9, 161 (1956).

exposing it to a stream of dry air,[43] by lyophilization,[44] or by heating with an infrared lamp.[40,45]

5. PHOSPHORUS PENTOXIDE

A. Suggested Procedures

Murray and Williams[46] have suggested several possibilities for the preparation of $P_2^{32}O_5$. (1) by the reaction of $Ag_3P^{32}O_4$ [47] with acetyl chloride[47] [3]; (2) by the reaction of $P^{32}OCl_3$ [24, 25] with silver acetate[47] [4]; and (3) by the reaction of $P^{32}OCl_3$ [24, 25] with potassium chlorate[48] [4].

The reader is referred to the collection by Murray and Williams[46] for details.

6. DISODIUM DIHYDROGEN HYPOPHOSPHATE HEXAHYDRATE

A. Procedure

$$2P^* + 2NaClO_2 + 2OH^- \longrightarrow Na_2H_2P_2^*O_6 + 2Cl^- \qquad [5]$$

Moeller et al.[38] prepared $Na_2H_2P_2^{32}O_6 \cdot 6H_2O$ by the direct oxidation of red phosphorus-P^{32} with sodium chlorite by an adaption of the procedure of Leininger et al.[49] in an apparatus shown in Fig. 3. In their experimental method, 1 g of red phosphorus-P^{32} is mixed with 25 g of inactive red phosphorus, and this (E) is inserted in a cylindrical pyrex reaction vessel on top of a layer of asbestos several centimeters thick (F) alternately with layers of glass beads (D). The reaction vessel is cooled internally with cold water by means of a pyrex tube (B) running along the axis. The chlorite solution [about 50 g of technical sodium chlorite (83 per cent) in 400 ml water] is allowed to drop from a funnel (A) into the reaction vessel at a rate of 1 to 2 ml per min. The bottom of the reaction vessel is connected with

43 Riley, R. F., J. Am. Chem. Soc., 66, 512 (1944).

44 Kalinsky, J. L., and Weinstein, A., J. Am. Chem. Soc., 76, 5882 (1954).

45 (*) Fejes, P., Magyar Tudomanyos Akad. Kŏzponti Fiz. Kutato Intezetenek Kŏzlemenyei, 3, 535 (1955); C.A., 53, 18716 (1959).

46 Murray, A., and Williams, D. L., "Organic Synthesis with Isotopes," Interscience, New York, 1958, Part II, p. 1927.

47 Bechamp, A., and Saintpierre, C., Compt. rend., 55, 59 (1862).

48 Oddo, G., Gazz. Chim. Ital., 29, 2, 333 (1899).

49 Leininger, E., and Chulski, T., J. Am. Chem. Soc., 71, 2385 (1949).

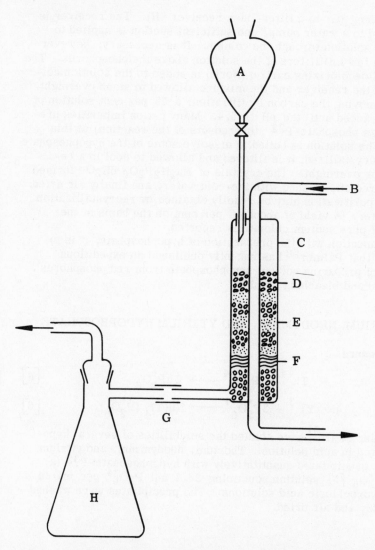

Fig. 3 Pyrex apparatus for preparation of hypophosphate-P^{32}: A, sodium chlorite dropping funnel; B, cooling water circuit; C, reaction vessel; D, glass beads; E, red phosphorus-P^{32}; F, glass or asbestos wool; G, Tygon tubing; and H, receiver.

Tygon tubing (G) to a filter-flask receiver (H). The receiver is
connected to a water pump, and sufficient suction is applied to
draw the solution through the column. It is necessary, however
to keep a few milliliters of the solution above the phosphorus. Ten
grams of decolorizing carbon (Norit) is added to the solution collected in the receiver and the mixture allowed to stand overnight.
After removing the carbon by filtration, a 15 per cent solution of
NaOH is added until the pH is 5.4. Many cation impurities precipitate as phosphate-P^{32} (byproducts of the reaction) at this
point. The solution is boiled to dissolve some of the hypophosphate
already crystallized; it is filtered and allowed to cool in a refrigerator overnight. The crystals of $Na_2H_2P_2O_6 \cdot 6H_2O$ formed
are filtered off, washed with ice-cold water, and finally air dried.
Further purification may be readily obtained by recrystallization
from water. A yield of about 40 per cent on the basis of the
weight of pure sodium chlorite is reported.

In connection with the preparation of hypophosphate, it is to
be noted that Palmer[50] has recently published an expeditious
method of preparing sodium hypophosphate from red phosphorus
(inactive) and bleaching powder.

7. THORIUM, NEODYMIUM, AND YTTRIUM HYPOPHOSPHATE

A. Procedure

$$Th^{+4} + P_2^*O_6^{-4} \longrightarrow ThP_2^*O_6 \qquad [6]$$

$$4Nd(Y)^{+3} + 3P_2^*O_6^{-4} \longrightarrow Nd(Y)_4 (P_2^*O_6)_3 \qquad [6]$$

Moeller et al.[51] have studied the solubilities of several hypo-
phosphates in acid solution. Thorium, neodymium, and yttrium
ions are precipitated quantitatively with hypophosphate-P^{32} (a
$Na_2H_2P_2^*O_6$ [5] solution containing 26.4 mg $P_2O_6^{-4}$ per ml) in
dilute hydrochloric acid solutions. The precipitates were washed
thoroughly and air dried.

B. Note

At higher normalities (6 $\underline{N}$) of HCl solutions, the ThP_2O_6
is still highly insoluble (solubility 2.1 × 10^{-4} mole per liter),
whereas $Nd_4(P_2O_6)_3$ and $Y_4(P_2O_6)_3$ are soluble, and can be removed by filtration.

---

50 Palmer, W. G., J. Chem. Soc., 1961, 1079.
51 Moeller, T., and Quinty, G. H., J. Am. Chem. Soc., 74,
6123 (1952).

8. PHOSPHORUS PENTASULFIDE

A. Procedure 1

$$2P^* + 5S \longrightarrow P_2^* S_5 \qquad [7]$$

Mühlmann et al.[52] synthesized $P_2^{32}S_5$ from red phosphorus-P^{32} and sulfur. No experimental details are given, but the method probably consists of melting the two components in the correct molar ratio of $2:5$ (see procedure 2).

B. Procedure 2

$$2P + 5S \xrightarrow{\quad P^*O_4^{-3}\quad} P_2^* S_5 \qquad [8]$$

Casida[53] used either carrier-free $H_3P^{32}O_4$ or carrier-free $Na_2HP^{32}O_4$ [33] as the labeled starting material. The acid is preferable, when the residue after evaporation is considerable, and the salt, when the residue amounts to no more than a few milligrams. To this dried starting material, red phosphorus and sulfur are added in a $2:5$ molar ratio (total weight 0.2 to 2.0 g). While flushing the reaction vessel with dry carbon dioxide, the mixture is carefully heated in one spot with a weak flame in order to initiate the vigorous reaction. After the liquified mixture has boiled for 10 minutes, the exchange is over 95 per cent complete, as is also the case after 2 hours heating at 300 to 500°C in a sealed ampoule. Recrystallization may be effected from carbon disulfide.

C. Discussion

The only obvious advantage of procedure 2 over procedure 1 is the higher specific activities obtainable with the latter.

9. PHOSPHORUS PENTAFLUORIDE

A. Procedure

$$2P^* + 5F_2 \longrightarrow 2P^*F_5 \qquad [9]$$

Rosen and Davies[5] obtained $P^{32}F_5$ in good yields by the direct reaction of fluorine gas with red phosphorus-P^{32}, with the surface temperature of the reaction vessel kept below 300°C. Circulation

---

[52] Mühlmann, R., and Schrader, G., Z. Naturforsch., 12b, 196 (1957).

[53] Casida, J. E., Acta Chem. Scand., 12, 1691 (1958).

of F_2 back and forth over the P^{32} sample was achieved by the alternate cooling (with liquid nitrogen) of two fluroine storage cans connected on either side of the reaction vessel. The $P^{32}F_5$ was purified by bulb-to-bulb distillation with liquid nitrogen.

B. Note

Because of the corrosive properties of PF_5 (b.p., -84.5°C), the apparatus to be used must be made of nickel and copper tubing in the customary manner.

10. PHOSPHORUS PENTACHLORIDE

A. Procedure

$$2P^* + 5Cl_2 \longrightarrow 2P^*Cl_5 \qquad [10]$$

The method consists essentially of the complete chlorination of red phosphorus-P^{32} with an excess of dry chlorine gas. Lockau et al.[54,55] and Oosterbaan et al.[40] passed the chlorine gas over elementary phosphorus-P^{32} for a period of 4 hours.

Maller et al.[56] dissolved the $P^{32}Cl_5$ formed after 2 hours of reaction in carbon tetrachloride and passed chlorine through the mixture for an additional 3 hours. After cooling to room temperature, the excess chlorine was removed with dry nitrogen gas. The carbon tetrachloride can be removed by distillation. An essentially similar procedure has been described by Crofts et al.[57]

The preparation of $P^{32}Cl_5$ has also been reported by Likins et al.[58] who modified a technique described by Maxson.[59] The use of an isotopic-exchange reaction for the preparation of $P^{32}Cl_5$ starting with the labeled trichloride appears feasable on the basis of the work of Becker and Johnson.[60] These workers studied the PCl_3-PCl_5 exchange in CCl_4 solution and suggested a mechanism

54 Lockau, S., Lüdicke, M., and Weygand, F., Naturwiss., 38, 350 (1951).

55 Lockau, S., and Lüdicke, M., Z. Naturforsch., 7b, 389 (1952).

56 Maller, R. K., and Heidelberger, C., Cancer Research, 17, 284 (1957).

57 Crofts, P. C., Downie, I. M., and Heslop, R. B., J. Chem. Soc., 1960, 3673.

58 Likins, R. C., Zipkin, I., and McCann, H. G., Proc. Soc. Exptl. Biol. Med., 95, 527 (1957).

59 Maxson, R. N., in H. S. Booth (ed.), "Inorganic Synthesis," McGraw-Hill, New York, 1939, Vol. I, p. 99.

60 Becker, W. E., and Johnson, R. E., J. Am. Chem. Soc., 79, 5157 (1957).

for the exchange that can serve to transfer both phosphorus and chlorine activity between the two reactants.

11. POTASSIUM HEXAFLUOROPHOSPHATE

A. Procedure

$$P^*Cl_5 + KCl + 6HF \longrightarrow KP^*F_6 + 6HCl \qquad [11]$$

The preparation of potassium hexafluorophosphate labeled with P^{32} starting from $P^{32}Cl_5$ [10] has been reported by Likins et al.[58] based on a method described by Woyski.[61] The reaction is carried out in a nickel, Monel, or stainless steel beaker. The $P^{32}Cl_5$ is slowly added to a solution of potassium chloride in anhydrous liquid hydrogen fluoride. Initially, the reaction should be cooled with a mixture of ice and salt. After all the $P^{32}Cl_5$ has been added, the reaction vessel is flushed with N_2 and then heated to about 150° to remove excess hydrogen fluoride. The yield of the reaction is essentially 100 per cent. The purity of the compound is better than 95 per cent and can be improved by recrystallization from hot water.

B. Note

CAUTION! The manipulations should be carried out in a well-ventilated hood, and heavy protective gloves should be worn.

12. PHOSPHORUS TRICHLORIDE

A. Procedure 1

$$2P^* + 3Cl_2 \longrightarrow 2P^*Cl_3 \qquad [12]$$

1a. The major problem in the direct conversion of red phosphorus to phosphorus trichloride is to prevent or minimize the simultaneous formation of phosphorus pentachloride. Saunders et al.[62, 63] found that the yield of PCl_5 was dependent on their choice of an optimal geometry of the apparatus and on their method of manipulation, especially developed for the small-scale conversion of labeled red phosphorus to PCl_3.

In their procedure, a mixture of 1 g red phosphorus-P^{32} and

---

[61] Woyski, M. M., in L. F. Audieth (ed.), "Inorganic Synthesis," McGraw-Hill, New York, 1950, Vol. III, p. 111.

[62] Saunders, B. C., and Worthy, T. S., Nature, 163, 797 (1949).

[63] Saunders, B. C., and Worthy, T. S., J. Chem. Soc., 1950, 1320.

1 ml of inactive phosphorus trichloride (as a solvent for the chlorination) is placed in the bottom of a small tubular reaction vessel
and exposed to a stream of Cl_2. If the rate of addition of the (dry)
chlorine is too high, the phosphorus begins to glow, and pentachloride
is formed. If the rate is too slow, on the other hand, the reaction
time is unduly long. It also appears essential to keep the phosphorus trichloride refluxing during the reaction and to introduce the
chlorine through a glass tube of the correct internal diameter
(1 cm) close to the top of the phosphorus trichloride-red phosphorus mixture. Purification was effected by sweeping the $P^{32}Cl_3$
twice with dry nitrogen gas into receivers cooled in liquid air.
These distillations freed the $P^{32}Cl_3$ from small quantities of
phosphorus and phosphorus pentachloride. A yield of about 90 per
cent is reported.

Mühlmann and Schrader[52] also converted red phosphorus-P^{32}
to $P^{32}Cl_3$ with chlorine, but no details are reported.

1b. A second procedure involving the direct combination of the
elements is very similar to the method of Saunders et al. [62, 63]
with the difference that fewer precautions are taken against the
possible production of phosphorus-P^{32} pentachloride. After the
chlorination process, the latter compound is reduced to the trichloride either by heating with red phosphorus[64] at 60°C or by the
addition of antimony[65] after cooling in an ice bath. In the latter
case, the reaction mixture was allowed to come slowly to room
temperature to avoid a too-violent reduction of $P^{32}Cl_5$ to $P^{32}Cl_3$.

Further purification of the $P^{32}Cl_3$ formed is achieved by
distillation into a second vessel at atmospheric pressure (b. p.,
76°C). Yields ranged from 62 to 87 per cent. [64, 65]

B. Procedure 2

$$3P^*Cl_5 + 2P \longrightarrow 5P^*Cl_3 \qquad\qquad [13]$$

Oosterbaan et al. [40] converted approximately 300 mg of
$P^{32}Cl_5$, [10] , dissolved in 1.5 ml of carbon tetrachloride to
$P^{32}Cl_3$ with 60 mg of red phosphorus by refluxing for 2 hours.
The $P^{32}Cl_3$-CCl_4 solution was separated from the residual red
phosphorus by flushing it with dry nitrogen into a trap cooled to
-75°C with a mixture of methylene dichloride and dry ice. No
further separation of the $P^{32}Cl_3$ from the carbon tetrachloride
was made.

64(*) Mandel'baum, Ya. A., Vladimirova, I. L., and Mel'nikov,
A. A., Doklady Akad. Nauk. S.S.S.R., 100, 77 (1955); C.A., 50,
1650 (1956).

65 Louloudes, S. J., Kaplanis, J. N., and Roan, C. C., J. Org.
Chem., 21, 685 (1956).

C. Note

The red phosphorus used was in a finely divided form, collected by decanting a suspension in water. This material was boiled with water and filtered until the supernatant was acid free. Finally, this red phosphorus was washed with dry acetone and dried over P_2O_5 in vacuo. The CCl_4 used was boiled with a small quantity of PCl_3, agitated with Na_2CO_3 solution, washed with water, dried with P_2O_5, and distilled.

D. Procedure 3

$$P^*OCl_3 + C \longrightarrow P^*Cl_3 + CO \qquad [14]$$

Murray and Spinks,[66] as well as Vigne et al.,[67] reduced $P^{32}OCl_3$ [24, 25] to $P^{32}Cl_3$ by passing the vapor over carbon granules in a silica tube heated to 1000°C. The transfer of the $P^{32}OCl_3$ vapor can be achieved by holding the receiving vessel for the $P^{32}Cl_3$ at -70°C while the $P^{32}OCl_3$, which is contained in a vessel at the other end of the silica tube, is allowed to warm slowly from -70°. Murray et al.[66] reported a 65 per cent yield for their procedure.

E. Procedure 4

$$H_3P^*O_4 + PCl_3 \longrightarrow H_3PO_4 + P^*Cl_3 \qquad [15]$$

Vigne et al.[68] reported 85 per cent exchange between carrier-free anhydrous $H_3P^{32}O_4$ [2] and phosphorus trichloride after 8 hours of heating at 150°C in a sealed glass tube. No such exchange occurred when anhydrous sodium phosphate-P^{32} was used instead of anhydrous $H_3P^{32}O_4$.

F. Procedure 5

$$P^*SCl_3 + (C_6H_5O)_3P \longrightarrow P^*Cl_3 + (C_6H_5O)_3PS \qquad [16]$$

According to Casida,[53] and on the basis of a well-known reaction,[69] $P^{32}Cl_3$ is formed in 91 per cent yield by the reaction

---

[66] Murray, D. H., and Spinks, J. W. T., Can. J. Chem., 30, 497 (1952).

[67] Vigne, J. P., Tabau, R. L., and Fondarai, J., Bull. soc. chim. France, 1956, 459.

[68] Vigne, J. P., and Tabau, R. L., Bull. soc. chim. France, 1958, 1194.

[69] Gottlieb, H. B., J. Am. Chem. Soc., 54, 748 (1932).

of 1 mole equivalent of $P^{32}SCl_3$ [19-23] with 1.1 mole equivalents of triphenyl phosphine at 130 to 140°C for 2 hours.

G. Procedure 6

$$KH_2P^*O_4 \longrightarrow Ca_2(HP^*O_4)_2 \longrightarrow Ca_2P^*O_7 \longrightarrow$$

$$P^*Cl_5 + P^*OCl_3 \longrightarrow P^*Cl_3 \qquad [17]$$

1a. Witten et al.[70] converted $KH_2P^*O_4$ by the precipitation of $Ca_2(HP^{32}O_4)_2$ to $Ca_2P_2^{32}O_7$ [56] [containing some $Ca_3(P^{32}O_4)_2$]. The pyrophosphate mixed with charcoal was chlorinated at 700°C, yielding a mixture of $P^{32}Cl_5$ and $P^{32}OCl_3$. The two compounds were converted to $P^{32}Cl_3$ with antimony[65] and carbon[66, 67] respectively. An over-all yield of 80 per cent is reported.

1b. On the basis of the above results,[70] Bocquet[42] has made an extremely detailed and critical study of possible ways to convert carrier-free phosphate-P^{32} to very pure $P^{32}Cl_3$. The following experimental technique appears to give a pure product in highest yield.

$$Ba_3(PO_4)_2 + 8C + 6Cl_2 \xrightarrow{\ P^*O_4^{-3}\ } 2P^*Cl_3 + 8CO + 3BaCl_2 \ [18]$$

About 2 g of dried inactive barium phosphate is intimately mixed with very pure activated charcoal. A silica tube (2.5 cm wide, 54 cm long) plugged near one end with filter paper is loaded with this mixture. While the tube is being held in a vertical position, a solution of carrier-free sodium phosphate-P^{32} is introduced dropwise on top of the phosphate-carbon mixture by means of a syringe. The tube is then placed in a cylindrical oven equipped with a receiver. Both ends are connected to bubblers of concentrated sulfuric acid. The receiving end of the tube should be close to the oven. The oven temperature is raised so as to reach 850 to 900°C after 1.5 hours. As soon as the filter-paper plug begins to burn, dry nitrogen is allowed to pass (initially at a slow rate) through the tube. The flushing with nitrogen is continued (ca. 3 hours) until all the tar produced by the combusion of the filter paper has been moved from the silica tube into the receiver, which is then replaced by a clean one. After the new receiver has been cooled with an ice-salt mixture, the stream of nitrogen is replaced by dry chlorine, which should be introduced very slowly at a rate of approximately 1 g per hour. After 1 to 2 hours, small droplets of $P^{32}Cl_3$ will appear at the receiving end of the reaction tube and

---

[70] Witten, B., and Miller, J. I., J. Am. Chem. Soc., 70 3886 (1948).

finally collect in the cooled receiver. The end of the reaction is clearly indicated when the receiving end of the reaction tube turns opaque, owing to the sudden conversion of the film of $P^{32}Cl_3$ to $P^{32}Cl_5$. At this moment the chlorine flow should be stopped immediately, and the receiving flask disconnected. A 95 per cent yield of pure $P^{32}Cl_3$ (free from phosphorus-P^{32} oxychloride!) is reported.

H. Note

1. The activated charcoal was purified prior to the actual synthesis, by heating at 1000°C in a silica tube flushed with dry nitrogen for 2 to 3 hours and with dry chlorine for an additional 3 hours.

2. For other procedures, see Sec. 50.

I. Discussion

Procedures 1 and 2 generally lead to lower specific activities than the other methods cited, since red phosphorus-P^{32} is the precursor reactant. As pointed out by Bocquet,[42] additional disadvantages of procedures 1b and 2 are (1) the decrease in specific activity when inactive red phosphorus is used as a reductant, and (2) the large hold-up and the danger of complex formation with $SbCl_3$ when antimony is used as a reductant.

Procedures 3, 5, and 6a involve starting materials generally not readily available. The reduction of $P^{32}OCl_3$ with carbon (procedure 3), moreover, has a tendency not to proceed quantitatively if not precisely controlled.[42] The presence of calcium in procedure 6a leads to calcium-chloride formation, which has a tendency to follow the $P^{32}Cl_3$ in the final distillation.[42]

This leads to the conclusion that procedures 4 and 6b which are relatively simple and safe one-step operations giving pure $P^{32}Cl_3$ in high specific activity and good yields are the methods of choice in the present instance. In case lower specific activities are acceptable, procedures 1 or 2 (using phosphorus as reducing agent) seem preferable.

13. THIOPHOSPHORYL CHLORIDE

A. Procedure 1

$$P^*Cl_3 + S \xrightarrow{\text{AlCl}_3 \text{ (anh)}} P^*SCl_3 \qquad\qquad [19]$$

On the basis of a method developed by Knötz, [71] thiophosphoryl-P32 chloride has been obtained[64, 65, 72-74] in high (up to 90 per cent) yields. The direct combination of sulfur and (labeled) phosphorus trichloride [12-18] is catalyzed by the addition of anhydrous aluminum chloride. One-tenth of the weight of the sulfur should be sufficient for the amount of $AlCl_3$. The more aluminum chloride added, however, the more rapidly and vigorously the reaction proceeds.

To 1 g of $P^{32}Cl_3$ and 0.24 g (a small excess) of powdered sulfur is added 0.03 to 0.2 g of anhydrous aluminum chloride. On heating on a water bath to the boiling point of phosphorus trichloride (76°C), the reaction proceeds rapidly. The mixture is heated under reflux for an additional 10 minutes. After cooling, the aluminum chloride is extracted with water in a separatory funnel. The thiophosphoryl-P^{32} chloride (bottom layer) is separated and dried over calcium chloride. The crude product is purified by distillation, and comes over as a colorless liquid at 124 to 126°C.

B. Procedure 2

$$P^*Cl_3 + S \longrightarrow P^*SCl_3 \qquad [20]$$

The direct reaction between $P^{32}Cl_3$ [12-18] and sulfur was also achieved by heating the mixture of the two compounds in a sealed glass tube for 2 hours at 150 to 180°C.[64, 66, 67] Yields of from 50 to 100 per cent are reported.

C. Procedure 3

$$3P^*Cl_5 + P_2^*S_5 \xrightarrow{\quad AlCl_3 \text{ (anh)} \quad} 5P^*SCl_3 \qquad [21]$$

The reaction is carried out in a sealed glass tube, heated for approximately 2 hours at 160°C. Lockau et al.[54, 55] used the phosphorus pentachloride [10] as the labeled component, whereas Casida[53] started with phosphorus pentasulfide [7, 8] as the labeled reactant. Casida added anhydrous aluminum chloride (1.5 times the weight of the sulfur) as a catalyst. Yields of from 60 to 70 per cent are reported.

---

[71] Knötz, F., Oesterr. Chemiker-Ztg., 50, 128 (1949); C.A., 43, 9394 (1949).

[72] Hein, R. E., and McFarland, R. H., J. Am. Chem. Soc., 74, 1856 (1952).

[73] Fukuto, T. R., and Metcalf, R. L., J. Am. Chem. Soc., 76, 5103 (1954).

[74] Hodnett, E. M., Moore, T. E., and Lothers, J. E., Jr., Proc. Okla. Acad. Sci., 39, 141 (1959).

D. Procedure 4

$$P^*Cl_5 + H_2S \longrightarrow P^*SCl_3 + 2HCl \qquad [22]$$

This reaction is reported by Maller et al. [56] A solution of $P^{32}Cl_5$ [10] in carbon tetrachloride was flushed with dry nitrogen gas to remove possible oxidants (Cl_2). The reaction vessel was then cooled in an ice bath, and a stream of dry hydrogen sulfide was bubbled through for a period of 6 hours. After nitrogen had replaced the excess hydrogen sulfide, the carbon tetrachloride (b. p., 76.8°C) was distilled off. The residual material (mainly $P^{32}SCl_3$) was distilled at 100 to 126°C. Relative to the original starting material (red phosphorus-P^{32}), a yield of 39 per cent is claimed.

E. Procedure 5

$$H_3P^*O_4(\text{anh}) + PSCl_3 \longrightarrow H_3PO_4 + P^*SCl_3 \qquad [23]$$

Vigne et al. [68] reported a 70 per cent exchange between carrier-free anhydrous $H_3P^*O_4$ [2] and thiophosphorylchloride after 60 hours of heating at 150°C in a sealed glass tube. No such exchange occurred when anhydrous sodium phsophate-P^{32} was used instead of anhydrous $H_3P^*O_4$.

F. Discussion

With respect to simplicity, none of the procedures described for preparing $P^{32}SCl_3$ has outspoken advantages or disadvantages over the other. In addition, except for procedure 4, all methods can lead to satisfactory or even very good yields.

With respect to the various labeled starting materials used, $P^{32}Cl_3$ is the most difficult to synthesize. Moreover, $P_2^{32}S_5$ is expeditiously labeled in high specific activities [7, 8] . Procedure 5 can also lead to high specific activities, since essentially carrier-free $H_3P^{32}O_4$ can be used as the starting material, but the method is relatively time consuming.

Procedures 1, 2, and 3 are especially suited for double labeling of thiophosphorylchloride as $P^{32}S^{35}Cl_3$. Moreover, since PCl_3 is readily labeled with Cl^{36}, (see Chap. 8), triple labeling to give $P^{32}S^{35}Cl_3^{36}$ should be possible. Since the beta-decay energies of the three nuclides (1.718, 0.167, and 0.716 Mev, respectively) are rather different, simple absorber techniques should suffice for the differential radioassay of this compound.

14. PHOSPHORYL CHLORIDE (PHOSPHORUS OXYCHLORIDE)

A. Procedure 1

$$H_3P^*O_4 + 3PCl_5 \longrightarrow 4P^*OCl_3 + 3HCl$$

$$H_2O + PCl_5 \longrightarrow POCl_3 + 2HCl \qquad\qquad [24]$$

$$\overline{H_3P^*O_4 + H_2O + 4PCl_5 \longrightarrow 5P^*OCl_3 + 5HCl}$$

The reaction between phosphorus pentachloride and $H_3P^{32}O_4$ has been the basis for a number of methods to synthesize $P^{32}OCl_3$. Axelrod, [75] Lindberg, [76] Murray et al., [66] and Fejes[45] started from $H_3P^{32}O_4$ [2] evaporated to dryness. Kalinsky et al., [44] however, pointed out that evaporation of the phosphoric-P^{32} acid to complete dryness is impractical and, in most cases, unnecessary.

In a procedure given by Kalinsky et al. [44] an aqueous solution containing 8 mmoles of $H_3P^*O_4$ is transferred to a 25-ml two-necked reaction vessel and evaporated under vacuum until approximately 1/4 ml (containing about 12.5 mmoles of H_2O) remains. The vessel is then fitted with a condenser with drying tube and a dropping funnel containing 2.7 g of phosphorus pentachloride (about 13 mmoles). After the vessel has been cooled in an acetone-dry ice mixture, a small quantity (ca. 0.1 g) of the pentachloride is added. Removing the coolant initiates the reaction. The cycle of alternate freezing, adding of PCl_5, and thawing should be continued until the reaction is controllable. Then the remainder of the PCl_5 is added as rapidly as possible. Finally the reaction mixture is brought to reflux for a period of about 15 minutes. The $P^{32}OCl_3$ so formed is purified by vacuum distillation. The radiochemical yield amounted to 96 per cent.

In this way, quantities as small as 400 mg (ca. 0.25 ml) of $P^{32}OCl_3$ have been successfully prepared. Depending on the specific activity (as high as 25 mc per mmole) required, the total synthesis takes 4 to 8 hours.

B. Procedure 2

$$Ag_3P^*O_4 + 3PCl_5 \longrightarrow 4P^*OCl_3 + 3AgCl \qquad\qquad [25]$$

Murray et al., [66] as well as Vigne et al., [67] allowed $Ag_3P^{32}O_4$ [47] to react with PCl_5 in a sealed tube for 10 to 30 minutes at 130°C to form $P^{32}OCl_3$.

---

[75] Axelrod, B., J. Biol. Chem., 176, 295 (1948).
[76] Lindberg, O., Arkiv. Kemi, 23A, (2) (1946).

C. Other Procedures

Gardiner et al. [77, 78] converted $FeP^{32}O_4$ [50] to $P^{32}OCl_3$ by treatment with phosgene at 400 to 450°C. A yield of 93 per cent was obtained. Banks et al. [79] followed a similar treatment but used calcium phosphate-P^{32} [55] as the starting material instead of iron phosphate-P^{32}. Vigne et al. [68] reported the observation of phosphorus exchange between anhydrous $H_3P^{32}O_4$ [2] and phosphorus oxychloride, without giving details. Chargaff[80] oxidized $P^{32}Cl_3$ [12-18] with potassium chlorate to $P^{32}OCl_3$. Crofts et al. [57] started with $P^{32}Cl_5$ [10] as the labeled component. The product $P^{32}OCl_3$ was formed from the reaction of P_2O_5 with the $P^{32}Cl_5$ in a carbon tetrachloride solution. An additional method for the preparation of $P^{32}OCl_3$ is given in Sec. 51.

D. Discussion

The experimental technique developed by Kalinsky et al. [44] (see Sec. 14-A) is certainly the most straightforward. The methods described by Gardiner et al. [78] and Banks et al. [79] (see Sec. 14-C) have the serious drawback[44] of needing elaborate and cumbersome equipment and the loss of one- to two-thirds of the P^{32} in the course of the synthesis.

15. IRON(II) PHOSPHIDE

A. Procedure

$$P^* \xrightarrow{\ Fe(C_2O_4)\ } Fe_3P_2^* \qquad\qquad [26]$$

Shikhov[81] prepared $Fe_3P_2^{32}$ by a high-temperature method. A mixture of red phosphorus-P^{32} and ordinary red phosphorus is dissolved in concentrated nitric acid. Ferrous oxalate is added to the solution, which is then dried, the residue ignited and reduced with hydrogen at 750°C in a tubular electric furnace.

---

[77] Gardiner, J. E., and Kilby, B. A., Research (London), 2, 590 (1949).

[78] Gardiner, J. E., and Kilby, B. A., J. Chem. Soc., 1950, 1769.

[79] Banks, T. E., Boursnell, J. C., Dewey, H. M., Francis, G. E., Tupper, R., and Wormall, A., Biochem. J., 43, 518 (1948).

[80] Chargaff, E., J. Am. Chem. Soc., 60, 1700 (1938).

[81](*) Shikhov, V. N., Zavodskaya Lab., 21, 1482 (1955); C. A. 50, 8419 (1956).

16. INDIUM PHOSPHIDE

A. Procedure

$$P^* + In \longrightarrow InP^*$$ [27]

Kafalas et al. [41] prepared InP^{32} by heating elementary phosphorus, containing P^{32}, and excess indium metal in an evacuated, sealed-off silica tube at 1050°C for 1 hour. (The danger of explosion is reduced by keeping one end of the tube at a lower temperature.) The resulting sample was treated briefly with cold concentrated HNO_3 in order to remove the excess indium. The formation of InP was confirmed by X-ray powder-pattern analysis. The product obtained in this procedure may be used in the synthesis of labeled phosphine [29].

17. MAGNESIUM PHOSPHIDE

A. Procedure

$$Mg_2P_2^*O_7 \longrightarrow Mg_2P_3^*$$ [28]

Elbek et al. [82] prepared $Mg_2P_3^{32(33)}$ by reduction of magnesium pyrophosphate-P^{32}($-P^{33}$) [60] with magnesium in a hydrogen atmosphere. No further details of their method are given.

18. PHOSPHINE ($-P^{32}$ and $-P^{33}$)

A. Procedure 1

$$InP^* + 3HCl \longrightarrow P^*H_3 + InCl_3$$ [29]

In a study of the hydrolysis of $A^{III}B^V$ intermetallic compounds, Kafalas et al. [41] obtained $P^{32}H_3$ from the acid hydrolysis of indium phosphide [27]. The quantity of the hydride recovered when the solution containing the solid phosphide and aqueous HCl was swept out with nitrogen was directly proportional to the concentration of the acid.

In view of the ease of formation of InP^{32}, this method is preferable over the reaction of yellow phosphorus with aqueous base or the thermal decomposition of $H_3P^{32}O_2$ or $H_3P^{32}O_3$, since these methods invariably give rise to impure products which are difficult to separate in small quantities.

---

[82] Elbek, B., Nielsen, K. O., and Nielsen, O. B., Phys. Rev., 95, 96 (1954).

B. Procedure 2

$$Mg_3P_2^* + 3H_2O \longrightarrow 3Mg(OH)_2 + 2P^*H_3 \qquad [30]$$

Elbek et al.[82] obtained labeled phosphine by starting with a solution containing orthophosphate labeled with both P^{32} and P^{33}. The phosphate was converted to $Mg_3P_2^*$ [28], which gave P^*H_3 on contact with water vapor. Unfortunately, no further details of their method are given.

C. Note

Kafalas et al.[41] have pointed out that PH_3 is best prepared from AlP and H_2SO_4,[83] but no radiosynthetic exploitation of this older method has yet been reported.

Additional methods for the preparation of $P^{32}H_3$ are given in Sec. 49.

19. ALUMINUM DIHYDROGEN ORTHOPHOSPHATE

A. Procedure

$$H_3P^*O_4 + (NH_4)H_2PO_4 \rightleftharpoons (NH_4)H_2P^*O_4 + H_3PO_4 \qquad [31]$$

Dion et al.[84] obtained $(NH_4)H_2P^{32}O_4$ by evaporation at temperatures of less than 45°C, of a solution of ammonium dihydrogen orthophosphate to which P^{32} as H_3PO_4 had been added. Crystal growth was controlled to some extent by the frequency of stirring during the evaporation.

20. SODIUM DIHYDROGEN ORTHOPHOSPHATE

A. Procedure

$$H_3P^*O_4 + NaH_2PO_4 \rightleftharpoons NaH_2P^*O_4 + H_3PO_4 \qquad [32]$$

Preparations of $NaH_2P^{32}O_4$ have been reported starting from an aqueous mixture of carrier-free $H_3P^{32}O_4$ and sodium dihydrogen orthophosphate.

Vogel et al.[39] dissolved 12 g of C.P. Na_2HPO_4 in 20 ml of

---

[83] Moser, L., and Brukl, A., Z. anorg. u. allgem. Chem., 121, 73 (1922).

[84] Dion, H. G., Dehm, J. E., and Spinks, J. W. T., Sci. Agr., 29, 512 (1949).

distilled water, added $H_3P^{32}O_4$, evaporated to the first appear-
ance of crystals, and stirred until complete crystallization occurred. The resulting crystals were powdered and dried at 100°C
for 2 hours, yielding anhydrous $NaH_2P^{32}O_4$.

Porthault et al.[85] precipitated the salt from a concentrated
aqueous solution by the addition of alcohol.

Götte et al.[86] and Dion et al.[84] obtained the salt by evaporation
of the aqueous solution to dryness at 45 to 50°C.

21. SODIUM MONOHYDROGEN ORTHOPHOSPHATE

A. Procedure

$$P^*O_4^{-3} + Na_2HPO_4 \rightleftharpoons Na_2HP^*O_4 + PO_4^{-3} \qquad [33]$$

Preparations of anhydrous $Na_2HP^*O_4$ start from an aqueous
solution of Na_2HPO_4 and carrier-free orthophosphate-P^{32}.
Shinagawa et al.[87] evaporated the solution (which had been made
slightly acid with HCl) at 110°C, overnight to dryness.

Porthault[85] precipitated the salt through the addition of alcohol
to the aqueous solution, as in the case of the dihydrogen compound [32].

22. DISODIUM DIHYDROGEN PYROPHOSPHATE

A. Procedure

$$NaH_2P^*O_4 \longrightarrow Na_2H_2P_2^*O_7 + H_2O \qquad [34]$$

Shinagawa et al.[87] prepared $Na_2H_2P_2^{32}O_7$ by heating
$NaH_2P^{32}O_4$ [32] in a platinum crucible. The temperature was
raised to 210°C and maintained for 12 hours. A purity of better
than 97 per cent is reported.

B. Discussion

According to Shinagawa et al.,[87] the product of the above-
mentioned heat treatment was $Na_4P_2^{32}O_7$. This conclusion is at

[85] Porthault, M., and Merlin, J. C., Bull. soc. chim. France,
1959, 359.

[86] Götte, H., and Frimmer, M., Angew. Chem., 65, 52
(1953).

[87] Shinagawa, M., Takanaka, J., Kiso, Y., Tsjukiji, A., and
Matama, Y., Bull. Chem. Soc. Japan, 28, 565, 568 (1955).

variance with the data presented by Van Wazer, [88] who has shown that the stable phase in the NaH_2PO_4-water system, between 169 and 343°C, is $Na_2H_2P_2O_7$. The final heating temperature, however, should be near 200°C, and under no circumstances should it be raised to about 250°C, since a further conversion to various metaphosphates will then proceed with reasonably rapid rates.

23. TETRASODIUM PYROPHOSPHATE

A. Procedure 1

$$Na_2HP^*O_4 \longrightarrow Na_4P_2^*O_7 \qquad [35]$$

The salt $Na_4P_2^{32}O_7$ is prepared[38, 85, 89-91] according to the usual procedure of dehydrating Na_2HPO_4 [33]., which consists of heating the reactant at 400 to 600°C for 2 hours. The product has a greater than 99 per cent purity, which can be raised to at least 99.8 per cent by a single recrystallization from water.[90] In view of the good yields, high purity, and simplicity of the method, this procedure is clearly preferable over other alternative syntheses.

B. Procedure 2

$$3Na_3P^*O_4 + Na_3P_3^*O_9 \longrightarrow 3Na_4P_2^*O_7 \qquad [36]$$

Porthault et al.[85] heated a mixture consisting either of anhydrous $Na_3P^{32}O_4$ [42] and trisodium trimetaphosphate or of anhydrous trisodium phosphate and $Na_3P_3^{32}O_9$ [40], in a 3:1 molar ratio, at 560°C for 24 hours, to obtain anhydrous $Na_4P_2^{32}O_7$.

24. THORIUM, RARE EARTH METALS, AND YTTRIUM PYROPHOSPHATES

A. Procedure

$$Th^{+4} + P_2^*O_7^{-4} \longrightarrow ThP_2^*O_7 \qquad [37a]$$

$$4M^{+3} + 3P_2^*O_7^{-4} \longrightarrow M_4(P_2^*O_7)_3 \qquad [37b]$$

[88] Van Wazer, J. R., "Phosphorus and its Compounds," Interscience, New York, 1958, Vol. I, p. 618.

[89] Moeller, T., and Schweitzer, G. K., Anal. Chem., 20, 1201 (1948).

[90] Quimby, O. T., Mabis, A. J., and Lampe, H. W., Anal. Chem., 26, 661 (1954).

[91] Berg, P., J. Biol. Chem., 233, 601 (1958).

Moeller et al.[89] have reported the feasibility of precipitating thorium, certain rare earth metals, (La, Ce, Yb), and yttrium as pyrophosphates-P^{32} in weakly (< 0.03 N) acid solutions by adding a standard solution of $Na_4P_2^{32}O_7$ [35, 36] (containing 2.00 mg $P_2O_7^4$ per ml) to the respective metal salt solutions.

B. Note

At higher normalities (0.3 N) of the acid medium, ThP_2O_7 is still highly insoluble (solubility, 0.5×10^{-4} mole per liter), whereas the rare earth(III) pyrophosphates are highly soluble. This fact can be exploited in effective ultimate separations of mixed, labeled pyrophosphates.

25. PENTASODIUM TRI(POLY)PHOSPHATE (HEXADRATE)

A. Procedures

$$NaH_2P^*O_4 + 2Na_2HP^*O_4 \longrightarrow Na_5P_3^*O_{10} + 2H_2O \qquad [38a]$$

$$NaH_2P^*O_4 + Na_4P_2^*O_7 \longrightarrow Na_5P_3^*O_{10} + H_2O \qquad [38b]$$

By following the method of Jones,[92] Shinagawa et al.[87] prepared $Na_5P_3^{32}O_{10}$ according to reaction [38a]. Sodium dihydrogen orthophosphate and sodium monohydrogen orthophosphate in a 1:2 molar ratio are evaporated to dryness at 110°C in a platinum crucible together with carrier-free $H_3P^{32}O_4$. The mixture is then held at 250°C for 2 hours before increasing the temperature to approximately 800°C. The mixture is allowed to remain at this temperature until the entire mass has melted. Then the temperature is lowered to about 650°C and maintained at this temperature for 18 hours. The temperature is then gradually lowered to 250°C over a period of 8 hours, and the product finally transferred to a desiccator to cool.

Quimby et al.[90] and Grunze[9] applied a different heat treatment (the latter according to reaction [38b]). The melt was held at 900°C for a sufficient length of time (2 hours) to ensure equilibration of the P^{32} atoms and was then quenched very rapidly to a glass.

Grunze[93] achieved this by decreasing the temperature within 30 seconds to 550°C, where it was held for about 9 hours, to allow the solid-state reaction, which yields the triphosphate-P^{32}, to proceed.

---

[92] Jones, L. T., Anal. Chem., 14, 536 (1942).

Quimby et al.[90] quenched from 900°C within 10 seconds to 400°C and then maintained this temperature for about 18 hours. The resulting crude product of 96 to 98 per cent purity was purified by 4 to 6 fractional crystallizations from water as the hexahydrate and then air dried to give the anhydrous compound.

B. Note

The heating procedure, as described by Shinagawa et al.[87] in their publication, is an incorrect quotation of Jones' method.[92]

C. Discussion

The essential differences between the techniques employed, on the one hand, by Jones[92] and Shinagawa[87] and, on the other hand, by Quimby[90] and Grunze,[9] concern the ultimate temperature of the melt (800°C and 900 to 1000°C, respectively) and the speed with which this melt is quenched (gradually and very rapidly). Grunze[9] has shown, by the use of chromatographic methods of analysis for the various tripolyphosphate labeled with P^{32} which had been formed by different heat treatments, that the procedure described above gives almost pure tripolyphosphate($-P^{32}$). At temperatures below 860°C (the actual point of liquifidation to a homogeneous melt), pyrophosphate crystals are still present. If the quenching speed is not very rapid, the resulting glass contains (among other products) relatively large pyrophosphate crystals. Because of their size, they anneal only slowly at temperatures of about 550°C to tripolyphosphate. Rapidly quenched, high-temperature melts ($>860°C$), however, contain only small amounts of small pyrophosphate crystals, which, at 550°C, gradually anneal almost quantitatively to give tripolyphosphate($-P^{32}$). (See also Van Wazer.[93]).

The procedure for synthesis according to Grunze[9] seems, therefore, preferable. The product as obtained by the Jones[92] method probably contains relatively large amounts of pyrophosphate-P^{32} (and other condensed labeled phosphates).

26. SODIUM HEXAMETAPHOSPHATE

A. Procedure

$$NaH_2P^*O_4 \longrightarrow NaP^*O_3 + H_2O \qquad [39]$$

Shinagawa et al.[87] and Götte et al.[86] have prepared sodium phosphate glass (also called Graham salt or sodium hexametaphosphate) with the over-all composition $NaP^{32}O_3$ ($Na_2O/P_2O_5 = 1:1$) by melting $NaH_2P^{32}O_4$ [32] in a platinum crucible to a liquid at

---

[93] Ref. 88, p. 604.

900°C and maintaining this temperature for 1/2 to 3 hours.[86,87] The melt was then cooled very rapidly (in an ice-water bath) to a clear glass.

B. Discussion

The glasses with the over-all metaphosphate composition $NaPO_3$ cover a wide range of compounds containing ring and long-chain phosphates in varying amounts depending on the method of formation.[94] Using the above method for syntheses will obviously lead to a more or less random distribution of the P^{32} label throughout the structure of the product material.

27. TRISODIUM TRIMETAPHOSPHATE

A. Procedure

$$3NaH_2P^*O_4 \longrightarrow Na_3P_3^*O_9 + 3H_2O \qquad\qquad [40]$$

On the basis of the method of Jones,[92] Vogel et al.,[39] Shinagawa et al.,[87] and Porthault[85] have prepared $Na_3P_3^*O_9$ from sodium dihydrogen orthophosphate-P^{32} [32] . In a platinum crucible the latter compound was first heated to 300°C. After maintaining this temperature for 1 hour (to allow the water that is formed to escape), the temperature was increased to 610°C, held there for 3 hours, and then slowly decreased to 390°C and maintained at that point for 14 hours.

According to the directions of Bell,[95] Quimby et al.[90] (after quenching to a glass) annealed at 535 to 545°C for 18 hours, whereas Ericson[96] annealed at 530°C, maintaining this temperature for 5 hours.

Quimby et al.[90] purified the crude product by several recrystallizations from water at 50 to 60°C. Qualitative tests with silver and barium ions indicated the absence of ortho-, pyro-, and triphosphate.

B. Discussion

The three different heat treatments all invariably lead[97] to the trimeric ring compound $NaP^{32}O_3$.

---

94 Ref. 88, pp. 607, 702, 775, 788.

95 Bell, R. N., in L. F. Andrieth (ed.), "Inorganic Synthesis," McGraw-Hill, New York, 1950, Vol. III, p. 103.

96 Ericson, Y., Intern. J. Appl. Radiation and Isotopes, 10, 177 (1961).

97 Ref. 88, p. 607.

28. SODIUM MONOFLUOROPHOSPHATE

A. Procedure

$$Na_3P^*_3O_9 + 3NaF \longrightarrow 3Na_2P^*O_3F \qquad [41]$$

According to Ericson,[96] labeled sodium monofluorophosphate is formed in high purity and with a yield of 100 per cent when sodium trimetaphosphate-P^{32} [40], mixed with sodium fluoride in a 1:3 molar ratio, is heated in a furnace at 800°C for 1 minute.

B. Note

The actual synthesis as reported by Ericson[96] describes a method for double labeling with P^{32} and F^{18} yielding $Na_2P^{32}OF^{18}$ ($t_{1/2} F^{18}$ = 1.87h).

29. TRISODIUM ORTHOPHOSPHATE

A. Procedure

$$Na_4P^*_2O_7 + Na_2CO_3 \longrightarrow 2Na_3P^*O_4 + CO_2 \qquad [42]$$

Porthault et al.[85] prepared anhydrous $Na_3P^{32}O_4$ by heating $Na_4P^{32}_2O_7$ [35, 36] with a stoichiometric quantity of anhydrous sodium carbonate. Before the heat treatment, the two components were intimately mixed by grinding in a ball mill for several hours. The mixture was then heated to 800°C for 12 hours.

B. Note

According to Porthault et al.,[85] this is the only method reported so far for the preparation of anhydrous $Na_3P^{32}O_4$.

30. POTASSIUM DIHYDROGEN ORTHOPHOSPHATE

A. Procedure

$$H_3P^*O_4 + KH_2PO_4 \longrightarrow KH_2P^*O_4 + H_3PO_4 \qquad [43]$$

Götte and Frimmer[86] prepared the labeled dihydrogen ortho-phosphate by mixing $H_3P^{32}O_4$ (the anhydride is specified by them) with an aqueous solution of KH_2PO_4 in a platinum dish and evaporating to dryness in an oven at 50°C. The crusty product is scraped into the bottom of the dish which is then transferred to an electric furnace for further heating. The nature of the final product (whether the simple orthophosphate, Graham's salt [39], or Tammann's salt [46]) depends on the subsequent heat treatment.

31. POTASSIUM MONOHYDROGEN ORTHOPHOSPHATE

A. Procedure

$$H_3P^*O_4 + 2KOH \longrightarrow K_2HP^*O_4 + 2H_2O \qquad [44]$$

Rudney[98] converted phosphoric-P^{32} acid to the dipotassium salt by titration with potassium hydroxide to the phenolphthalein end point. The solution was then evaporated to dryness to yield the labeled product in quantitative yield.

32. POTASSIUM PYROPHOSPHATE

A. Procedure

$$2K_2HP^*O_4 \longrightarrow K_4P_2^*O_7 + H_2O \qquad [45]$$

De Moss et al. [99] prepared $K_4P_2^{32}O_7$ from $K_2HP^{32}O_4$ [44] by high-temperature fusion. The temperature should be raised gradually to about 400°C. The product contained less than 0.1 per cent orthophosphate.

33. "TAMMANN PHOSPHATE", $KNa_2(P^{32}O_3)_3$

A. Procedure

$$3KP^*O_3 + NaCl \longrightarrow KNa_2(P^*O_3)_3 + 2KCl \qquad [46]$$

Götte et al. [86] prepared metaphosphate-P^{32} with an over-all composition of $KNa_2(P^{32}O_3)_3$ by first bringing $KH_2P^{32}O_4$ [43] to a dark-red heat within 25 minutes. The glassy substance so formed, is allowed to cool to room temperature, powdered, and weighed. The powdered potassium metaphosphate-P^{32} glass is then treated with saturated aqueous NaCl solution so that the

---

[98] Rudney, H., J. Biol. Chem., 210, 353 (1954).
[99] De Moss, J. A., and Novelli, G. D., Biochim. et Biophys. Acta, 22, 49 (1956).

molar ratio of potassium and sodium is 1:2. After standing for
12 hours at room temperature, the supernatant is decanted. The
residual compound is washed twice with a small amount of distilled water and then dissolved in distilled water (30 to 50 ml per
0.6 g $KH_2P^{32}O_4$) by careful heating in a water bath. The
$KNa_2(P^{32}O_3)_3$ is precipitated as a dough-like substance by the
addition of 50 ml of alcohol. The precipitate is washed with 50
per cent alcohol until completely free of chloride.

B. Note

Tammann salt is a highly condensed phosphate and is said to
have a molecular weight of about 1.3×10^5. As is true of the
other polymeric phosphates, the P^{32} label will be distributed
essentially randomly throughout the extended structure.

34. SILVER ORTHOPHOSPHATE

A. Procedure

$$P^*O_4^{-3} + 3Ag^+ \longrightarrow Ag_3P^*O_4 \qquad [47]$$

Baldwin et al.[100] precipitated $Ag_3P^{32}O_4$ by adjusting an
aqueous solution of silver nitrate (56.1 g = 0.33 mole) in dilute,
P^{32}-labeled phosphoric acid (0.1 mole) to a pH of 6 to 7 with
3 N ammonium hydroxide. The precipitation should be done with
stirring. After the pH remains constant at 6 to 7, the precipitate
is allowed to digest (again with stirring) at room temperature for
16 hours. The supernatant is then removed, the precipitate washed several times with a minimum quantity of water, and oven-dried
at 110°C. The P^{32} is recovered as the silver phosphate in
essentially quantitative yield.

Murray et al.[66] and Vigne et al.[67] used $Na_2HP^{32}O_4$ as the
starting material, in a precipitation method and an exchange study
with inactive silver phosphate. The obvious isotopic dilution in
the latter case makes the exchange method unsuitable for the
preparation of a high-specific-activity product.

35. ALUMINUM ORTHOPHOSPHATE

A. Procedure

$$Al^{+3} + P^*O_4^{-3} \longrightarrow AlP^*O_4 \qquad [48]$$

---

[100] Baldwin, W. H., and Higgins, C. E., J. Am. Chem. Soc.,
74, 2431 (1952).

Amorphous $AlP^{32}O_4$ was prepared by Ivanov[101] by adding
0.1 $\underline{N}$ $KH_2P^{32}O_4$ to a corresponding quantity of aluminum sulfate.
The precipitate was kept on a water bath at 60 to 70°C for 21(?)
days, filtered, washed with acetone, and dried at 60°C.

36. CHROMIC ORTHOPHOSPHATE HEXAHYDRATE AND CHROMIC ORTHOPHOSPHATE COLLOID

A. Procedure

$$Cr(H_2O)_6^{+3} + P^*O_4^{-3} \longrightarrow CrP^*O_4 \cdot 6H_2O \xrightarrow{-H_2O} CrP^*O_4 \quad [49]$$

Radiophosphorus-labeled $CrPO_4 \cdot 6H_2O$ has been prepared
largely to serve as the starting material from which the colloidal
anhydrous solid can be obtained. Morton[102] evaporated to dryness
by infrared heating, an aqueous mixture of $H_3P^{32}O_4$ and $Cr(NO_3)_3$
(in a 2 1/2 per cent molecular excess). The solid was then heated
overnight to 500°C to obtain $CrPO_4$ in a form suitable for ball
milling.

Burstone,[103] using the method of Taylor et al.,[104] Gabrieli,[105]
Armbrustor et al.,[106] and Lahr et al.,[107] and on the basis of the
work of Ness and co-workers[108] precipitated hydrated chromic
phosphate-P^{32} from an aqueous solution of $Na_2HP^{32}O_4$ (obtained
from Na_2HPO_4 and carrier-free $H_3P^{32}O_4$) in a similar fashion.
The following experimental technique is essentially that described
by Ness et al.[108]

A 0.10-M $Na_2HP^{32}O_4$ solution is added dropwise to a stirred,
20 per cent excess of 0.10 $\underline{M}$ (violet) $CrCl_3$ [alternatively,
$KCr(SO_4)_2$ or $Cr(NO_3)_3$] solution until violet, crystalline
$CrP^{32}O_4 \cdot 6H_2O$ is precipitated. To reduce the acidity to pH 4 to
5, a 1.0-$\underline{M}$ solution of sodium acetate is added dropwise with
continued stirring in the ratio of 1 ml of sodium acetate to each

---

101(*) Ivanov, S. N., Pochvovedenie, 7, 44 (1955); C.A., 50,
6871 (1956).

102 Morton, M. E., Nucleonics, 10, (11), 92 (1952).

103 Burstone, M. S., J. Am. Dental Assoc., 42, 418 (1951).

104 Taylor, R. M., and Saenz, A. C., J. Immunol., 63,
319 (1949).

105 Gabrieli, E. R., Acta Physiol. Scand., 23, 283 (1951).

106 Armbrustor, E. H., and Ridenour, G. M., Soap Chem.
Specialties, 31 (7), 47 (1955).

107 Lahr, T. N., Olsen, R., Gleason, G. I., and Tabern,
D. L., J. Lab. Clin. Med., 45, 66 (1955).

108 Ness, A. T., Smith, R. E., and Evans, R. L., J. Am.
Chem. Soc., 74, 4685 (1952).

10 ml of the reaction mixture. The bluish-green precipitate is
allowed to stand for at least 2 hours. After filtration or centrifugation the precipitate is washed thoroughly with water and ethanol
and finally air dried. The yield of the $CrP^{32}O_4 \cdot 6H_2O$ should
be quantitative.

After drying at 100°C for 1 hour to give a green material, the
compound is completely dehydrated to black anhydrous $CrP^{32}O_4$
by gradually heating it to 800°C and maintaining this temperature
for 1 hour. The product is leached with water for 2 hours and
dried at 60°C.

For biological studies, it is recommended that the compound be
ignited at 500°C for 3 to 4 hours to yield a relatively soft, black,
inert, and insoluble product, which can be reduced satisfactorily to
colloidal dimensions by ball milling (for several hours to days) with
rust resistant, polished chrome-steel balls.

B. Notes

Too large an amount of sodium acetate for complete precipitation
is to be avoided in order to prevent the irreversible formation of
green $Cr(OH)_3$ or basic salts. Ness et al. [108] also pointed out that
heating in air at 300 to 800°C resulted in appreciable decomposition, with oxidation, to form chromium trioxide; no such oxidation
occurred upon heating in vacuo or in a nitrogen atmosphere.

Ball milling of the anhydrous material is more efficient if a
little water is added. [102,106] Carboxymethyl cellulose (50 mg per
100 ml) serves as an excellent colloid stabilizer. [106]

37. FERRIC ORTHOPHOSPHATE

A. Procedure

$$Fe^{+3} + P^*O_4^{-3} \longrightarrow FeP^*O_4 \qquad\qquad [50]$$

Gardiner et al. [78] prepared $FeP^{32}O_4$ starting with 20 ml of a
phosphoric-P^{32} acid solution (31.92 g per liter) diluted to 100 ml.
This solution was added slowly with vigorous stirring to about 50
ml of ferric acetate solution in acetic acid (8.25 g of iron and 120
ml of acetic acid per liter). After adding 5 g solid ammonium
acetate, the mixture was boiled for 5 minutes. The precipitate
of $FeP^{32}O_4$ was then centrifuged, washed with alcohol and ether,
dried at 120°C, powdered, and finally transferred to a quartz tube,
and heated for 90 minutes to red heat.

Ivanov[101] precipitated (amorphous) $FeP^{32}O_4$ by mixing 0.1 N
$KH_2P^{32}O_4$ with the corresponding concentration of ferric sulfate.
The precipitate was kept on a water bath at 60 to 70°C for 21(?)
days, filtered, washed with acetone, and dried at 60°C.

38. ZIRCONYLPHOSPHATE (COLLOID)

A. Procedure

$$K_2HP^*O_4 + ZrOCl_2 \longrightarrow Zr(OH)P^*O_4 + 2KCl \qquad [51]$$

Mayer et al.[109] prepared $Zr(OH)P^{32}O_4$ in a precipitated colloidal form (particle size, 50 mμ diameter) by neutralizing with 0.2 $\underline{M}$ NaOH, an aqueous mixture of 2.7 ml of 0.1096 $\underline{M}$ K_2HPO_4, $\overline{3}$ ml of 0.1096 $\underline{M}$ $ZrOCl_2$, and carrier-free P^{32} as orthophosphate. After adjustment to isotonicity and sterilization in an autoclave, the supernatant was drawn off and used in further investigations.

A stable colloidal form of $Zr(OH)P^{32}O_4$ (particle size, 25 mμ diameter) was also obtained by adding a fourfold excess of 0.22 $\underline{M}$ zirconyl nitrate to a 0.05-$\underline{M}$ K_2HPO_4 solution containing P^{32}.

B. Note

The influence of excess zirconyl reagent and the presence of other ions on the precipitation is described in great detail by Bailey et al.[110] to which the reader is referred.

39. MONOCALCIUM ORTHOPHOSPHATE MONOHYDRATE

A. Procedure

$$Ca(H_2PO_4)_2 + H_3P^*O_4 + H_2O \rightleftharpoons$$
$$Ca(H_2P^*O_4)_2 \cdot H_2O + H_3PO_4 \qquad [52]$$

Dion et al.[84] prepared $Ca(H_2P^{32}O_4)_2 \cdot H_2O$ by dissolving monocalcium orthophosphate and carrier-free $H_3P^{32}O_4$ in water and recovering the material by evaporation at less than 45°C. Crystal growth was controlled to some extent by the frequency of stirring during evaporation.

40. DICALCIUM ORTHOPHOSPHATE DIHYDRATE

A. Procedure

$$CaHPO_4 + H_3P^*O_4 + 2H_2O \rightleftharpoons CaHP^*O_4 \cdot 2H_2O + H_3PO_4 \quad [53]$$

---

[109] Mayer, S. W., and Morton, M. E., Nucleonics, **13** (11), 98 (1955).

[110] Bailey, P. H., and Broadbank, R. W. C., Analyst, **83**, 675 (1958).

Dion et al.[84] have prepared $CaHP^{32}O_4 \cdot 2H_2O$ based on a procedure suggested by Larson.[111]

Carrier-free $H_3P^{32}O_4$ was added to a solution of anhydrous commercial dicalcium orthophosphate in 25 per cent aqueous acetic acid at 50°C. The filtered solution was evaporated at 25 to 33°C by exposing to a stream of dry air. The salt, which collected on the side of the beaker, was pushed down into the solution. A pure preparation was obtained when about 75 per cent of the added salt had crystallized. The crystalline mass was filtered, washed by decantation with absolute alcohol, and finally with ether. The crystals were dried at room temperature.

B. Procedure 2

$$KH_2P^*O_4 + KOH + CaCl_2 \longrightarrow$$

$$CaHP^*O_4 \cdot 2H_2O + 2KCl + H_2O \qquad [54]$$

According to Witten et al.,[70] $CaHP^{32}O_4 \cdot 2H_2O$ is precipitated by adding, with stirring, a mixture of 1 g of labeled potassium dihydrogen orthophosphate and 0.412 g of KOH dissolved in 3.5 ml of water to 2.2 g of calcium chloride in 7 ml of water. The precipitate was centrifuged and washed three times with a small amount of water to remove both the potassium chloride formed, as well as the excess of calcium chloride. The crude product contained some tricalcium orthophosphate-P^{32}.

41. TRICALCIUM ORTHOPHOSPHATE

A. Procedure

$$3Ca^{+2} + 2P^*O_4^{-3} \longrightarrow Ca_3(P^*O_4)_2 \qquad [55]$$

Crystalline $Ca_3(P^{32}O_4)_2$ was prepared by Ivanov[101] by mixing 0.1 N $KH_2P^{32}O_4$ with 0.1 N calcium nitrate in the presence of NH_3. The precipitate was kept on a water bath for 5 days at a temperature of 60 to 70°C, filtered, washed with acetone, and dried at 60°C.

B. Discussion

Precipitated "tricalcium orthophosphate" is actually a type of hydroxyapatite compound for which the Ca/P mole ratio ranges near a value of 3:2.[112] Larson[111] recommends maintaining a

[111] Larson, H. W. E., Anal. Chem., 7, 401 (1935).
[112] Ref. 88, p. 511.

pH of 7 to 8 during the precipitation.

42. CALCIUM PYROPHOSPHATE

A. Procedure

$$2CaHP^*O_4 \cdot 2H_2O \longrightarrow Ca_2P_2^*O_7 + 5H_2O \qquad [56]$$

Witten et al.[70] converted $CaHP^{32}O_4 \cdot 2H_2O$ [53, 54] to $Ca_2P_2^{32}O_7$ by heating at 500°C for 3 hours in an electric furnace.

43. CALCIUM METAPHOSPHATE GLASS

A. Procedure

$$Ca_3(P_3O_9)_2 \xrightarrow{KH_2P^*O_4} Ca_3(P_3^*O_9)_2 \qquad [57a]$$

$$3Ca(H_2P^*O_4)_2 \cdot H_2O \longrightarrow Ca_3(P_3^*O_9)_2 + 9H_2O \qquad [57b]$$

Hill et al.[113] prepared a labeled glass with the over-all composition $Ca_3(P_3O_9)_2$ by melting calcium metaphosphate in the presence of a very small amount of $KH_2P^{32}O_4$ of high specific activity at 1100°C [57a]. The melt was then rapidly cooled by pouring onto a cooling tray. Reaction [57b] is basically no different from reaction [57a] but is less attractive as a consequence of the necessary but troublesome dehydration of the active starting material, $Ca(H_2P^{32}O_4)_2 \cdot H_2O$ [52] .

44. PHOSPHATE FERTILIZERS

Because of their considerable importance in the investigation of biochemical problems related to agriculture, a brief review of procedures for labeling phosphate fertilizers with P^{32} will be given [58] .

A. Superphosphate-P^{32}

Hendricks et al.,[114] Hill and co-workers,[113] and Carlsen[115]

113 Hill, W. L., Fox, E. J., and Mullins, J. F., Ind. Eng. Chem., 41, 1328 (1949).

114 Hendricks, S. B., and Dean, L. A., Proc. Soil Sci. Soc. Amer., 12, 98 (1947).

115 Carlsen, B., Ingeniøren, 61, 233 (1952).

have prepared superphosphate-P^{32} [$Ca(H_2P^{32}O_4)_2 \cdot 2H_2O$ + $CaSO_4 \cdot H_2O$] by dissolving orthophosphate-P^{32} [53] in the dilute sulfuric acid that is added to the rock phosphate. This was followed by the normal procedures of successively stirring, curing, breaking up, drying, and grinding, which were performed in the usual manner. Special precautions to avoid air-borne phosphate dust should be observed, especially if large quantities of material are to be handled.

B. Other Phosphate-P^{32} Fertilizers

In addition to superphosphate-P^{32}, Hill et al. [113] have also prepared several other phosphate-labeled fertilizers. Ammoniated (3 per cent) superphosphate-P^{32} was obtained by treating superphosphate-P^{32} with liquid NH_3. Dicalcium orthophosphate-P^{32} was obtained by the hot neutralization of monocalcium phosphate (mixed with a small amount of $KH_2P^{32}O_4$ of high specific activity [43]) according to the reaction

$$Ca(H_2P^{32}O_4)_2 + CaCO_3 \longrightarrow 2CaHP^{32}O_4 + H_2CO_3$$

Tricalcium orthophosphate-P^{32} was made according to the reaction

$$Ca(H_2P^{32}O_4)_2 + 2CaCO_3 \longrightarrow Ca_3(P^{32}O_4)_2 + 2H_2CO_3$$

Calcium trimetaphosphate-P^{32} was obtained by heating the inactive metaphosphate in the presence of labeled KH_2PO_4 [43] at a temperature of 1100°C.

$$Ca_3(P_3O_9)_2 \xrightarrow{\quad KH_2P^{32}O_4 \quad} Ca_3(P^{32}_3O_9)_2$$

The melt was rapidly quenched to a glass by pouring on a cooling tray. (See [57a].)

45. MAGNESIUM AMMONIUM ORTHOPHOSPHATE HEXAHYDRATE

A. Procedure

$$Mg^{+2} + NH_4^+ + P^*O_4^{-3} + 6H_2O \longrightarrow MgNH_4P^*O_4 \cdot 6H_2O \qquad [59]$$

The essentially insoluble (0.52 g per liter at 20°C) salt $MgNH_4PO_4 \cdot 6H_2O$ is probably one of the most commonly prepared compounds labeled with radiophosphorus, as it is generally used for quantitative determinations of radiophosphorus. Wilson[35] was one of the first to apply the procedure in the separation of P^{32} present as orthophosphate.

The method is described in detail in most handbooks on inorganic quantitative analysis and consists essentially of the precipitation of orthophosphate($-P^{32}$) by adding to the solution a small excess of magnesia mixture (a slightly acid, aqueous solution of $MgCl_2 \cdot 6H_2O$, NH_4Cl, and HCl) followed by a large excess of concentrated ammonia.

46. MAGNESIUM PYROPHOSPHATE

A. Procedure

$$2MgNH_4P^*O_4 \cdot 6H_2O \longrightarrow Mg_2P^*_2O_7 + 2NH_3 + 13H_2O \qquad [60]$$

Ignition of $MgNH_4P^{32}O_4 \cdot 6H_2O$ [59] to constant weight, preferably in an oven, at 1000 to 1100°C yields $Mg_2P^{32}_2O_7$. This procedure is commonly used in the quantitative determination of phosphorus and is also described in most handbooks on inorganic analysis. This method was used by Elbek et al.[82] in the preparation of $Mg_3P^*_2$ and P^*H_3.

47. AMMONIUM PHOSPHOMOLYBDATE

A. Procedure

$$P^*O_4^{-3} \xrightarrow{\quad NH_4Mo_4 + HNO_3 \quad} (NH_4)_3P^*O_4 \cdot 12Mo_3 \cdot 2HNO_3 \cdot H_2O$$

$$[61]$$

Ammonium phosphomolybdate is a precipitate generally used for the quantitative separation of phosphorus as phosphate and therefore, can also be used[116] for the determination of orthophosphate-P^{32}. The ideal composition of the precipitate is $(NH_4)_3P^{32}O_4 \cdot 12Mo_3.2HNO_3.H_2O$. The method is described in detail in textbooks of inorganic analysis and consists of the precipitation of orthophosphate($-P^{32}$) from a nitric acid solution at temperatures not higher than 50°C, by the addition of a large excess of ammonium molybdate and ammonium nitrate. A dilute solution of ammonium nitrate is a suitable wash liquid.

---

[116] MacKenzie, A. J., and Dean, L. A., Anal. Chem., 20, 559 (1948).

48. PHOSPHO-HETEROPOLY COMPOUNDS

A. Procedure [62]

Spitsyn et al.[117] described a method, based on electrolysis, for synthesizing heteropoly compounds such as the phosphotungstates and phosphomolybdates. Thus trisubstituted sodium phospho-tungstate-P^{32} and phosphomolybdate-P^{32} are formed in the anode region of the electrolyzer from a mixture of the normal salt (either Na_2WO_4 or Na_2MoO_4) and $H_3P^{32}O_4$ at a pH of 2.5 to 2.0. The yield in solution is 60 to 65 per cent and, in the crystalline form, 50 to 55 per cent. The free acids are prepared at a pH of about 1. At pH 7.5 to 7.0, unsaturated heteropoly compounds with Na_2WO_4 or their double salts, are formed; at a pH of less than 2.3, phosphotungstate of the saturated series (P/W ration is 1:12) is formed.

RECOIL SYNTHESES

As has already been pointed out, information on the application of recoil processes as a practical means for labeling compounds with P^{32} is still somewhat limited. Nevertheless, the literature on recoil labeling with phosphorus is considerable, since its nature is rather fundamental from the viewpoint of hot-atom chemistry. For this reason, only the most pertinent information will be surveyed in the present discussion (see Fig. 4).

49. PHOSPHINE-P^{32}

A. Procedure 1

$$PH_3 \xrightarrow{\text{n}, \gamma} P^{32}H_3 \qquad [63]$$

Sellers et al.[118] have irradiated phosphine at about 0.5 atm pressure for 2 days in a nuclear reactor at a flux of 10^{13} n per cm^2 sec. As a result of radiation damage, 44 per cent of the gaseous PH_3 had disintegrated, quantitatively yielding H_2. The residual PH_3 appeared to be "strongly" radioactive, but no exact figure is given for the percentage of P^{32} retained as phosphine.

---

[117] Spitsyn, V. I., and Koneva, K. G., Zhur. Neorg. Khim., 1, 941, 2488 (1956); C.A., 51, 3327 (1957); C.A., 51, 12722 (1957).
[118] Sellers, P. A., Sato, R. T., and Strain, H. H., J. Inorg. & Nuclear Chem., 5, 31 (1957).

$$PH_3 \xrightarrow{\quad (n,\gamma) \quad}_{63}$$

$$Ca_3P_2 \xrightarrow{\quad (n,\gamma) \quad}_{64}$$

$$KCl \xrightarrow{\quad (n,a) \quad}_{65}$$

$$CaS \xrightarrow{\quad (n,p) \quad}_{66}$$

$$P^{32}H_3$$

$$PCl_3 \xrightarrow{\quad (n,\gamma) \quad}_{67} P^{32}Cl_3$$

$$POCl_3 \xrightarrow{\quad (n,\gamma) \quad}_{68} P^{32}OCl_3$$

$$Cu\text{-}P \xrightarrow{\quad (d,p) \quad}_{69} P^{32}I$$

$$\text{Phosphates} \xrightarrow{\quad (n,\gamma) \quad}_{70} \text{corresponding phosphate-}P^{32}$$

Fig. 4 Diagram for recoil syntheses.

B. Procedure 2

$$Ca_3P_2 \xrightarrow{\quad (n,\gamma) \quad} P^{32}H_3 \qquad [64]$$

Elen et al.[119] have irradiated calcium phosphide in a nuclear reactor. In a closed, all-glass system, the irradiated material was treated with dilute hydrochloric acid. The $P^{32}H_3$ formed on hydrolysis was collected in a gas buret.

---

119 Elen, J. D., and van Gelder, L. J., Reactor Institute, Delft, The Netherlands, private communication.

C. Procedure 3

$$KCl \xrightarrow{(n,\alpha)} P^{32}H_3 \qquad\qquad [65]$$

Carlson et al. [120] have demonstrated that the yield of P^{32} in the -3 oxidation state, produced in KCl with fast neutrons by the reaction $Cl^{35}(n,\alpha)P^{32}$, depends on the pre-irradiation treatment as well as on the irradiation conditions. Outgassing of the KCl crystals prior to irradiation and a reduction in the accompanying γ-ray flux during activation, resulted in higher yields of $P^{32}H_3$. Pile irradiations of outgassed KCl yielded only $P^{32}H_3$, whereas irradiations with the fast neutrons generated by accelarators gave only 30 to 40 per cent $P^{32}H_3$. The P^{32} was recovered from the activated KCl samples as phosphine by dissolving the irradiated crystals in oxygen-free dilute acid while sweeping with inactive phosphine.

D. Procedure 4

$$CaS \xrightarrow{(n,p)} P^{32}H_3 \qquad\qquad [66]$$

Lindner[36] has demonstrated that of the several sulfides investigated, calcium sulfide on fast-neutron irradiations yields a considerable percentage of the P^{32} formed as $P^{32}H_3$, if the irradiated material is dissolved in oxygen-free dilute hydrochloric acid.

E. Discussion

When high yields and high specific activities are desired, pile irradiation of calcium phosphide (procedure 2) is recommended. Procedures 3 and 4 both have the disadvantage of being sensitive to radiation annealing leading to oxidation of the -3 oxidation state.

50. PHOSPHORUS-TRICHLORIDE

A. Procedure

$$PCl_3 \xrightarrow{(n,\gamma)} P^{32}Cl_3 \qquad\qquad [67]$$

Hein and co-workers (Conn et al. [121] and Setser et al. [122]) have

[120] Carlson, T. A., and Koski, W. S., J. Chem. Phys., 23, 1596 (1955).

[121] Conn, R. K., and Hein, R. E., J. Am. Chem. Soc., 79, 60 (1957).

[122] Setser, D. W., Moser, H. C., and Hein, R. E., J. Am. Chem. Soc., 81, 4162 (1959).

produced $P^{32}Cl_3$ by reactor-activation of inactive doubly distilled reagent-grade phosphorus trichloride. For bombardments at fluxes on the order of 10^{11} n per cm^2 sec, the percentage of P^{32} as $P^{32}Cl_3$ increased from 60 to 90 per cent with increasing irradiation time. The increase in retention is due to annealing processes taking place during the irradiation, and the "plateau" value of about 90 per cent retention is reached within a few hours. The separation of pure $P^{32}Cl_3$ was achieved by fractional distillation at atmospheric pressure (after the addition of $POCl_3$, $PSCl_3$, and decane as holdback carriers), using a jacketed column (3 feet by 1 inch) packed with glass helices.

51. PHOSPHORYL-CHLORIDE (PHOSPHORUS-OXYCHLORIDE)

A. Procedure

$$POCl_3 \xrightarrow{(n, \gamma)} P^{32}OCl_3 \qquad [68]$$

Both Setser et al.[122] and Clark and Moser[123] have produced $P^{32}OCl_3$ by neutron activation of redistilled, reagent-grade phosphoryl chloride in fluxes of several times 10^{11} n per cm^2 sec. The amount of P^{32} recovered as $P^{32}OCl_3$ increased from about 30 per cent to greater than 80 per cent with increasing irradiation time. This increase in retention appeared to be mainly a result of annealing processes that convert the $P^{32}Cl_3$ initially formed to $P^{32}OCl_3$. The saturation (plateau) value of greater than 80 per cent $P^{32}OCl_3$ was reached within a 1-hour irradiation period. The separation of pure $P^{32}OCl_3$ was performed by distillation at atmospheric pressure in a jacketed column with 11.7 theoretical plates. Prior to the distillation PCl_3, $PSCl_3$, and decane were added as holdback carriers.

52. PHOSPHORUS TRIIODIDE

A. Procedure

$$Cu\text{-}P \text{ alloy} \xrightarrow{(d, p)} Cu\text{-}P^{32} \text{ alloy} \xrightarrow{I_2} P^{32}I_3 \qquad [69]$$

Baba et al.[124] bombarded a Cu-P alloy with deuterons in a cyclotron to produce, among other activities, P^{32} by a (d, p)-reaction on the phosphorus. The activated alloy was immersed in

[123] Clark, T. J., and Moser, H. C., J. Inorg. & Nuclear Chem., 17, 210 (1961).
[124] Baba, H., Nozaki, T., and Azaki, H., Bull. Chem. Soc. Japan, 32, 537 (1959).

a refluxing solution of iodine in toluene for about 2 hours. This leaching process yielded $P^{32}I_3$. The toluene solution containing the $P^{32}I_3$, however, was slightly contaminated with copper iodide.

B. Note

The Cu-P alloy can be made by heating pure copper foil and red phosphorus at 300°C in a vacuum-sealed quartz tube for about 10 hours.

53. VARIOUS PHOSPHATES-P^{32}

A. Procedure

$$\text{Phosphates} \xrightarrow{(n,\gamma)} \text{corresponding phosphate-}P^{32} \qquad [70]$$

According to Sato et al., [125, 126] the neutron irradiation of phosphoric acid, of its salts, and of its linear and cyclic condensation products produces primarily the corresponding P^{32}-labeled compounds. Not more than a trace of reduced products, such as phosphite and hypophosphite, is formed. It was reported that the relative quantities of the products did not vary with the intensity of the neutron irradiation (1 to 5×10^{13} n per cm^2 sec for 2 days and ca. 8×10^{11} n cm^2 sec for 5 days). From this observation, it was concluded that the large amount of energy liberated as a result of the neutron capture by the phosphorus atoms is dissipated without disruption of the existing chemical bonds as well as without extensive condensation. The compounds that have been investigated are: (1) orthophosphates—crystalline phosphoric acid, the mono- and diammonium salts, the mono-, di-, and trisodium and potassium salts; (2) linear polyphosphates—di- and tetrasodium pyrophosphate, pentasodium tripolyphosphate, guanidine salt of tetrapolyphosphoric acid; and (3) cyclic metaphosphates—trisodium metaphosphate, tetrasodium tetrametaphosphate. The analytical technique used in this work was primarily paper electrophoresis.

B. Discussion

Recent studies have indicated that the findings of Strain and

[125] Sato, T. R., Sellers, P. A., and Strain, H. H., J. Inorg. & Nuclear Chem., 11, 84 (1959).

[126] Sato, T. R., and Strain, H. H., Proc. I. A. E. A. Conf. on Chem. Effects of Nuclear Transformations, Prague 1960 (preprint CENT/41); published by the I. A. E. A., Vienna, 1961.

co-workers are open to some doubt. Lindner et al. [127, 128] report, in contrast to the earlier results, that the maximum probability of non-bond-rupture in crystalline phosphates is not greater than ca. 10 per cent and may well be lower. They demonstrated that combined thermal and radiation annealing during, and/or thermal annealing after, bombardment may lead to the complete conversion of several other species (at least eight, representing approximately 90 per cent of the total P^{32} activity) initially formed. Thus, only intensive neutron irradiations at high ambient temperatures, which are accompanied by high radiation-dose rates, are expected to give the results reported by Strain and co-workers. [125, 126]

[127] Lindner, L., and Harbottle, G., J. Inorg. & Nuclear Chem., 15, 386 (1960).

[128] Lindner, L., and Harbottle, G., Proc. I. A. E. A. Conf. of Chem. Effects of Nuclear Transformations, Prague, 1960 (preprint CENT/70); published by the I. A. E. A., Vienna, 1961.

7

Sulfur-35

ROLFE H. HERBER
Rutgers, The State University
New Brunswick, New Jersey

1. NUCLEAR PROPERTIES

A The nuclear properties and related characteristics of the radionuclides of sulfur are summarized[1] in Table 1. Of the four

Table 1
Radionuclides of Sulfur

Nuclide	Half–life	Decay mode	Energy, mev	Typical reactions
$_{16}S^{31}$	2. 66s	β^+	4.1	$P^{31}(p, n)$; $S^{32}(n, 2n)$; $Si^{28}(\alpha, n)$; $Si^{29}(\alpha, 2n)$
S^{35}	86. 35d	β^-	0.1674	$Cl^{35}(n, p)$; $S^{34}(n, \gamma)$; $S^{38}(n, 2n)$; $S^{34}(d, p)$
S^{37}	5. 04m	β^-	3.6 (90 %) 4.3 (10 %)	$Cl^{37}(n, p)$; $Cl^{37}(d, 2p)$
		γ	3. 09 (90 %)	
S^{38}	2. 87h	β^-	1.1 (95 %) 3.0 (5 %)	$Cl^{37}(\alpha, 3p)$; spall
		γ	1. 9 (95 %)	

radio tracers that have been characterized, only S^{35} and S^{38} have half-lives appropriate for most chemical investigations. Although S^{38} has been employed to some extent in physicochemical

---

[1] Strominger, D., Hollander, J. M., and Seaborg, G. T., Revs. Modern Phys., 30, 585 (1958).

studies,[2,3] the possible modes of production of this activity—
either by the Cl^{37} (α, 3p) or Ar^{40} (p, 3pn) reaction—require the
use of medium- to high-energy electronuclear machines, and the
application of S^{38} as a tracer nuclide in chemical problems has
been very little explored. For these reasons, the present discussion will be limited to the tracer S^{35} and its incorporation into
a variety of inorganic compounds.

2. AVAILABILITY OF S^{35}

The primary source of S^{35} in the United States is Oak Ridge
National Laboratory, operated for the U.S. Atomic Energy Commission, from which labeled sulfate, sulfide, and elementary sulfur can be purchased at prices (1961) of \$2 to \$4 per mc.[4] A
number of commercial United States firms offer S^{35}-labeled inorganic compounds, such as $KS^{35}CN$, $S^{35}OCl_2$, and H_2S^{35} at
prices of \$120 to well over \$200 per mc. The availability of
elementary S^{35} and S^{35}-labeled compounds from various foreign
suppliers is summarized in a recent publication[5] of the I.A.E.A.,
which gives price quotations for 0.05, 0.1, 0.5, and 1.0 mc
quantities.

3. DETECTION AND RADIOASSAY OF S^{35} RADIATION

Because of the "softness" of the S^{35} β^- radiation (which
corresponds[6] to a half thickness of 2.3 mg Al per cm^2 and a
range of about 35 mg Al per cm^2) special methods must be employed in the quantitative determination of this activity. However,
since the maximum beta-decay energy of S^{35} (0.1675 mev) is very
close to that of C^{14} (0.155 mev), most of the methods that have
been developed for radiocarbon assay are also applicable to S^{35}.

---

[2] Nethaway, D. R., and Caretto, A. A., Jr., Phys. Rev., 109,
504 (1958).

[3] Herber, R. H., Conference on Chemical Effects of Nuclear
Transformations, Prague, 1960, Paper No. 40, Vol. II, pp. 201-208,
I.A.E.A., Vienna.

[4] Catalogue and Price List, Oak Ridge National Laboratory,
Post Office Box X, Oak Ridge, Tenn.

[5] "International Directory of Radioisotopes," Vol. II, Compounds
of C^{14}, H^3, I^{131}, P^{32} and S^{35}, I.A.E.A. Vienna, 1959, 216 pp;
available in U.S. from National Agency for Intern. Pub., 801 Third
Ave., New York 22, N.Y.

[6] Libby, W. F., Phys. Rev., 103, 1900 (1956).

The relatively long half-life[7] (86.35 ± 0.17 days) makes the use of decay corrections unnecessary in most relative-activity measurements with this nuclide, or in experiments completed within a few days.

By far, the most common method of S^{35} radioassay is the precipitation of $BaS^{35}O_4$ and subsequent measurement of the activity of thin layers of this material with a thin-window (1 to 2 mg per cm^2) Geiger-Müller tube.[8] It is particularly in this connection that many of the techniques developed for the radioassay[9] of C^{14} can be readily adapted for work with S^{35}. Quantitative radioassay of solid samples requires the application of corrections for self-absorption within the sample. A number of self-absorption correction tabulations have appeared in the literature,[10-16] but, in practice, empirical self-absorption corrections are best determined for the particular geometry, detector, and mounting material that are to be used in the subsequent radioassay. An extensive review of self-absorption corrections, backscattering effects, the distribution of counting time, and related factors for barium sulfate has been reported in the Russian literature.[17] The backscattering of S^{35} radiation by Al, Zn, Pb, and Sb has been measured using a G. M. detector, and correction factors for this effect, as well as for source coverings and geometry, have been discussed by Hisada and Watanabe.[18]

[7] Cooper, R. D., and Cotton, E. S., Science, 129, 1360 (1959).

[8] Overman, R. T., and Clark, H. M., "Radioisotope Techniques," McGraw-Hill, New York, 1960, pp. 240-242.

[9] Calvin, M., Heidelberger, C., Reid, J. C., Tolbert, B. M., and Yankwich, P. E., "Isotopic Carbon," Wiley, New York, 1949.

[10] Aten, A. H. W., Jr., Nucleonics, 6, 68 (1950).

[11] Armstrong, W. D., and Schubert, J., Anal. Chem., 20, 270 (1948).

[12] Katz, J., Science, 131, 1886 (1960).

[13] Katz, J., and Golden, S., J. Lab. Clin. Med., 53, 658 (1959).

[14] Hendler, R. W., Science, 131, 1887 (1960).

[15] Massini, P., Science, 133, 877 (1961).

[16] Berson, S. A., and Yalow, R. S., Science, 131, 606 (1960).

[17] (*) Keirim-Markus, I. B., and L'vova, M. A., Issledovaniya v Oblasti Dozimetrii Ioniziruyush chikh Izluchenii Sbornik Statei, 1957, 3; C.A., 52, 15283 (1958).

[18] (*) Hisada, T., and Watanabe, T., Repts. Govt. Ind. Research Inst. Nagoya, 1, 127 (1952)

The radioassay of other solids labeled with S^{35}, such as benzidene sulfate[19-21] and dimethylmercapto mercury(II), [22] can usually be carried out by methods similar to those used for $BaSO_4$. The absolute counting of S^{35} in 4π geometry[23] has been discussed in considerable detail by Pate and Yaffee. [24,25] These authors have considered the corrections for gas and wall backscattering as well as the scattering due to the ultrathin (5 to 10 μg per cm^2) source mount, for soft-beta radiations. They also describe in detail a 4π counter that has a plateau in the region 1800 to 3400 volts and is suitable for S^{35} radioassay.

A method for counting S^{35}-labeled gases directly in a thin-window counting cell has been discussed by Norris. [26] This technique has the advantage that the counting characteristics of the detector (essentially a thin-window G. M. tube) are uneffected by the chemical nature of the gas sample. Wolfgang and Rowland, [27] as well as Dobbs, [28] have described gas-flow proportional detectors for radioassay of the effluent from a gas chromatography column, suitable for C^{14} work. Such systems, in which the sample gas is diluted with the helium carrier gas of the chromatographic procedure, as well as with methane, should be equally suitable for S^{35}-labeled compounds with similar volatilities. The direct radioassay of labeled gases has also been investigated. [29,30] A counter tube

19 (*) Brodskii, A. I., and Eremenko, R. K., Zhur. Obshchei Khim., 25, 1189 (1955).

20 (*) Gur'yanova, E. N., Syrkin, J. K., and Kuzina, L. S., Doklady Akad. Nauk S.S.S.R., 85, 1021 (1952); C.A., 47, 5877 (1953).

21 (*) Nazarenko, Y. P., and Fialkov, Y. A., Doklady Akad. Nauk S.S.S.R., 107, 413 (1956); C.A., 50, 15180 (1956).

22 Herber, R. H., Paper No. 37, Div. Phys. Chem., A. C. S. Meeting, New York, September, 1960; Anal. Chem., 34, 340 (1962).

23 Bay, Z., Mann, W. B., Seliger, H. H., and Wyckoff, H. O., Radiation Research, 7, 558 (1957).

24 Pate, B. D., and Yaffee, L., Can. J. Chem., 33, 1656 (1955).

25 Pate, B. D., and Yaffee, L., Can. J. Chem., 33, 610 (1955).

26 Norris, T. H., J. Am. Chem. Soc., 74, 2396 (1952).

27 Wolfgang, R., and Rowland, F. S., Anal. Chem., 30, 903 (1958).

28 Dobbs, H. E., J. Chromatog., 2, 572 (1959).

29 Alcock, C. B., Intern. J. Appl. Radiation Isotopes, 3, 135 (1958).

30 Merritt, W. F., and Hawkings, R. C., Anal. Chem., 32, 308 (1960).

with a tungsten anode and a colloidal graphite (Aquadag) cathode suitable for $S^{35}O_2$ radioassay has recently been described.[31] Sulfur dioxide in the concentration range 10 to 30 per cent is counted with an alcohol and argon mixture over a 100- to 150-volt plateau with a 2 to 3 per cent slope.

Condenser-electrometer systems useful for soft beta emitters have been reported,[32] and the sensitivity of such detectors appears not to be influenced by the presence of H_2O and oxygen in the gas mixture, a fact that is useful in many routine laboratory situations. A 4π-radiochromatogram scanner suitable for C^{14} and S^{35} has recently been described by Salomon.[33]

A number of scintillometric techniques for the radioassay of weak-beta emitters have been developed. Filter-paper radioassays not requiring sample preparation have been reported[34] for I^{131}, P^{32}, C^{14}, and Na^{22}, and should be equally suitable for work with S^{35}. Scintillometry of aqueous solutions and gases labeled with weak-beta emitters can be effected[35] by allowing the samples to flow through a plastic spiral made of a scintillation phosphor encapsulated in Dow Corning 200 silicone fluid in a container mounted on the usual photomultiplier. A similar technique, in which the whole sample container is made of a beta-scintillating material, has been reported by Greenfield.[36] The use of liquid-solution scintillator materials is especially useful[37] for the detection of weak-beta emitters, and a number of applications to S^{35}-labeled compounds have appeared in the recent literature.[38,39] The absolute radioassay of $Na_2S^{35}O_4$ using solution scintillometric techniques has recently been reported[40] and makes use of a 75 per

---

[31] (*) Korshunov, I., Amenitskaya, R. V., and Aivazov, B. V., Primenenie Mechenykh Atomova Anal. Khim., Akad. Nauk S.S.S.R., Inst. Geokhim. Anal. Khim. im. V. I. Vernadskogo, 1955, 219; C.A., 50, 3911 (1956).

[32] Fox, S., and Frank, R. B., IRE Trans. on Nuclear Science, 5, 27 (1958).

[33] Salomon, L. L., Science, 131, 415 (1960).

[34] Funt, B. L., and Hetherington, A., Science, 131, 1608 (1960).

[35] Funt, B. L., and Hetherington, A., Science, 129, 1429 (1959)

[36] Greenfield, S., Analyst, 83, 114 (1958).

[37] Price, W. J., "Nuclear Radiation Detection," McGraw-Hill, New York, 1958, Chap. 7.

[38] Radin, N., and Fried, R., Anal. Chem., 30, 1926 (1958).

[39] Helf, S., Castorina, T. C., White, R. G., and Graybush, R. J., Anal. Chem., 28, 1465 (1956).

[40] Horrocks, D. L., and Studier, M. H., Anal. Chem., 33, 615 (1961).

cent dioxane solvent for water-soluble samples.[41] A convenient method for the scintillometric radioassay of S^{35}-labeled precipitates employs[42] a suspension of the sample in a solution of 4 g per liter of PPO and 0.05 g per liter of POPOP in toluene. A drawback in this method, however, is that the precipitates tend to settle; hence an extrapolation to zero time (or periodic shaking) must be done to obtain quantitative data.

Additional techniques developed in connection with special radioanalytic problems have been reported. A low-level anti-coincidence system, by which as little as 1 μc of S^{35} can be detected, has been described by Hosain.[43] The preparation of ultra-thin sources of S^{35}, which are stable under high-vacuum conditions and can be used in beta-ray spectroscopy, has been discussed by Juillard.[44]

4. ELEMENTARY SULFUR

When target materials that are to be irradiated have been carefully prepared, elementary S^{35} can be recovered directly from the target. Ames and Willard[45] have reported the recovery of amorphous (μ) sulfur from the S^{34} (n, γ) and Cl^{35} (n, p) reaction. When the target is treated for 10 hours at 100° C, the sulfur is converted to the organic soluble (λ) form and can be recrystallized from its toluene solution. The formation of $S^{35}(0)$ in carefully outgassed KCl targets by the Cl^{35}(n, p) reaction has been discussed by Koski[46,47] in a series of studies of hot-atom phenomena. Some $S^{35}(0)$ is also formed[48,49] in neutron-irradiated PCl_3 and other chlorine-containing target materials.

A number of methods are available for the reduction of sulfur from positive oxidation states to the elementary form. Thus

[41] Davidson, J. D., and Feigelson, P., Intern. J. Appl. Radiation Isotopes, 2, 1 (1957).

[42] Hayes, F. N., Rogers, B. S., and Langham, W. H., Nucleonics, 14 (3), 48 (1956).

[43] Hosain, F., Naturwiss., 45, 107 (1958).

[44] Juillard, A., J. phys. radium, 21, 467 (1960).

[45] Ames, D. P., and Willard, J. E., J. Am. Chem. Soc., 73, 164 (1951).

[46] Koski, W. S., J. Am. Chem. Soc., 71, 4042 (1949).

[47] Koski, W. S., J. Chem. Phys., 17, 582 (1949).

[48] Conn, P. K., and Hein, R. E., J. Am. Chem. Soc., 79, 60 (1957).

[49] Gueronniere, E., and Henry, R., C.E.A. Rappt. (France) 858; U.S. Atomic Energy Comm. Nuclear Sci. Abs., 13, 16034 (1959).

$S^{35}(0)$ can be obtained[50] from $S^{35}O_2$ by reacting the latter with H_2S in the ration of 1:2, as well as when the S^{35} is originally present in the H_2S. Since no isotopic exchange between H_2S and SO_2 occurs under these conditions, any excess unreacted material can be recovered without reduction of specific activity. A similar reaction involving either CaS^{35} or $S^{35}O_2$ according to the stochiometry

$$CaS^{35} + 2SO_2 \longrightarrow CaSO_4 + S^{35} + S$$
or
$$CaS + 2S^{35}O_2 \longrightarrow CaS^{35}O_4 + S^{35} + S$$

has been reported.[51] However, in contrast to the reaction with H_2S, which proceeds rapidly (even explosively) at room temperatures, the alkaline earth sulfides require treatment at 600 to 1100° C.

The oxidation of H_2S^{35} and metal sulfides by 1 $\underline{N}$ KI saturated with I_2 leads[52] to amorphous $S^{35}(0)$, which can be converted to the soluble CS_2 form by heating in an autoclave for appropriate time intervals. The sulfides to be oxidized can be obtained from $BaS^{35}O_4$ by reduction with carbon,[53] or by thermal reduction[54] at 900° C.

5. HYDROGEN SULFIDE AND METAL SULFIDES

The extensive work of Koski[46,47] on the chemical consequences of the $Cl^{35}(n, p)$ reaction has shown that carefully outgassed and dried samples of KCl can yield up to 84 per cent of the total S^{35} activity in the -2 oxidation state. Where high-neutron fluxes are available, the irradiation of such targets is probably the simplest method of obtaining S^{35}-labeled sulfides in high specific activities. All other reported methods depend either on the reduction of radiosulfate or on the combustion of elementary sulfur.

—————
[50] van der Heijde, B. H., and Aten, A. H. W., Jr., J. Am. Chem. Soc., 75, 754 (1953).
[51] (*) Diev, N. P., Paduchev, V. V., Toporova, V. V., and Upenskii, N. F., Doklady Akad. Nauk S.S.S.R., 118, 782 (1958).
[52] Cooley, R. A., Yost, D. M., and McMillan, E., J. Am. Chem. Soc., 61, 2970 (1939).
[53] Aten, A. H. W., Jr., Kriek, E., Hovenkamp, S. G., De-Roos, A. M., and Spoon, W. A., J. Inorg. & Nuclear Chem., 2, 203 (1956).
[54] Cooley, R. A., and Yost, D. M., J. Am. Chem. Soc., 62, 2474 (1940).

The reduction of $BaS^{35}O_4$ with elementary carbon, employed by Aten et al. [53] is an adaptation of a method suggested by Wells, [55] in which 60 per cent yields are obtained at 800° C and 92 per cent yields at 1000° C for the reaction

$$BaSO_4 + 2C \longrightarrow BaS + 2CO_2$$

The sulfide so formed is then treated[44] with HCl to yield the desired H_2S. A similar reduction using "sugar" carbon (i. e., very finely divided carbon obtained by the dehydration of sugar) has been reported by Tuck. [56] The BaS^{35} so formed was treated with trichloroacetic acid to liberate H_2S, which was in turn bubbled through H_2O and dried over $CaCl_2$ and P_2O_5.

The use of carbon monoxide as a reductant for $BaS^{35}O_4$ has been reported by Eldjarn. [57] A reaction system maintained at 850 to 900° C for 20 to 30 minutes gives rise to BaS^{35} in essentially quantitative (99.5 to 100 per cent) yield.

The reduction of elementary sulfur by hydrogen to yield H_2S has been reported. [58] Essentially quantitative yields can be obtained by maintaining the reaction system at 380° C for 20 hours. In a similar procedure, $BaS^{35}O_4$ is reduced at 900 to 1000° C in an atmosphere of hydrogen to yield BaS^{35}, from which H_2S^{35} is obtained by treatment with HCl. [59] Reduction of $BaS^{35}O_4$ at 700° C has been reported by Alcock. [29]

An interesting exchange reaction between Na_2S and $S^{35}(0)$ has been reported[60] in toluene, although this solvent does not dissolve either reactant appreciably. These authors[60] also report the formation of polysulfides by the reaction

$$Na_2S^{35} + xS \rightleftharpoons Na_2S^{35}_{x+1}$$

A convenient method for the preparation of labeled bisulfide

[55] Wells, A. E., Ind. Eng. Chem., 8, 770 (1916); see also Heisig, G. B., and Holt, R., J. Am. Chem. Soc., 74, 1597 (1952).

[56] Tuck, J. L., J. Chem. Soc., 1939, 1292.

[57] Eldjarn, L., Acta Chem. Scand., 7, 343 (1953).

[58] Grigg, E. C. M., and Lauder, I., Trans. Faraday Soc., 46, 1039 (1950). The authors did not use radiotracer-labeled materials in their study.

[59] (*) Neiman, M. B., Torsueva, E. S., Fedoseeva, A. I., and Shantorovich, P. S., Doklady Akad. Nauk S.S.S.R., 86, 317 (1952); C.A., 47, 438 (1953).

[60] Koros, E., Maros, L., Feher, I., and Schulek, E., Magyar Kem. Folyóirat, 63, 213 (1957); J. Inorg. & Nuclear Chem., 4, 185 (1957).

and labeled polysulfide employs[61] ethanol suspensions of metallic sodium. $NaHS^{35}$ is recovered when the organic phase is saturated with H_2S^{35} or when the sodium suspension is saturated with inactive H_2S and then treated with elementary radiosulfur. $Na_2S_2^{35}$ is similarly obtained when an H_2S-saturated sodium alcoholate solution is treated with $S^{35}(0)$ and heated for 3 to 5 hours.

Alkali metal bisulfides have also been obtained[62] from $S^{35}O_4^{-2}$ that has been reduced with hydrogen iodide in an 85 per cent formic acid solution containing sodium hypophosphite. An 80 per cent yield of KHS^{35} by this procedure has been reported.

The transfer of radiosulfur between cuprous sulfide and FeS and Ni_3S_2 has been reported.[63] This exchange is of some preparative interest, since Ni_3S_2 and FeS can be selectively separated from the cuprous sulfide. In the case of the Cu_2S-FeS system, 82 per cent exchange was noted after 30 minutes at 1200°C. In the Cu_2S-Ni_3S_2 system, 50 to 54 per cent exchange was observed after 30 minutes at 1000°C.

Labeled thallous sulfide can be precipitated from $Tl(NO_3)$ or $Tl(O_2CCH_3)$ solutions with Na_2S^{35} over a wide pH range. $Tl_2S^{35} \cdot PbS^{35}$ can also be prepared.[64]

A series of labeled transition metal sulfides has also been prepared by Alcock[29] in connection with a study of high-temperature equilibria. Using both direct fusion of the metals with elementary sulfur in a Pyrex ampoule at elevated temperatures and aqueous sulfide precipitation techniques, he was able to prepare FeS^{35}, CoS^{35}, $Co_4S_3^{35}$, and $Co_9S_8^{35}$. The equilibrium between various metal sulfides (Fe, Co, Mn) and H_2S is also discussed with respect to the transfer of sulfur activity from one metal to another through the common H_2S reaction product.

6. SULFUR DIOXIDE AND SULFITES

A convenient synthesis of $S^{35}O_2$ has been reported by Johnson and Huston,[65] who ignited a mixture of high-specific-activity

---
61 (*) Vasiliyeva, V. N., and Gur'yanova, J. N., Zhur. Obshchei Khim. 26, (88) 677 (1956); Chem. Zentr., 128, 4942 (1957).

62 Wieland, T., and Krantz, H., Chem. Ber., 91, 681 (1958).

63 (*) Chizhikov, D. M., and Ustinskii, B. Z., Trudy Inst. Met., im. A. A. Baikova, 1957, 101; C.A., 52, 17913 (1957).

64 (*) Nanobashvili, E. E., Shelia, N. G., and Ivanitskaya, L. V., Soobshcheniya Akad. Nauk Gruzin. S.S.R., 19, 557 (1957).

65 Johnson, R. E., and Huston, J. L., J. Am. Chem. Soc., 72, 1841 (1950).

$BaS^{35}O_4$ and red phosphorus in a stream of oxygen in a reaction flask attached to a high-vacuum system. The major advantage of this procedure is the low contamination of the final product with sulfur trioxide (less than 0.1 per cent). A similar procedure, using elementary radiosulfur, has been reported by Ames and Willard,[45] who used ignition in a stream of O_2 to give $S^{35}O_2$. The product was bubbled through toluene to trap any sulfur entrained in the gas, and the final product hydrolyzed to sulfite in 3 $\underline{M}$ NaOH. A similar technique employing combustion of $S^{35}(0)$ in air has also been reported.[66,83,105]

Masters and Norris[67] have exploited the preparation of $H_2S^{35}O_4$ (reported below) in the synthesis of $S^{35}O_2$. The labeled acid is allowed to react with gaseous sulfur dioxide in a sealed tube at 350°C for 6 days. Shorter reaction times are required if the acid is exposed in the form of a thin film in the reaction tube, since the exchange is probably heterogeneous in nature. In a typical experiment reported, some 64 per cent of the S^{35} activity initially used to prepare the $H_2S^{35}O_4$ could be isolated in the SO_2 fraction.

The recovery of high-specific-activity $S^{35}O_2$ from neutron-irradiated carbon tetrachloride has recently been reported.[68] The recoiling S^{35} atom produced by the $Cl^{35}(n,p)$ reaction is presumed to form binary halogen compounds, such as S_2Cl_2, SCl_2, and possibly SCl_4, by reaction with chlorine atoms produced by radiation damage in the target. When the CCl_4 is scavenged with SO_2, the radiosulfur-labeled product is formed either by isotopic exchange or by hydrolysis of the binary halides with minute traces of moisture.[3,68] Since the vapor pressures of CCl_4 and SO_2 are very different at room temperature, the separation of the desired product from the target material is easily effected.

The synthesis of the 1:1 addition compound of triethylamine and SO_2 has been reported by Norris and Herber.[69] The lability of the SO_2 ligand in sulfur dioxide solvent can be exploited to introduce S^{35} into the compound, since the exchange

$$(CH_3CH_2)_3N \cdot SO_2 + S^{35}O_2 \rightleftharpoons (CH_3CH_2)_3N \cdot S^{35}O_2 + SO_2$$

is complete in less than 4 minutes even at -78°C. The addition of a stoichiometric quantity of water converts the oily, liquid anhydrous addition compound into the crystalline hydrate,

---

[66] Elkeles, H., Acta. Chem. Scand., 8, 1557 (1954).

[67] Masters, B. J., and Norris, T. H., J. Am. Chem. Soc., 74, 2395 (1952).

[68] Herber, R. H., J. Inorg. & Nuclear Chem., 16, 361 (1961).

[69] Herber, R. H., and Norris, T. H., J. Am. Chem. Soc., 76, 3849 (1954).

$(CH_3CH_2)_3NH \cdot S^{35}O_3H$, which can be recovered quantitatively
from the reaction system.

7. SULFUR TRIOXIDE, SULFURIC ACID, AND SULFATES

Most of the methods reported for the synthesis of S^{35}-labeled
sulfuric acid depend on isotopic exchange equilibria for the introduction of the radionuclide into the molecule directly, or into SO_3,
which is then hydrolyzed to the acid.

Huston[70] has reported the heterogeneous exchange between
liquid SO_3 and solid barium sulfate of high specific activity to
yield $S^{35}O_3$. Since the solid catalyzes the conversion of sulfur
trioxide to the high-melting beta form, the solid SO_3 so formed
must be warmed, distilled off, and returned to the reaction system, since the solid-solid exchange is extremely slow. Some 28.5
per cent exchange between $SO_3(\ell)$ and $BaS^{35}O_4(s)$ has been reported in 3 days. The exchange is most conveniently carried out
at 60° C.

The preparation of carrier-free $H_2S^{35}O_4$ has been reported by
French investigators.[49] In their method, neutron-irradiated KCl
targets are dissolved in water, and the resultant solution passed
through Dowex-50(H). The eluate is evaporated to reduce the volume and then heated almost to dryness with hydrogen peroxide to
yield an aqueous solution of the labeled acid at a pH of approximately 1. The ion-exchange step serves to remove extraneous
radioactive cation, whereas the major anionic radiochemical
contaminant (Cl^{36}) is driven off in the evaporation procedure. No
specific decontamination step from P^{32} is reported.

The preparation of 97 per cent sulfuric acid labeled with S^{35}
exploits the small but significant solubility of $BaSO_4(s)$ in the concentrated acid. In the reported procedure,[67, 71] 91 mg of
$BaS^{35}O_4$ was dissolved in 5 ml of 96 per cent H_2SO_4 to give a
clear solution, from which the barium salt was again precipitated
on the addition of 5 ml H_2O. After centrifugation, the supernate
was decanted off and the acid reconcentrated by the addition of
fuming H_2SO_4. Although considerable isotopic dilution occurs
during this procedure, the use of high-specific-activity barium
sulfate yields a final acid of sufficiently high activity to be suitable
for further tracer applications. As has been noted above, the
$H_2S^{35}O_4$ so obtained[62] can be used as an intermediate in the preparation of $S^{35}O_2$.

The treatment of fuming sulfuric acid with SO_3 to give pyro-
sulfuric acid as an intermediate in the synthesis of organic
sulfuric acids labeled with S^{35} has also been reported.[72]

[70] Huston, J. L., J. Am. Chem. Soc., 73, 3049 (1951).

[71] Norris, T. H., J. Am. Chem. Soc., 72, 1220 (1950).

[72] (*) Vainshtein, F. M., and Shilov, E. A., Zhur. Obshchei
n., 28, 782 (1958).

The isotopic-sulfur exchange between $K_2S^{35}O_4$ and SO_3 has been observed[73, 74] as a consequence of radiation damage in the solid, owing to the S^{35} beta decay. With a 10-minute contact time at $840 \pm 5°$ C, a K_2SO_4 sample having a specific activity of 20 to 30 μc per g gave about 12 per cent exchange, whereas a specific activity of 2 mc per g gave approximately 67 per cent exchange. At higher specific activities (up to 16.2 mc per g), the extent of exchange decreased somewhat. Blank runs with $K_2S^{35}O_4$ (of high specific activity) alone showed no decomposition or loss in weight under the conditions of the exchange. Activity calculations suggest that as many as 10^{14} exchanges took place per beta decay. A similar study of the formation of $S^{35}O_2$ in a radiation field has employed betatron radiations as a method of bringing about exchange between $K_2S^{35}O_4$ and SO_3.[75] Dosage rates of up to 10^{15} ev in 10 minutes do not influence the exchange rate observed from β^- decay; dosage rates of 10^{16} to 10^{17} ev in 10 minutes give a logarithmic dependence on the dosage rate.

The use of such techniques for radiosynthetic purposes on a routine basis must await a more definitive study of radiation-produced exchange phenomena and the factors that govern the optimal recovery of the desired product.

The exchange of radiosulfur between $S^{35}O_3$ and several alkali metal sulfates appears to proceed through an $M_2S_2O_7$ intermediate.[76] Thermal decomposition of the intermediate at 800° C for 90 to 120 minutes suggests that, only in the case of the lithium salt, has complete exchange taken place. However, significant extents of exchange for the Na, K, Rb, and Cs sulfates are also observed.

$Ag_2S^{35}O_4$ has been obtained by King and Levy,[77] presumably by the reaction between silver nitrate and labeled sulfuric acid.

Although Cr(III) aquo complexes do not react at appreciable rates with sulfate ions at room temperature, the reactions

$$Cr(H_2O)_6^{+3} + S^{35}O_4^{-2} \rightleftharpoons Cr(H_2O)_4S^{35}O_4 + 2H_2O$$

and

$$Cr(H_2O)_6^{+3} + 2S^{35}O_4^{-2} \rightleftharpoons Cr(H_2O)_2(S^{35}O_4)_2^- + 4H_2O$$

[73] Spitsyn, V. I., Doklady Akad. Nauk S.S.S.R., 7, 1296 (1958).

[74] Mikhailenko, I. E., and Spitsyn, V. I., Doklady Akad. Nauk S.S.S.R., 131, 129 (1960).

[75] (*) Spitsyn, V. I., Mikhailenko, I. E., Vereshinskii, I. V., and Glazunov, P. J., Doklady Akad. Nauk S.S.S.R., 131, 360 (1960); U.S. Atomic Energy Comm. Nucl. Sci. Abs., 14, 16667 (1960).

[76] (*) Spitsyn, V. I., and Mikhailenko, I. E., Zhur. Neorg. Khim., 3, 526 (1958); C.A., 52, 19361 (1958).

[77] King, C. V., and Levy, B., J. Phys. Chem., 60, 374 (1956).

can be observed[78] when the solution is briefly heated to the boiling point.

A chromatographic separation of $S^{35}O_4^{-2}$ from P^{32}-labeled phosphate has been reported by Deshpande.[79] Neutron-irradiated KCl is dissolved in water to give an 0.1-$\underline{M}$ solution, to which is added 5 mg of phosphate carrier. The sample is placed onto an Amberlite IRA-400 (40 to 60 mesh) column in the chloride form. The column is washed with water and then with 0.1 $\underline{M}$ HCl. The sulfate fraction is found to have about 5.5 times the retention of the phosphate fraction, and hence a clean radiochemical separation can be obtained by chromatographic means.

The preparation of metal sulfates and their hydrates from aqueous solutions containing $S^{35}O_4^{-2}$ usually follows in a straight-forward matter. $CaS^{35}O_4 \cdot 2H_2O$ has been prepared from the analogous carbonate solution,[80] and $PbS^{35}O_4$ by the electrolysis of aqueous sodium sulfate with lead electrodes.[81]

8. THIOSULFATE, POLYTHIONATES, AND RELATED ANIONS

Because of the nonequivalence of the two sulfur atoms of the thiosulfate ion, a number of studies have been made of the formation and decomposition of this ion using radiotracer techniques. The earliest reference to S^{35}-labeled thiosulfates is by Anderson,[82] who prepared $S^{35}SO_3^{-2}$ by the reaction of elementary sulfur labeled with S^{35} and sulfite ion. That this procedure introduces the tracer only into the S(0) position was shown by subsequent decomposition of the thiosulfate with HCl, followed by separate radioassay of the two sulfur fractions, or by analogous formation of $Ag_2S^{35}SO_3$, which was decomposed to Ag_2S^{35} and H_2SO_4.

Voge and Libby[83] and Voge[84] showed that S^{35}-labeled thiosulfate could be prepared by exploiting the isotopic exchange

$$H_2S^{35} + S_2O_3^{-2} \rightleftharpoons H_2S + S^{35}SO_3^{-2}$$

[78] Kertes, S., and Lederer, M., Anal. Chem. Acta, 16, 40 (1957).

[79] Deshpande, R. G., J. Chromatog., 2, 117 (1959).

[80] Ketelaar, J. A. A., and Heijmann, H., Rec. trav. chim., 73, 278 (1954).

[81] (*) Maeda, M., Denki Kagaku, 25, 195 (1957).

[82] Anderson, E. B., Z. Physik. Chem., 32B, 237 (1936).

[83] Voge, H. H., and Libby, W. F., J. Am. Chem. Soc., 59, 2474 (1937).

[84] Voge, H. H., J. Am. Chem. Soc., 61, 1032 (1939).

Their method consists essentially of passing hydrogen sulfide into a basic (1 $\underline{M}$ NaOH) oxygen-free solution of thiosulfate. This is sealed in a Pyrex glass tube and maintained at 100° C for 23 hours, during which time the exchange has gone to completion. Labeled thiosulfate can also be prepared by the reaction[85]

$$S_3O_6^{-2} + S^{35-} \longrightarrow S^{35}SO_3^{-2} + S_2O_3^{-2}$$

at 100° C, but the final specific activity of the product will be limited by the necessary isotopic dilution inherent in the stoichiometry.

The isotopic synthesis of $SS^{35}O_3^{2}$ can be effected[59] by the reaction between SO_2 and H_2S^{35} in basic solution. Detailed studies of the decomposition products of the thiosulfate so produced confirm the hypothesis that the "inner" sulfur atom comes from the SO_2 and the "outer" sulfur atom from both the SO_2 and H_2S.

Ames and Willard[45] have reported the synthesis of thiosulfate labeled selectively in either the S(0) or S(IV) position. Their synthesis of $S^{35}SO_3^{2}$ is essentially identical to that of Anderson,[82] followed by the extraction of excess S(0) with toluene and the removal of excess sulfite by precipitation as $SrSO_3$. The labeled thiosulfate is then precipitated as the tris-ethylenediamine nickel(II) salt. The related synthesis of $SS^{35}O_3^{2}$ can be brought about by isotopic-exchange methods, since the reaction

$$S^{35}O_3^{-2} + S_2O_3^{-2} \rightleftharpoons SS^{35}O_3^{-2} + SO_3^{-2}$$

has a conveniently rapid rate at 60 to 100° C. Essentially identical preparative methods for the two labeled thiosulfates have been reported in the Russian literature.[59]

The selective oxidation of thiosulfate and tetrathionate has been reported by van der Heijde and Aten,[86, 87] who studied the reaction

$$2SS^{35}O_3^{-2} \rightleftharpoons O_3S^{35}SSS^{35}O_3^{-2} + 2e^-$$

and found no exchange of activity between the S(0) and S(IV) atoms. They decomposed the thiosulfate by the use of mercuric chloride:

[85] Schoon, N. S., Acta Chem. Scand., 14, 2009 (1960).

[86] van der Heijde, H. B., and Aten, A. H. W., Jr. J., Am. Chem. Soc., 74, 3706 (1952).

[87] van der Heijde, H. B., Rec. trav. chim., 72, 510 (1953).

$$2SS^{35}O_3^{-2} + 3HgCl_2 + 2H_2O \longrightarrow$$

$$HgCl_2 \cdot 2HgS + 2S_3{}^{35}O_4^{-2} + 4Cl + 4H^+$$

Complementary to the above is the reported[88,89] synthesis of $S_4O_6^{-2}$ in which the two inner sulfur atoms are labeled. The reaction sequence involves the partial hydrolysis of sulfur mono-chloride

$$S^{35}SCl_2 + 2H_2O \longrightarrow S^{35}S(OH)_2 + 2HCl$$

followed by reaction of the product with inactive sulfite

$$S^{35}S(OH)_2 + 2SO_3^{-2} \longrightarrow O_3SSS^{35}SO_3^{-2} + 2OH^-$$

These authors also report the unusual double synthesis of $S^{35}SO_3^{-2}$ and $S^{35}CN^-$ by the reaction of the inner-sulfur-labeled $S_4O_6^{-2}$ prepared as above with excess cyanide ion by the reaction

$$O_3SS^{35}S^{35}SO_3^{-2} + 3CN^- + H_2O \longrightarrow$$

$$SO_4^{-2} + S^{35}SO_3^{-2} + S^{35}CN^- + HCN$$

Elkeles[66,90] has reported the use of triiodide ion at pH 5 in the oxidation of thiosulfate to tetrathionate. As noted above, the S^{35} label will be on the inner sulfur atom of the tetrathionate if its original site was the S(0) of the thiosulfate, and on the outer sulfur atom if its original site was the S(IV) of the thiosulfate.

The reaction between labeled sulfite and inactive persulfate has been used[91] to prepare S^{35}-labeled dithionate ion in which the radiotracer is largely in the S(IV) position; i. e.,

$$S^{35}O_3^{-2} + S_2O_8^{-2} \longrightarrow SO_4S^{35}O_3^{-2} + SO_4^{-2}$$

[88] Brodskii, A. I., and Eremenko, R. K., Zhur. Obshchei Khim., 25, 1189 (1955); discussed in Ref. 89, pp. 841-842.

[89] Stranks, D. R., and Wilkins, R. G., Chem. Revs., 57, 743 (1957).

[90] Elkeles, H. Acta Chem. Scand., 7, 1012 (1953).

[91] Aten, A. H. W., Jr., Louwrier, K. P., Coppens, P., Kok, H. A., De Roos, A. M., Kriek, E., Hillege, A., Vollbracht, L., and Hartog, F., J. Inorg. & Nuclear Chem., 3, 296 (1956).

Reaction of labeled sulfite with pyrosulfate results in 48 to 51 per cent of the activity incorporated in the $S_2O_6^{-2}$ ion

$$S^{35}O_3^{-2} + S_2O_7^{-2} \longrightarrow O_3SS^{35}O_3^{-2} + SO_4^{-2}$$

The formation of labeled $S_5O_6^{-2}$ and $S_3O_6^{-2}$ has been described by Brodski and Jeremenko[92,93] using labeled thiosulfate as the source of the tracer atom. In the presence of trivalent arsenic (either as As_2O_3 or Na_3AsO_3), the reaction

$$3Na_2S^{35}SO_3 + As(III) \longrightarrow$$

$$S^{35}(S^{35}SO_3)_2^{-2} + 6Na^+ + S^{35}O_3^{-2} + As(V)$$

can be observed[84] in acid solution with 75 per cent of the sulfur activity incorporated in the pentasulfur ion. A similar reaction is observed[93] when a solution of $S^{35}SO_3^{-2}$, to which a small amount of arsenous oxide has been added, is saturated with SO_2. The precipitate of sodium tetrathionate that forms is filtered off and the solution treated with potassium acetate. The $K_2S_3O_6$ recovered accounts for 25 per cent of the total activity and is specifically labeled in the central sulfur atom. The same product is obtained by the treatment of $S^{35}SO_3^{-2}$ with 30 per cent H_2O_2 and removal of sulfate as the barium salt, and this method (in which 50 per cent of the S^{35} activity is found in the product) is probably the most convenient synthetic route to $O_3S^{35}SSO_3^{-2}$.

An isotopic-exchange method (complementary to the foregoing)[93] to effect the synthesis of $O_3S^{35}SSO_3^{-2}$ was suggested at about the same time by Fava and Pajaro,[94] who carried out the reaction between $S^{35}O_3^{-2}$ and $S_3O_6^{-2}$ in concentrated alkali nitrate solutions over the pH range 5.7 to 10 at 25 to 50° C. Under these conditions, the isotopic exchange is conveniently rapid for isotopic synthetic purposes.

9. THIONYL AND SULFURYL HALIDES

The synthesis of $S^{35}OCl_2$ from labeled sulfur dioxide and

[92] Brodski, A. I., and Jeremenko, R. K., Doklady Acad. Nauk S.S.S.R., 101, 487 (1955); Chem. Zentr., 127, 2681 (1956).

[93] Brodski, A. I., and Jeremenko, R. K., Doklady Akad. Nauk S.S.S.R., 95, 539 (1954); Chem. Zentr., 126, 4542 (1955).

[94] Fava, A., and Pajaro, G., Ann. Chim. (Rome), 44, 545 (1954); Ricerca sci., 24, 1905 (1954).

phosphorus pentachloride has been reported by several research groups.[95],[96] The usual procedure is to allow the SO_2 to react with a tenfold excess of PCl_5 for 2 hours at room temperature. After the addition of inactive carrier $SOCl_2$, the two volatile components can be separated by vacuum fractionation. The reaction appears to be free of contaminating side reactions.

A somewhat more convenient method for the preparation of $S^{35}OCl_2$ exploits the isotopic exchange with sulfur dioxide. Although the uncatalyzed exchange is very slow,[95] the reaction proceeds rapidly enough in the presence of homogeneous catalysts, such as $(CH_3)_4NCl$ and $RbCl$, to be of general utility.[97] The catalysis of the $S^{35}O_2$-$SOCl_2$ exchange by $SbCl_3$ has also been reported,[98] but exchange rates appear to be about 10^{-2} as rapid as in the case of basic catalysis. The suggested mechanism involves the formation of an antimony pentachloride addition product, which then exchanges slowly (but more rapidly than in the uncatalyzed system) with SO_2.

Radiosulfur-labeled thionyl bromide is prepared[99] by analogous isotopic exchange between $S^{35}O_2$ and $SOBr_2$, using $(CH_3)_4NBr$ or KBr as a catalyst. Complete exchange in 24 hours at 25° C can be attained using millimolar amounts of $SOBr_2$ in an excess of SO_2.

Radiosulfur exchange between $SOCl_2$ and $SOBr_2$ occurs rapidly in SO_2 solutions with a half-time of less than 2 minutes,[100] even at -50° C, as well as between the two pure compounds ($t_{1/2} \sim 80$ minutes at -50°C), but little use can be made of these observations for radiosynthetic purposes.

The isotopic-exchange synthesis of sulfuryl chloride has been described by Bruno and Fiorani,[101] using $Ag_2S^{35}O_4$ as the source of the radiosulfur. SO_2Cl_2 and Ag_2SO_4 are maintained at 200 to 300° C for 18 hours. At the end of this time, the volatiles are passed through a column that retains SO_3 but allows SO_2Cl_2 to pass. The suggested mechanism for this exchange involves the

[95] Johnson, R. E., Norris, T. H., and Huston, J. L., J. Am. Chem. Soc., 73, 3052 (1951).

[96] Becke-Goehring, M., and Heincke, J., Z. anorg. u. allgem. Chem., 278, 53 (1955).

[97] Masters, B. J., and Norris, T. H., J. Am. Chem. Soc., 77, 1346 (1955).

[98] Burge, D. E., and Norris, T. H., J. Am. Chem. Soc., 81, 2324 (1959).

[99] Herber, R. H., Norris, T. H., and Huston, J. L., J. Am. Chem. Soc., 76, 2015 (1954).

[100] Johnson, L. F., Jr., and Norris, T. H., J. Am. Chem. Soc., 79, 1584 (1957).

[101] Bruno, M., and Fiorani, M., Ricerca sci., 28, 749 (1958).

equilibrium

$$SO_2^{+2} + S^{35}O_4^{-2} \rightleftharpoons \left[SS^{35}O_6\right] \rightleftharpoons S^{35}O_2^+ + SO_4^{-2}$$

so that the trioxide contaminant must be removed from the reaction product.

10. CARBON DISULFIDE

Radiosulfur-labeled CS_2 can be obtained from direct-recoil synthesis[102] when a carbon tetrachloride solution of the disulfide is exposed to a thermal-neutron flux. CS_2^{35} has also been obtained[102] from a neutron-irradiated solution of C_2Cl_6 in CS_2 with about 12 per cent of the total radiosulfur that is produced by the $Cl^{35}(n,p)$ reaction stabilized in the carbon disulfide. These authors also report the exchange between radiosulfide and CS_2 to have a half-time of 40 minutes. This observation is at variance, however, with results of a similar study,[103] which showed that less than 1 per cent exchange between CS_2 and H_2S had occurred in a benzene solution after 95 hours at 120° C.

The formation of CS_2^{35} from polysulfides appears to be a useful synthetic method[104] when high specific acitvities are not needed. Sodium sulfide monohydrate and elementary sulfur labeled with S^{35} in ethanol are maintained overnight under an atmosphere of nitrogen. The resulting solution is treated with CS_2, and the Na_2CS_3 that forms is decomposed with HCl. About one-third of the activity is found in the H_2S that is evolved, and about two-thirds remain in the carbon disulfide.

The heterogeneous exchange between CS_2 and H_2S in an atmosphere of nitrogen is slow, giving 5 to 6 per cent exchange after 3 hours at 400° C. In the presence of an iron-chromium catalyst, however, this exchange proceeds at a sufficiently rapid rate[105] to be convenient for the synthesis of CS_2^{35}.

S^{35}-labeled H_2S is also employed as the starting material in the recovery of CS_2^{35} from the decomposition of the product formed with phenylisocyanate. The activity balance, which has

102 Edwards, R. R., Nesbett, F. B., and Solomon, A. K., J. Am. Chem. Soc., 70, 1670 (1948).
103 Douglas, D. L., Cooley, R. A., and Yost, D. M., J. Am. Chem. Soc., 71, 3237 (1949).
104 (*) Vasil'eva, V. N., and Gur'yanova, E. N., Zhur. Obshchei Khim., 26, 677 (1956); C.A., 50, 14615 (1956).
105 (*) Ivanovskii, F. P., Kal'varskava, R. S., Beskova, G. S., and Sokolava, N. P., Zhur. Fiz. Khim., 30, 2358 (1956); C.A., 51, 9275 (1957).

been observed, is consistent[106] with the mechanism

$$2\phi NCS + H_2S^{\overline{35}} \longrightarrow \begin{matrix} \phi NC \\[-2pt] \phi NC \end{matrix} \!\! \begin{matrix} S \\[-2pt] \diagdown \\[-2pt] S^{35} \\[-2pt] \diagup \\[-2pt] S \end{matrix} \longrightarrow \begin{matrix} \phi N \\[-2pt] \phi N \end{matrix} \!\! C\!=\!S + CSS^{35}$$

The recovery of radiosulfur-labeled CS_2 from CCl_4 and labeled P_2S_5 maintained for 7 hours at 300 to 315° C in a sealed tube has been reported in the Russian literature.[107]

11. MISCELLANEOUS SULFUR COMPOUNDS

A. Thiocyanates

$KCNS^{35}$ can be obtained[108] when K_2S^{35}, KCN, and elementary sulfur are digested for several hours. The product appears to be contaminated with about 5 per cent thiosulfate. A similar procedure involves the addition of boric acid and KCN to a solution of $Na_2S_x{}^{35}$ at a pH of 7.5. After 1 hour at reflux temperature, the solution is made slightly acid, H_2S is allowed to escape, and $S^{35}CN^-$ can be recovered from the solution.

Eldjarn[57] has suggested a method based on an earlier paper by Gutman[109] in which K_2S^{35} is allowed to react with cyanogen bromide

$$K_2S^{35} + BrCN \longrightarrow KS^{35}CN + KBr$$

to form the labeled thiocyanate. The procedure, which has been adapted to the 30- to 40-mg scale, gives the product in high (~86 per cent) yield.

$KS^{35}CN$ can also be obtained[110] from elementary radiosulfur. The latter is dissolved in xylene by gentle heating and then added

[106] Wieland, T., Merz, H., and Rennecke, A., Ber., 91, 683 (1958).

[107] (*) Markova, Y. W., Posharskaya, A. M., Maimind, W. I., Schukova, T. F., Kossolopova, N. A., and Schtschukina, M. N., Doklady Akad. Nauk S.S.S.R., 91, 1129 (1953); Chem. Zentr., 126, 9065 (1955).

[108] Heisig, G. B., and Holt, R., J. Am. Chem. Soc., 74, 1597 (1952).

[109] Gutman, A., Ber., 42, 3628 (1909).

[110] Tabern, D. L., Gleason, G., and Dunnigan, D., cited in a review by Crompton, C. E., and Woodruff, N. H., Nucleonics, 7, (4) 44 (1950).

to an acetone solution of inactive elementary sulfur and potassium cyanate. The solution is refluxed for 2 hours, filtered, and the acetone is removed by evaporation. After appropriate washing of the precipitate and removal of H_2S and HCN, the thiocyanate can be recovered in approximately 49 per cent yield.

The absence of exchange between KSCN and sulfide[60, 108, 111] and thiosulfate[60] has repeatedly been verified and the direct-exchange synthesis for the preparation of $KS^{35}CN$ is thus not feasible.

B. Sulfur-Nitrogen Compounds

Much of the study reported on sulfur nitrogen compounds has come from the work of Frau Becke-Goehring and her co-workers. Their work has shown that labeled $S_3N_2O_2$ can be obtained[112] from labeled thionyl chloride by the reaction

$$S_4N_4 + 2S^{35}OCl_2 \longrightarrow S_3^{35}N_2O_2 + S_2N_2 + 2Cl_2 + S$$

When the product so formed is decomposed by treatment with moist nitrogen, the radiosulfur appears only in the SO_2 product

$$2S_3^{35}N_2O_2 \xrightarrow[\text{(H}_2\text{O)}]{\text{N}_2} S_4N_4 + 2S^{35}O_2$$

and consequently, this procedure cannot be used to prepare the labeled tetranitride.

The reaction between S_4N_4 and $S^{35}O_3$ to yield $S_3N_2O_5$ gives a product[113] in which the two S(VI) atoms carry the label. The reaction is carried out by allowing liquid SO_3 to drop onto the tetranitride, which is cooled with ice water. The product is subsequently sublimed off at 60° C. The reaction between $S_3N_2O_2$ and $S^{35}O_3$ results only in the transfer of oxygen (in consonance with a similar mechanism proposed by Huston[114]), and the $S_3N_2O_5$ formed is not labeled.

Tetrasulfur tetranitride and thionyl chloride react in the presence of SO_2 to yield[96] $S_3N_2O_3$. When the sulfur dioxide is labeled with S^{35}, no activity appears in the product. When the $SOCl_2$ is

[111] Adamson, A. W., and Magee, P. S., J. Am. Chem. Soc., 74, 1590 (1952).

[112] Becke-Goehring, M., in F. A. Cotten (ed.) "Progress in Inorganic Chemistry," Interscience, New York, 1959, Vol. I., p. 219.

[113] Becke-Goehring, M., Hohenschutz, H., and Ebert, J., Z. anorg. u. allgem. Chem., 276, 47 (1954).

[114] Huston, J. L., J. Am. Chem. Soc., 72, 3049 (1951).

labeled, however, it can be shown that one of the three sulfur atoms in $S_3N_2O_3$ comes from the thionyl chloride, and the resultant product will be proportionately labeled. Sulfur-labeled S_4N_2 can be obtained[112] from labeled carbon disulfide by the reaction

$$S_4N_4 + CS_2^{32} \longrightarrow S_4^{35}N_2 + (CNS)_x$$

for which a detailed activity balance indicates that 30 to 35 per cent of the sulfur in S_4N_2 comes from the disulfide and the remainder from the tetrasulfide. A detailed discussion of the structure and reactions of S_4N_4 has been published. [115]

The complex reaction between $S^{35}O_3$ and NH_3 has been reported[116] to give a wide variety of labeled products. When the trioxide (carried in a stream of dry nitrogen) is passed into a 25 per cent aqueous ammonia solution, among the reaction products which have been isolated are $H_2NS^{35}O_3H$, $HN(S^{35}O_3)_2^{-2}$, and $N(S^{35}O_3)_3^{-2}$.

C. Miscellaneous Compounds.

The formation of a variety of polysulfoxides by the reaction

$$H_2S^{35} + SO_2(\text{excess}) \longrightarrow S_{8-16}^{35}O_2$$

has been reported. [117] A detailed activity balance shows that about 60 per cent of the sulfur in the product is derived from H_2S, even though the SO_2 is present in large excess, and that the polysulfoxides will thus be proportionately labeled with the tracer.

Radiosulfur-labeled sulfur sesquioxide has been prepared by Appel[118] by the reaction of liquid SO_3 with elementary radiosulfur. When the product is allowed to react with dioxane, the dioxane·SO_3 addition product is inactive in consonance with the Lewis acid-base mechanism, which has been suggested for the formation of S_2O_3.

The isotopic-exchange reaction between liquid $S^{35}O_2$ and $[(CH_3)_4N]_2S_2O_5$ has been exploited[95] to yield labeled pyrosulfite. With 92 per cent exchange in 150 minutes reported at $-21°$ C and about 80 per cent exchange in 20 minutes at $-75°$ C, the reaction is convenient for isotopic synthetic purposes.

$S_2^{35}Cl_2$ can be synthesized[119] by a sealed-tube method either by the isotopic exchange between $S^{35}(0)$ and S_2Cl_2 or by the metathesis with Cl_2. After 1 hour at $100°$ C, the labeled monochloride is separated by vacuum distillation. A similar reaction

[115] Goehring, M., Chem. Ber., 80, 110 (1947).

[116] Appel, R., and Huber, W., Ber., 89, 386 (1956).

[117] Becke-Goehring, M., and Rommel, E., Z. Naturforsch., 11B, 422 (1956).

[118] Appel, R., Naturwiss., 40, 509 (1953).

[119] Cooley, R. A., and Yost, D. M., J. Am. Chem. Soc., 62, 2474 (1940).

has been reported in a preliminary communication by Fava and Salsilli,[120] who observed the exchange between S_2Cl_2 and $S^{35}(0)$ in CCl_4 under pressure at 125° C. The reaction, which is first order in S_2Cl_2, is 50 per cent complete in 170 minutes.

Muxart[121] has reported the slow sulfur exchange between $S^{35}OCl_2$ and SCl_2 to yield the radiotracer-labeled dichloride. The exchange is 45 per cent complete in 2 hours at 60° C, and 100 per cent complete in 2 hours at 89° C. The exchange mechanism may involve the migration of an oxide ion between thionyl chloride and sulfur monochloride, and is thus probably insensitive to catalysis.

The reaction between carbon monoxide and an excess of elementary radiosulfur, based on a procedure of Lewis and Lacy,[122] has been reported[123] to yield COS^{35} in good yield when the reactants are held at 425° C for 16 hours. Detailed directions for the synthesis of COS^{35}, starting with 0.75 mg of elementary sulfur have been reported.[124] In this procedure, sulfate is reduced to sulfide with carbon[53, 54] and oxidized to elementary sulfur with iodine. The dried sulfur is distilled and then allowed to react with carbon monoxide for 16 hours at 450° C to yield the labeled carbonyl sulfide.

Labeled SO_2Cl_2 with Cl^{36} and/or S^{35} markers has been prepared by Ovezall-Klaasen and Halberstadt.[125] In their procedure, elementary chlorine (either labeled or normal) and sulfur dioxide (labeled or normal) are distilled into a reaction vessel containing a small quantity of charcoal catalyst. On warming the reaction mixture to room temperature, the formation of SO_2Cl_2 is complete, and the product can immediately be purified by gas-phase fractionation. The quantity of sulfuryl chloride which can be prepared in this manner is limited only by the pressure limitation imposed by the size of the reaction vessel.

Acknowledgment   The preparation of this chapter has been supported in part by the U.S. Atomic Energy Commission under contract AT(30-1)-2472. The author is grateful for the assistance of Miss A. Rust in the preparation of the bibliographic data and the technical assistance of his wife in completing this work.

120 Fava, A., and Salsilli, L., Ricerca sci., 24, 375 (1954).
121 Muxart, R., Compt rend., 231, 1489 (1950).
122 Lewis, G. N., and Lacey, W. N., J. Am. Chem. Soc., 37, 1976 (1915).
123 Koski, W. S., J. Am. Chem. Soc., 71, 4042 (1949).
124 Wentink, T., Koski, W. S., and Cohen, V. W., Phys. Rev., 81, 948 (1951).
125 Ovezall-Klaasen, G. A., and Halberstadt, J., Intern. J. Appl. Radiation Isotopes, 7, 145 (1959).

8

Radiochlorine

B. J. MASTERS
Los Alamos Scientific Laboratory
Los Alamos, New Mexico

1. INTRODUCTION

A. The Chlorine Nuclides

A number of chlorine isotopes, which are of possible interest in the preparation of chlorine-labeled compounds, are listed in Table 1. For brevity, only the predominant mode of decay and the methods of preparation most commonly employed by the nuclear chemist are tabulated for each nuclide. The isotopes Cl^{32}, Cl^{33}, Cl^{34}, Cl^{38m}, and Cl^{40}, each with half-lives of 2 seconds or less, are not included in this compilation.

Table 1
Nuclear Data for Some Chlorine Isotopes[1]

Isotope	Half-life	Type of decay, energy, mev	Method of preparation
Cl^{34m}	32 min	β^+, 2.5 max	$Cl^{35}(p,pn)$
Cl^{35}	stable		(Natural abundance, 75.5%)
Cl^{36}	4×10^5 yr	β^-, 0.714	$Cl^{35}(n,\gamma)$ or (d,p)
Cl^{37}	stable		(Natural abundance, 24.5%)
Cl^{38}	38 min	β^-, 4.8 max	$Cl^{37}(n,\gamma)$ or (d,p)
Cl^{39}	56 min	β^-, 3.5 max	$A^{40}(\gamma,p)$

Of the nuclides listed in Table 1, Cl^{36} has attained, by far, the greatest degree of use in tracer applications. Among the many advantages it offers, particular attention may be called to its con-

---

[1] Strominger, D., Hollander, J. M., and Seaborg, G. T., Revs. Modern Phys., 30, 615 (1958).

veniently long half-life, its relatively simple decay scheme (98.3 per cent by β^- emission, 1.7 per cent by K-electron capture, no accompanying gamma), and its ready availability at moderate cost. Probably more than 90 per cent of the studies discussed throughout this chapter have been carried out with Cl^{36} tracer, and its use may be assumed in the procedures that follow unless specified otherwise.

For studies in which a long half-life is not a primary consideration, Cl^{38} offers the advantage of a high initial specific activity combined with a lowered level of activity in waste materials, so that disposal is considerably less of a problem than in the case of Cl^{36}. Highly enriched preparations of this isotope may be obtained by making use of Szilard-Chalmers techniques, such as that employed by Erbacher and Philipp.[2] In their procedure, purified dichloroethane is subjected to neutron irradiation, after which the target material is extracted with water to remove a large fraction of the Cl^{38}-recoil atoms. An enrichment factor (ratio of the specific activity of the extracted chlorine to that of the unseparated target material) on the order of 10^6 or greater appears to be readily attainable.[3]

Neither Cl^{34m} nor Cl^{39} has received appreciable usage as a chemical tracer; however, these isotopes may be of some interest in hot-atom chemistry studies. Although enriched mixtures of the stable chlorine isotopes have been shown to be quite suitable for exchange studies,[4] they are not employed extensively for labeling purposes, owing no doubt to the present availability of the chlorine radioisotopes.

B. Methods of Isotopic Analysis

With the obvious exception of the stable isotopes Cl^{35} and Cl^{37}, for which mass-spectrometric-analysis methods are most suitable, quantitative analyses for the chlorine nuclides are usually carried out by beta-particle radioassay techniques. For routine specific-activity determinations, Geiger-counting or proportional-counting instruments are most frequently employed, although scintillation detectors, particularly those using liquid or gel scintillators with internal counting samples,[5] appear to be suitable.

---

[2] Erbacher, O., and Philipp, K., Z. Physik. Chem. (Leipzig), A176, 169 (1936).

[3] Barnes, J. W., Burgus, W. H., and Miskel, J. A., in Wahl, A. C., and Bonner, N. A. (eds.), "Radioactivity Applied to Chemistry," Wiley, New York, 1951, p. 261.

[4] Clusius, K., and Haimerl, H., Z. Physik. Chem (Leipzig), 51B, 347 (1942).

[5] Helf, S., White, C. G., and Shelley, R. N., Anal. Chem., 32, 238 (1960).

Owing to their solubility both in water and in many slightly ionizing solvents, the quaternary ammonium radiochlorides are frequently used as intermediates in labeling semicovalent and covalent chloride compounds. Tetramethylammonium radiochloride and tetraethylammonium radiochloride are readily prepared by the neutralization of the appropriate hydroxide with labeled hydrochloric acid.[38, 39] Tetramethylammonium bromide, available commercially in somewhat higher purity than the hydroxide, may be converted to the radiochloride via the heterogeneous metathetical reaction[20] of $(CH_3)_4NBr$ with excess AgCl.[36] Radiochlorine-labeled thionyl chloride,[40] phosphorous oxychloride,[20, 41, 42] nitrosyl chloride,[39] boron trichloride,[38] arsenic trichloride,[42] selenium oxychloride,[42] silicon tetrachloride,[43] and trimethylchlorosilane[43] have all been prepared by taking advantage of the rapid exchange between the unlabeled compounds and tetramethylammonium radiochloride. Phosphorus pentachloride in liquid methyl cyanide has also been shown to undergo exchange with tetraethylammonium chloride.[44] Pyridinium radiochloride, obtained by the reaction of labeled hydrogen chloride with pyridine in dry ether, has been employed as an intermediate in the preparation of labeled boron trichloride, phosphorous trichloride, thionyl chloride, sulfuryl chloride, and acetyl chloride.[45] Under anhydrous conditions, these compounds undergo rapid exchange with pyridinium radiochloride in chloroform solution, whereas the chlorine atoms of the solvent do not enter into the exchange process.

Nitrosyl radiochloride, obtained via the tetramethyl ammonium radiochloride-exchange procedure[39] has been used by Lewis and Sowerby[46, 47] as an intermediate in the preparation of a number of radiochlorine-labeled anhydrous salts. For example, zinc radiochloride may be prepared by condensing radioactive nitrosyl chloride onto a metallic zinc surface at -40° and allowing the temperature to rise slowly to room temperature. The yellow complex $ZnCl_2 \cdot NOCl$ that forms is separated from the unreacted zinc and heated to 120° to yield[47] unsolvated $ZnCl_2^{36}$. Mercuric

[38] Herber, R. H., J. Am. Chem. Soc., 80, 5080 (1958).

[39] Lewis, J., and Wilkins, R. G., J. Chem. Soc., 1955, 56.

[40] Herber, R. H., Ref. 14, Vol. VII, in press.

[41] Herber, R. H., J. Am. Chem. Soc., 82, 792 (1960).

[42] Lewis, J., and Sowerby, D. B., J. Chem. Soc., 1957, 336.

[43] Herber, R. H., J. Phys. Chem., 62, 379 (1958).

[44] Kolditz, L., and Haas, D., Z. anorg. u. allgem. Chem., 294, 191 (1958).

[45] Frazer, M. J., J. Chem. Soc., 1957, 3319.

[46] Lewis, J., and Sowerby, D. B., J. Chem. Soc., 1957, 1617.

[47] Lewis, J., and Sowerby, D. B., J. Chem. Soc., 1956, 150.

radiochloride may be synthesized in a similar manner.[47] Alternatively, labeled zinc chloride[47] and mercuric chloride,[47] as well as labeled cadmium chloride,[47] ferric chloride,[46] antimony pentachloride,[46] and arsenic trichloride[46] may be prepared by taking advantage of the rapid exchange between these salts and nitrosyl chloride. A typical exchange procedure involves mixing the finely divided metal chloride with liquid nitrosyl radiochloride at about -15°, followed by removal of the nitrosyl chloride by vacuum distillation. In some cases a gentle heating is required to decompose the 1:1 complexes that form with nitrosyl chloride. Ferric chloride, antimony pentachloride, and arsenic trichloride are soluble in nitrosyl chloride and undergo complete exchange with the solvent within the time required for separation. In the case of the insoluble salts, zinc chloride, mercuric chloride, and cadmium chloride, rapid exchange of the metal chloride occurs only with that nitrosyl chloride which enters into complex formation with the salt; heterogeneous exchange between the complex and excess nitrosyl chloride is slow at -15°. The exchange method appears to be general for all salts that form solvate complexes with nitrosyl chloride.

Several miscellaneous exchange reactions may be employed for the introduction of radiochlorine into chloride compounds that are generally considered covalent. Labeled selenium oxychloride and stannic chloride may be prepared via the rapid exchange between potassium radiochloride and solvent selenium oxychloride,[20] and between hydrogen radiochloride and solvent stannic chloride,[48] respectively. At elevated temperatures, phosphorous trichloride undergoes exchange with anhydrous sodium radiochloride.[49] Trimethylchlorosilane may be labeled by equilibration with anhydrous hydrogen radiochloride,[50] or with radioactive antimony trichloride in benzene solution.[51] Radioactive arsenic trichloride[4,52] and silicon tetrachloride[53] may be conveniently obtained by allowing the unlabeled compounds to exchange at 100° with hydrogen radiochloride. Chlorine exchange between hydrogen chloride and phosphorus trichloride[4] or phosphorus oxy-

---

[48] Howald, R. A., and Willard, J. E., J. Am. Chem. Soc., 77, 2046 (1955).

[49] Downs, J. J., and Johnson, R. E., J. Am. Chem. Soc., 77, 2098 (1955).

[50] Herber, R. H., and Chang, S. C., J. Inorg. & Nuclear Chem., 17, 385 (1961).

[51] Reid, A. F., and Mills, R., J. Chem. Soc., 1960, 703; ibid., 1960, 708.

[52] Owen, J. H., and Johnson, R. E., J. Inorg. & Nuclear Chem., 2, 260 (1956).

[53] Herber, R. H., J. Chem. Phys., 27, 653 (1957).

chloride,[4] between phosphorus oxychloride and boron trichloride,[41] between phosphorus trichloride and phosphorus pentachloride,[54] and between thionyl chloride and antimony trichloride[20] all proceed rapidly enough to suggest the use of these
systems in exchange-labeling procedures.

Radioactive elemental chlorine is frequently used as a starting
material for the preparation of labeled chlorides, both in direct-
synthesis methods and in exchange procedures. Examples of
direct syntheses are provided by the reaction of radiochlorine
with an excess of red phosphorus at 100° to form phosphorus
trichloride,[54] and the combination with metallic antimony to form
antimony trichloride.[51] In the latter procedure, the reaction
mixture is subjected to a final heating of 200 to 300° to decompose any antimony pentachloride that may be formed, after
which the product is purified by vacuum sublimation. An interesting result is obtained when radiochlorine is added to unlabeled
phosphorus trichloride, equatorially labeled phosphorus pentachloride being produced with little or no intramolecular exchange
between the three equatorial and two apical positions of the product.[49] Elemental chlorine undergoes rapid exchange with tellurium tetrachloride in benzene solution,[55] with arsenic trichloride in the presence of hydrogen chloride,[52] and with both
phosphorus trichloride and phosphorus pentachloride in carbon
tetrachloride solution,[56] exchange of the equatorial chlorides being favored in the last instance.[49]

B. Compounds of the Higher Oxidation States

The preparation of labeled elementary chlorine is of particular
interest, owing to the extensive use of this material in obtaining
other radiochlorine-labeled compounds via either direct syntheses
or exchange procedures. The observed rapid exchange between
free radiochloride ion and chlorine in aqueous solution[57] suggests
a possible method of obtaining radiochlorine. Also worthy of
consideration as a preparative method is the exchange between
hydrogen radiochloride and elementary chlorine in the gaseous
state. Although true homogeneous exchange in this system is
slow, the reaction proceeds rapidly via surface catalysis by the

[54] Becker, W. E., and Johnson, R. E., J. Am. Chem. Soc.,
79, 5157 (1957).

[55] Johnson, R. E., "Exchange Between Labeled Halogens and
Certain Inorganic Halides," Office of Technical Services, Department of Commerce, Washington, D.C., 1952.

[56] Koskoski, W., and Fowler, R. D., J. Am. Chem. Soc.,
64, 850 (1942).

[57] Long, F. A., and Olson, A. R., J. Am. Chem. Soc., 58,
2214 (1936).

walls of ordinary containing vessels or when the reactants are exposed to ultraviolet illumination.[58] The high-temperature equilibration of chlorine with silver radiochloride has been employed by Downs and Johnson[49] as a method of preparing radiochlorine. In this procedure, silver chloride is fused in vacuo, to remove moisture, and heated to 450° with a large molar excess of chlorine, the heterogeneous-exchange reaction being complete within a few hours. In a procedure reported by McNeill,[59] palladous chloride is dissolved in an aqueous solution of labeled hydrochloric acid to allow the exchange of chlorine. After removal of hydrochloric acid and water by distillation, the palladous radiochloride is dried at 120°, and labeled chlorine is obtained by thermal decomposition of the anhydrous salt in vacuo at about 450°.

Although the foregoing exchange procedures appear to be eminently suitable for the quantitative introduction of radiochlorine into a vacuum system for further synthetic or analytical exploitation, they carry the obvious disadvantage of dilution of the radiochloride starting material with chlorine of normal isotopic composition. This objection is overcome in a number of well-defined procedures for the quantitative oxidation of radiochloride to radiochlorine. In Sorenson's procedure,[60] labeled silver chloride is treated with an excess of potassium dichromate in concentrated sulfuric acid. The generator is swept with air while being gradually heated to a final temperature of 200°. The radiochlorine yield is 95 to 98 per cent of the theoretical amount. The classic procedure for oxidizing sodium chloride by means of manganese dioxide and sulfuric acid has been adapted by Townes and Aamodt[61] for the production of radiochlorine. Woeber's method[62] involves the addition at 0° of fuming (15 per cent SO_3) sulfuric acid to 30 per cent hydrogen peroxide containing dissolved sodium radiochloride; radiochlorine is evolved in 95 to 100 per cent yield. A seemingly less-hazardous procedure, in which an inert gas stream is bubbled through an aqueous solution of 0.5 $\underline{M}$ hydrogen radiochloride containing excess potassium peroxysulfate at 75°, has been described by Brown et al.[63] The reaction rate is easily controlled by slight warming or cooling, and radiochlorine yields of 98 to 100 per cent are obtained. It should be pointed out that the chlorine produced by these oxidation methods

---

[58] Johnston, W. H., and Libby, W. F., J. Am. Chem. Soc., 73, 854 (1951).

[59] McNeill, I. C., J. Chem. Soc., 1961, 639.

[60] Sorenson, P., Anal. Chem., 26, 1581 (1954).

[61] Townes, C. H., and Aamodt, L. C., Phys. Rev., 76, 691 (1949).

[62] Woeber, H. H., J. Am. Chem. Soc., 74, 1355 (1952).

[63] Brown, F., Gillies, A., and Stevens, W. H., Can. J. Chem., 31, 768 (1953).

may be expected to contain appreciable amounts of water,
hydrogen chloride, or oxygen; however, the removal of these impurities in appropriate traps should present no serious difficulty.
Although the oxidations are most conveniently performed in
vacuum systems in which liquid nitrogen traps are used to collect
the radiochlorine product, the procedures may safely be carried
out in conventional apparatus in which aqueous sodium hydroxide
traps are used to prevent the escape of radioactive material.

Exchange reactions of some of the interhalogen compounds in
the gaseous phase have been studied by Phelps. [64] Radiochlorine
monofluoride may be prepared via the exchange at room temperature between radiochlorine and chlorine monofluoride, whereas
chlorine trifluoride may be labeled by equilibration at 180° C
with radiochlorine. The latter exchange reaction is accompanied
by chlorine monofluoride formation.

Relatively few preparations of compounds containing radiochlorine in the positive oxidation states have been reported in the
literature; however, the conventional procedures for oxidizing
chloride ion or chlorine to the higher valency states appear to be
readily adaptable for labeling purposes. For example, Lee[65]
has prepared labeled potassium chlorate from potassium radiochloride by means of a standard electrolytic method.[16] In this
procedure, the addition of a gas-trapping system seems advisable.
in order to insure the retention of small amounts of radiochlorine
or radiochlorine oxides that might be evolved during the electrolysis. In another convenient method for the production of labeled
chlorate ion, radiochlorine is allowed to disproportionate in
aqueous buffer solution at elevated temperature, and the radiochloride ion, which results as a by-product, is removed by precipitation as silver chloride.[66] Dodgen and Taube[67] have prepared labeled chlorine dioxide by heating neutron-bombarded
potassium chlorate, oxalic acid, and water to 60° and collecting
the evolved radiochlorine dioxide in water after first removing
other radioisotopic contaminants.

Dodgen and Taube's observations of certain tracer chlorine
redox reactions in solution[66] are of possible interest as preparative methods. When chlorite ion reacts with elemental chlorine
or hypochlorous acid to form chloride ion and chlorine dioxide or
chlorate ion, most of the chlorine atoms in the chlorine dioxide or
chlorate are derived from the chlorite. Conversely, when chlorate
ion is reduced by chloride ion to give elemental chlorine and

[64] Phelps, J. P., Dissertation Abstr., 19, 58 (1958).

[65] Lee, D. A., J. Am. Chem. Soc., 76, 2590 (1954).

[66] Dodgen, H., and Taube, H., J. Am. Chem. Soc., 71,
3330 (1949).

[67] Dodgen, H., and Taube, H., J. Am. Chem. Soc., 71,
2501 (1949).

chlorine dioxide, the chlorine atoms in the dioxide are derived
predominantly from the chlorate.

The exchange reactions of the higher oxidation states of
chlorine in water solution appear to offer few possibilities for
application as labeling procedures. Neither chlorite nor chlorate
ions undergo rapid exchange with chloride ion in acid solution.[66, 68] Perchlorate and chlorate ions do not exchange chlorine
in either acidic or basic solution.[65] Chlorine dioxide does not
exchange appreciably with perchlorate, chlorate, chlorine, or
chloride in either acid or slightly alkaline solution, and chlorine
dioxide-hypochlorite exchange is very slow.[67] The exchange reactions between hypochlorite and chlorite ions in base, and between chlorine and chlorate ion in acid, are both slow.[66] Possible routes to labeled hypochlorite and chlorite compounds are
suggested by the observations of rapid exchange in the chloride
ion-hypochlorous acid system[69] and in the chlorine dioxide-
chlorite ion exchange system.[67]

—————
[68] McCallum, K. J., and Holmes, O. G., Can. J. Chem.,
29, 691 (1951).

[69] Anbar, M., Guttmann, S., and Rein, R., J. Am. Chem.
Soc., 81, 1816 (1959).

9

Iodine-131

MILTON KAHN
University of New Mexico
Albuquerque, New Mexico

1. INTRODUCTION

I^{131} is available from the U.S. Atomic Energy Commission as carrier-free I^{131-} dissolved in dilute aqueous sodium sulfite. This
active solution is generally used to inoculate an aqueous solution
of an inactive alkali iodide, which subsequently serves as the
starting material for the preparation of other labeled iodine compounds.

The conversion of carrier-free I^{131} from one oxidation state
to another requires special consideration because the chemical
behavior of iodine at tracer concentrations is significantly different
from that at ordinary concentrations.

2. DETECTION OF I^{131}

The radioactivity of I^{131} can be measured by detection of either
the beta or gamma radiation associated with its decay (see Fig. 1).[1]

A. Beta Counting

Solid samples for beta counting can be prepared by the collection
of a precipitate on filter paper, the transference of a slurry to a
solid surface with subsequent evaporation, the formation of a precipitate on a solid surface followed by evaporation, or by the direct
evaporation of aqueous solutions containing iodide or iodate.

Silver iodide is precipitated from nearly boiling dilute nitric
acid solutions of iodide by the dropwise addition of aqueous silver
nitrate.[2] The precipitate is digested for 1 minute, filtered with

[1] Slack, L., and Way, K., "Radiations from Radioactive
Atoms," U.S. Atomic Energy Commission, Washington, D.C.,
1959, p. 33.
[2] Glendenin, L. E., and Metcalf, R. P., Natl. Nuclear Energy
Ser., Div. IV, 9, Book 3, 1625 (1951).

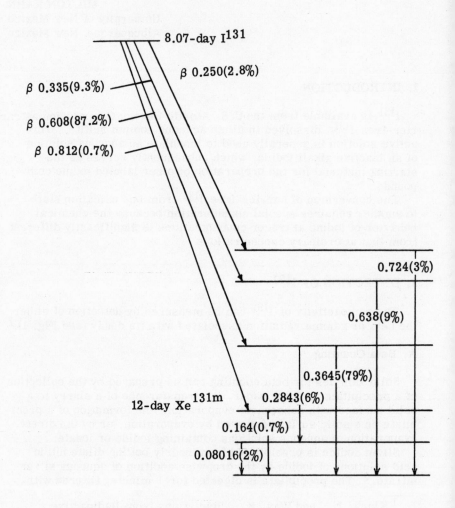

Fig. 1 Decay scheme for I^{131}. (Based on Ref. 1.)

suction onto a filter-paper disc, washed with water and then ethanol, and dried for 10 minutes at 110° C. Katcoff et al.[3] precipitated palladium iodide from hot dilute nitric acid solutions of iodide by slow addition of aqueous palladium nitrate. The precipitate was prepared for counting according to the procedure described previously for silver iodide.

Jenkins and Harris[4] prepared samples of silver iodide by transferring an alcohol slurry of the precipitate to a steel planchet and evaporating the alcohol under a heat lamp.

The formation of a precipitate of silver iodide directly on a microscope cover glass[5] or on discs of aluminum, stainless steel, or copper[6] has been effected by the transference of an appropriate aliquot of an aqueous solution of radioactive iodide to the disc, followed by addition of a slight excess of aqueous silver nitrate; the suspension was evaporated to dryness.

Attempts to prepare samples by direct evaporation of alkaline solutions of carrier-free iodide on aluminum or glass discs resulted in some loss of activity.[7] However, it has been found that this loss could be avoided by the addition of a small amount of silver nitrate to the solution prior to evaporation in a gentle stream of warm air. Similar losses were detected on evaporation of neutral or slightly acid solutions of macro amounts of iodide.[6] Samples of silver iodate have been prepared by the evaporation of ammoniacal solutions of the salt on glass discs.[5]

Barreira et al.[8] found that the effective half-life of I^{131} in thin samples of silver iodide and cuprous iodide decreased when exposed to gamma radiation from Co^{60}.

The radioactivity of liquid samples of I^{131} is rarely measured by detection of the beta radiation with a Geiger-Müller tube because of the relative inefficiency of the method. Rose and Emery,[9] using a type of jacketed Geiger-Müller tube to detect the I^{131} betas, have studied the dependence of the counting rate of liquid samples on the composition of the medium.

---

[3] Katcoff, S. , Dillard, C. R. , Finston, H. , Finkle, B. , Seiler, J. A. , and Sugarman, N. , Natl. Nuclear Energy Ser. Div. IV, 9, Book 3, 1635 (1951).

[4] Jenkins, F. E. , and Harris, G. M. , J. Phys. Chem. , 61, 249 (1957).

[5] Myers, O. E. , and Kennedy, J. W. , J. Am. Chem. Soc. , 72, 897 (1950).

[6] Pinajian, J. J. , Univ. Microfilms, Publ. No. 13,939; Dissertation Abstr. , 15, 2241 (1955).

[7] Weisburger, J. H. , and Lipner, H. J. , Nucleonics, 12 (5), 21 (1954).

[8] Barreira, F. C. , Laranjeira, M. , and Neves, E. M. , Rev. fac. cien. Univ. Lisboa, 2a Ser. B, 87 (1956); C.A. , 53, 18666g. (1959).

[9] Rose, G. , and Emery, E. W. , Nucleonics, 9 (1), 5 (1951).

Herber[10] has suggested the possibility of measuring gaseous I^{131} activity by detection of the betas with a Geiger-Müller tube incorporated into the manifold of a gas-transfer high-vacuum system.

B. Gamma Counting

The radioactivity of I^{131} is most conveniently measured by detection of the gamma radiation from liquid samples with a type of well scintillation counter. Geiger-Müller tubes have been used[11,12,13] to detect the gamma radiation of I^{131}, but, because of the relatively low efficiency of G. M. detectors for gamma radiation, this method of detection is seldom employed.

It is good practice to determine empirically variations in counting rate with composition of the liquid samples. However, such variations are usually within experimental error and can be minimized by avoiding the detection of the 0.080-Mev gamma radiation through the use of absorbers or an electronic discriminator.[12,13] In the preparation of liquid samples, an aliquot of the active solution is added to the counting tube and then diluted with the appropriate solvent to a standard volume; the samples can then be mixed with a stream of air or inert gas. The tubes can be sealed with rubber stoppers wrapped in aluminum foil; the foil serves to prevent the stoppers from becoming contaminated or from swelling, in the case of nonaqueous solvents. In some instances it may be necessary to make the aqueous sample alkaline to prevent the loss of activity through volatilization during the mixing process. The counting tubes are calibrated by comparing the counting rates of liquid samples prepared, in each instance, by diluting an aliquot of an aqueous I^{131-} solution to the standard height with water.[12,13] The variation in counting rates with sample volumes for a particular detector geometry has been investigated by Weisburger and Lipner,[7] and Kahn.[14]

The primary advantage of gamma-solution counting over beta counting of solid samples lies in the relative ease of preparation of liquid samples; the counting efficiencies of the two methods are essentially equal. Anger,[15] using a type of well scintillation counter with a thallium-activated sodium iodide crystal and a 5819 RCA

[10] Herber, R. H., Rev. Sci. Instr., 28, 1049 (1957).

[11] Reilly, W. A., Bayer, D. I., and Siegel, J. M., Proc. Soc. Exptl. Biol. Med., 75, 1 (1950).

[12] Keneshea, F. J., Jr., and Kahn, M., J. Am. Chem. Soc., 74, 5254 (1952).

[13] Kahn, M., and Wahl, A. C., J. Chem. Phys., 21, 1185 (1953).

[14] Kahn, M., doctoral dissertation, Washington University, 1950.

[15] Anger, H. O., Rev. Sci. Instr., 22, 912 (1951).

phototube, detected I^{131} in liquid samples with an efficiency of about 32 per cent. Weisburger and Lipner[7] counted liquid samples similarly with an efficiency of 46 per cent and, furthermore, found detection of the beta radiation from solid samples with a Geiger-Müller tube or a gas-flow proportional counter to be equally efficient.

C. Standardization of I^{131}

The standardization of I^{131} has been comprehensively reviewed and studied by Pinajian.[6] He reports the results of studies involving the use of an electroscope, absolute beta counting with G.M. tubes, the use of simulated I^{131} reference sources with G.M. tubes, and the gamma counting of liquid samples with G.M. tubes employing standard solutions of I^{131} obtained from the National Bureau of Standards.

D. Effect of 12.0-day Xe^{131m_2} on Counting Rates

The amount of Xe^{131m_2} (see Fig. 1) associated with I^{131} in a counting sample will depend on the preparation and age of the sample and, consequently, may represent a source of counting error. Thus, the preparation of a solid sample by precipitation or evaporation, or the preparation of a liquid sample by precipitation with subsequent dissolution, will result in complete separation of the xenon from the I^{131}; the amount of xenon subsequently present will depend on the age and emanating power of the sample. The possibility of this error can be eliminated by employing beta counting or gamma-scintillation counting with discrimination against gamma rays of energy less than 0.17 mev. Where samples are to be counted with a scintillation detector that does not discriminate against the 12.0-day xenon gamma, an estimate of this error is obtained by considering of the growth of xenon under nonemanating conditions in a sample initially free of xenon. Assuming equal detection efficiencies for the gammas from the 12.0-day xenon and from the short-lived excited states of xenon, the percentage of the sample activity attributable to the 12.0-day xenon will be 0.04 per cent after 1 day, 0.13 per cent after 3 days, and 3 per cent after 40 days. Therefore, if samples of I^{131} are compared within a few days after preparation, the error resulting from the detection of 12.0-day xenon would be no greater than a few tenths of 1 per cent, even though the emanating power of the samples vary widely.

3. PRODUCTION OF I^{131}

I^{131} can be produced in the pile by the fission of uranium or the capture of slow neutrons by tellurium, and with a cyclotron by the bombardment of tellurium with deuterons. The I^{131} separated from these targets is generally carrier-free.

A. Production of Carrier-Free Fission-Product I^{131}

The present-day large-scale production of I^{131} at the Oak
Ridge National Laboratory depends on the separation of carrier-
free fission-product I^{131} from neutron-irradiated uranium metal.
The I^{131} produced in this manner will not be carrier-free or isotopically pure because[16,17] of the unavoidable presence of I^{127} and
I^{129}. Indeed, to realize yields as high as 85 per cent, it has been
found necessary[16] to irradiate the uranium metal long enough to
produce sufficient I^{127} and I^{129} to act as carriers for the I^{131}.
The irradiation time is usually about 60 days.

The first step, which is common to all fission-product-separation
procedures, involves the dissolution of the irradiated fissile material in an appropriate solvent. In the case of the actinide metals
this is commonly strong nitric acid. According to the procedure
reported by Rupp,[18,19] the iodine, some of which accompanies the
oxides of nitrogen during dissolution of the uranium and the remainder which is distilled, is efficiently condensed in a bubble-cap
scrubbing tower containing water at 3°C. Iodine is separated from
the resulting aqueous solution, which contains relatively small
amounts of nitrous and nitric acids, by adjusting to 20 per cent by
volume of sulfuric acid and distilling through a column in the presence of hydrogen peroxide. The activity, which is trapped in
dilute sulfurous acid, is of high chemical and radiochemical purity.
This distillate is eventually filtered through a type of bacterio-
logical filter and the pH adjusted to 9 with sodium bicarbonate.

In the process reported by Arrol et al.,[16] the crude distillate,
which is trapped in dilute sodium hydroxide, is acidified with sulfuric acid, treated with hydrogen peroxide, and redistilled into
10 per cent sodium hydroxide. The nitrate is removed completely
from the second distillate by addition of chromium (VI) oxide and
strong sulfuric acid with subsequent distillation; during this distilla-

---

[16] Arrol, W. J., Chadwick, J., and Eakins, J., in Bruce,
F. R., Fletcher, J. M., Hyman, H. H., and Katz, J. J. (eds.),
Progress in Nuclear Energy, Series 3, "Process Chemistry,"
McGraw-Hill, New York, 1956, pp. 356-362.

[17] Ballantine, D. S., and Cohn, W. E., U. S. Atomic Energy
Comm. Report, MDDC-1600.

[18] Rupp, A. F., Proc. Intern. Conf. Peaceful Uses Atomic
Energy, Geneva, 1955, 14, 68.

[19] Rupp, A. F., in Bruce, F. R., Fletcher, J. M., Hyman,
H. H., and Katz, J. J. (eds.), Progress in Nuclear Energy,
Series 3, "Process Chemistry," McGraw-Hill, New York, 1956,
pp. 345-355.

tion, the I^{131} is oxidized to iodic acid; the latter remains in the
still pot. The iodic acid is then reduced to iodine with oxalic acid
or phosphorous acid, steam distilled, and trapped in dilute sodium
bisulfite. This procedure has been varied by using potassium permanganate to oxidize the iodine to iodic acid.[20,21]

In an early procedure reported by Ballantine and Cohn[17] the
nitric acid condensate, which contained a large fraction of the I^{131},
was treated with chromium(VI) oxide and concentrated sulfuric acid
and distilled until dense white fumes of sulfur trioxide appeared.
During this treatment, the iodine was oxidized to iodic acid and
freed of nitric acid. The I^{131} was distilled from the solution after
the addition of excess oxalic acid; the distillate was found to be about
0.001 N in reducing agents.

B. Separation of Carrier-Free I^{131} from Neutron-Irradiated Tellurium

On irradiation of tellurium with slow neutrons, three isotopes of
iodine are formed via the transformations summarized below.[22]

$$Te^{131m} \; (30h) \xrightarrow{\;\beta^-\;} Te^{131}(24.8m) \xrightarrow{\;\beta^-\;} I^{131} \; (8.07d)$$

$$Te^{129m} \; (33.5d) \xrightarrow{\;\beta^-\;} Te^{129} \; (72m) \xrightarrow{\;\beta^-\;} I^{129} \; (1.72 \times 10^7 y)$$

$$Te^{127m} \; (115d) \xrightarrow{\;\beta^-\;} Te^{127} \; (9.3h) \xrightarrow{\;\beta^-\;} I^{127} \; (stable)$$

The method most commonly used to extract carrier-free I^{131}
from neutron-irradiated tellurium metal is based on the procedure
first described by Perlman, Morton, and Chaikoff.[23] They dissolved the tellurium metal in a hot concentrated sulfuric acid solution of chromium(VI) oxide. The cooled solution was treated with
oxalic acid to reduce the chromium(VI) to chromium(III) and the
iodate to molecular iodine; the iodine was subsequently distilled
into dilute sodium hydroxide. Ballantine and Cohn,[17] using this
procedure, recovered only about 60 per cent of the total I^{131}, with
a radiochemical purity greater than 99 per cent in the first 25 to
30 ml of distillate. Continued distillation yielded additional I^{131},
but only slowly. The distillate was found to be contaminated with
reducing agents (0.001 $\underline{N}$).

[20] Rupp, A. F., Beauchamp, E. E., and Farmakes, J. R.,
ORNL 1047, 1951.
[21] Rupp, A. F., and Binford, F. T., J. Appl. Phys., 24,
1069 (1953).
[22] Strominger, D., Hollander, J. M., and Seaborg, G. T.,
Revs. Modern Phys., 30 (2), 585 (1958).
[23] Perlman, I., Morton, M. E., and Chaikoff, I. L., J. Endo-
crinol., 30, 487 (1942).

Kenney and Spragg,[24,25] in testing this procedure, obtained similar results and were able to recover essentially all the I^{131} by continuing distillation until fuming of the distilland occurred. The distillate, which was contaminated with oxalic and formic acids, was subjected to alkaline and acid permanganate oxidation; the excess permanganate was back-titrated with oxalic acid and the I^{131} subsequently distilled without the accompaniment of organic acids. By carefully controlling the amount of oxalic acid added to the original sulfuric acid-chromium(VI) solution, it was found possible to recover essentially all the I^{131} free of organic acids. These workers concluded that it is molecular iodine and not hydrogen iodide that distills, and that excess oxalic acid partly inhibits distillation by reducing sulfuric acid to sulfurous acid which in turn reduces molecular iodine to iodide. A similar explanation was offered for the inhibition of the distillation of I^{131} by the presence of undissolved metallic tellurium. Because of its greater purity, potassium dichromate was eventually substituted for chromium(VI) oxide.

Taugböl and Blix[26] purified the I^{131} in the crude distillate described previously as follows: The distillate was made slightly acid, titrated to a fast pink color with permanganate, made strongly acid with sulfuric acid, warmed to 70 to 80° , and then titrated with oxalic acid to a colorless end point. The I^{131} was distilled following the addition of a small quantity of nitrite to ensure the presence of elemental iodine.

Details of the construction and manipulation of the apparatus used to extract carrier-free I^{131} from tellurium metal by the above-mentioned procedure have been described by several workers.[25-28]

Neutron-irradiated tellurium metal has been dissolved by fusion with solid sodium hydroxide slightly above the melting point of tellurium (452° C) for about 5 minutes. The cooled solid mass was extracted with water; the extract was filtered, concentrated, and treated with permanganate to oxidize the lower oxidation states of iodine to iodate. The solution was then acidified with sulfuric acid, treated with oxalic acid, and the I^{131} recovered by distillation in yields of 85 to 90 per cent.[29] In an alternative

---

[24] Kenney, A. W., and Spragg, W. T., J. Chem. Soc. 1949, S323.

[25] Kenney, A. W., and Spragg, W. T., AERE (Gt. Brit.) C/R-349, 1957, 14 pp.

[26] Taugböl, K. and Blix, U., JENER Publs., No. 18 (1953).

[27] Seligman, H., Angew. Chem., 66, 95 (1954).

[28] Miles, B. J., Fletcher, C. W., Faires, R. A., Payne, B. R., and Hudswell, F., AERE, 1/R 1038, 1952, 7 pp.

[29] Levy, M., Keston, A. S., and Udenfriend, S., J. Am. Chem. Soc., 70, 2289 (1948).

procedure,[30] the alkaline water extract was acidified with hydrochloric acid and passed through a column of Amberlite IRA-400
resin in the chloride form. The I^{131} activity was retained on the
column and eventually eluted with 6 $\underline{f}$ hydrochloric acid. The
yield of carrier-free I^{131} varied from 50 to 60 per cent; when
carrier was added, the yield was greater than 99 per cent.

Some workers have used tellurium dioxide or telluric acid as
target material to avoid the dissolution of tellurium metal. Evans
and Stevenson[31] separated I^{131} from irradiated tellurium dioxide
by heating the oxide to 650 to 700° C in a slow stream of oxygen
for 24 hours. The I^{131} was recovered by bubbling the oxygen
through dilute sodium hydroxide. Samsahl and Taugböl[32] heated
the irradiated oxide to 680 to 700°C for 2 to 4 hours under a
pressure of about 0.02 mm Hg. The distilled I^{131} was eventually
recovered in aqueous sodium bisulfite with an over-all yield of
nearly 100 per cent. No activity distilled below 500° C, even
after prolonged heating.

Ryabchikov et al.[33] dissolved the irradiated oxide in aqueous
10 per cent sodium hydroxide. The filtered solution was acidified
with sulfuric acid, ferric sulfate was added, and the I^{131} was
distilled into dilute aqueous sodium sulfite with a yield of about 90
per cent.

Constant[34,35] dissolved neutron-irradiated telluric acid in
dilute sulfuric acid and distilled the I^{131} from this solution into
aqueous sodium bicarbonate; about 90 per cent of the I^{131} was recovered.

Carrier-free I^{131} can be obtained from neutron-irradiated
telluric acid in an adsorption method suggested by Tóth.[36] The
acid is dissolved in 1 $\underline{N}$ H_2SO_4 in a platinum vessel agitated for
40 minutes to distribute the increasingly depleted solution evenly
over the surface. After removing the telluric acid and washing
the platinum dish with distilled water, the container is filled again
with distilled water and the I^{131} plated onto a platinum disc (acting

[30] Inarida, M. , Nippon Kagaku Zasshi, 80, 400 (1959); C. A. ,
53, 16739f (1959).

[31] Evans, C. C. , and Stevenson, J. , Brit. Pat. No. 763,865,
Dec. 19, 1956.

[32] Samsahl, K. , and Taugböl, K. , Proc. Intern. Conf. Peaceful Uses Atomic Energy, Geneva, 1955, 14, 89.

[33] Ryabchikov, D. I. , Ermakov, A. N. , Kozyreva, L. S. , and
Oreshko, V. F. , Primenenie Mechenykh At. v Analit. Khim. ,
Akad. Nauk SSSR, Inst. Geokhim. Anal. Khim. , 1955, 179; C. A. ,
50, 3918c (1956).

[34] Constant, R. , J. Inorg. & Nuclear Chem. , 7, 133 (1958).

[35] Constant, R. , Belg. Pat. No. 555,601, Mar. 30, 1957;
C. A. , 53, 18677i (1959).

[36] Tóth, G. , J. Inorg. & Nuclear Chem. , 19, 186 (1961).

as a cathode) at a potential of 2 to 3 volts with respect to the container. Up to 85 per cent of the iodine activity can be transferred in 90 minutes with less than 0.05 per cent contamination of the I^{131} with other activities.

C. Separation of I^{131} from Deutron-Bombarded Tellurium Metal

Bombardment of tellurium with 16 mev deuterons produces I^{131} via the nuclear reaction $Te^{130}(d,n)I^{131}$.

Overstreet and Jacobson[37] obtained carrier-free I^{131} by dissolving deuteron-bombarded tellurium metal in 6 f nitric acid with subsequent distillation. The distillate was collected over carbon tetrachloride, which was then washed with water, treated with chlorine gas in direct sunlight for at least 1 hour, and finally extracted with aqueous sodium sulfite. The yield of this procedure was substantially improved by adding carrier iodide prior to the distillation step.[38,39]

Süe and Occhi[40] extracted I^{131} from deuteron-bombarded tellurium metal by dissolving the tellurium in a sulfuric acid-chromium(VI) oxide mixture containing carrier iodide; the iodine was subsequently distilled into toluene following the usual oxalic acid treatment described previously.

D. Purification of Carrier-Free I^{131}

Carrier-free I^{131} is available from the U.S. Atomic Energy Commission in dilute sodium sulfite solutions adjusted to a pH from 8 to 9. These solutions usually contain on the order of 5 mg of total solids per ml, and the contamination by heavy metals is less than 10 ppm.

This iodine activity can be further purified by distillation and collection in pure water with yields of about 90 per cent.[41,42] The carrier-free I^{131} is added to 8 f sulfuric acid containing 0.01 f ceric bisulfate, refluxed for about 1 hour, cooled and treated with an an excess of ferrous sulfate, and then distilled into water.

---

[37] Overstreet, R., and Jacobson, L., Natl. Nuclear Energy Ser., Div. IV, 9, Book 3, 1638 (1951).

[38] Hamilton, J. G., and Soley, M. H., Am. J. Physiol., 127, 557 (1939).

[39] Perlman, I., Chaikoff, I. L., and Morton, M. E., J. Biol. Chem., 139, 433 (1941).

[40] Süe, P., and Occhi, A., Bull. soc. chim. France, 1948, 430.

[41] Kahn, M., Freedman, A. J., and Shultz, C. G., Nucleonics, 12(7), 72 (1954).

[42] Kahn, M., Freedman, A. J., and Shultz, C. G., in T. Moeller (ed.), "Inorganic Synthesis," Vol. V, McGraw-Hill, New York, 1957, pp. 166-167.

Eiland[43] found that the activity purified in this manner did not behave reproducibly when subjected to extraction with pure benzene and with benzene 0.007 $\underline{f}$ in carrier iodine. The amount of activity present in each type of benzene extract varied over wide limits from solution to solution, indicating a variable ratio of molecular iodine to iodide. Solutions of purified carrier-free I^{131} with a constant ratio of elemental iodine to iodide (for at least 10 days) were prepared by making the active aqueous solution 0.005 $\underline{f}$ in sodium sulfite. Under these conditions, about 90 per cent of the activity assumed a form (probably iodide) that underwent rapid isotopic exchange with carrier molecular iodine in benzene; about 2 per cent of the total sample activity remained in the pure benzene extract even after back extraction with 0.01 $\underline{f}$ potassium iodide. In 0.0005 $\underline{f}$ sodium sulfite, the "iodide" form dropped to about 83 per cent; the activity that could not be extracted from benzene with 0.01 $\underline{f}$ potassium iodide increased to about 3.5 per cent.

4. CHEMICAL BEHAVIOR OF CARRIER-FREE I^{131}

The marked difference in the behavior of iodine at tracer concentrations from that at ordinary concentrations was first evidenced by the difficulty in achieving complete isotopic exchange between the traces of radioactive iodine isotopes formed in fission, and those formed by beta decay, with macro quantities of the stable inorganic forms of iodine (iodide, iodine, iodate, and periodate) added as carrier.[2,3,44-47]

In a subsequent study[13] of the behavior of iodine at low concentrations, it was found that oxidation of carrier-free I^{131} by chromium(VI) or cerium(IV) in 1 $\underline{f}$ sulfuric acid, at room temperature for several minutes, resulted in the formation of several radioactive fractions that do not correspond to any of the known stable oxidation states of iodine. All the unidentified fractions were characterized by a slow exchange, if at all, with iodide, iodine,

[43] Eiland, H. M., doctoral dissertation, University of New Mexico, 1957.

[44] Glendenin, L. E., and Metcalf, R. P., Natl. Nuclear Energy Ser., Div. IV, 9, Book 2, 997 (1951).

[45] Katcoff, S., Dillard, C. R., Finston, H., Finkle, B., Seiler, J. A., and Sugarman, N., Natl. Nuclear Energy Ser., Div. IV, 9, Book 2, 1007 (1951).

[46] Glendenin, L. E., Metcalf, R. P., Novey, T. B., and Coryell, C. D., Natl. Nuclear Energy Ser., Div. IV, 9, Book 3, 1629 (1951).

[47] Campbell, G. W., and Brady, E. L., Natl. Nuclear Energy Ser., Div. IV, 9, Book 3, 1623 (1951).

or iodate. One fraction, which represented about 10 per cent of the total activity, could not be back-extracted with 0.2 $\underline{f}$ potassium iodide or 0.1 $\underline{f}$ sodium hydroxide after extraction into benzene. These anomalous fractions, once formed, were destroyed very slowly, if at all, by prolonged reduction with iron(II). Furthermore, it was observed that these anomalous fractions formed to a small extent even where the total iodine concentration was as high as 6×10^{-5} $\underline{f}$.

It was suggested that the anomalous fractions extracted into benzene are most likely formed through reaction between a reactive form of iodine, such as hypoiodous acid, and trace impurities. The anomalous fraction that did not extract to an appreciable extent into benzene was thought to be the product of a reaction involving a type of inorganic impurity, or a true simple inorganic oxidation state of iodine, which is intermediate between +1 and +5 (e.g., HIO_2) and which exists only at low concentrations. During a detailed investigation of this water-soluble inorganic fraction, Eiland[43] had occasion to repeat some of the experiments reported by Kahn and Wahl[13] and obtained essentially the same results. Thus, although the idiosyncrasies of carrier-free I^{131} are only slightly understood at present, they are at least reproducible.

5. PREPARATION OF AQUEOUS SOLUTIONS OF INORGANIC COMPOUNDS OF CARRIER-FREE I^{131}

Because tracer quantities (10^{-10} $\underline{M}$ or less) are generally beyond the reach of ordinary analytical procedures, the oxidation state of iodine in a carrier-free inorganic compound can be determined only by assuming that extrapolation of macro behavior to tracer concentrations is valid.[48] For example, it is assumed that iodine activity, which does not exchange rapidly with carrier elemental iodine and which follows carrier iodate isotopically during fractional precipitation, is indeed iodate.[13] Activity which does not extract into benzene but which is rapidly exchangeable with carrier iodine in benzene can be ascribed to either iodide or hypoiodite; if the activity were contained in a dilute solution of sodium sulfite it would be assigned the -1 oxidation state. The assignment of the 0 oxidation state is difficult because the extrapolation of the chemical behavior of macro amounts of elemental iodine to carrier-free concentrations is not valid.[13,14,49,50] Periodate can be distinguished from

[48] Bonner, N. A., and Kahn, M., in Wahl, A. C., and Bonner, N. A. (eds.), "Radioactivity Applied to Chemistry," Wiley, New York, 1951, Chap. 6.

[49] Good, M. L., and Edwards, R. R., J. Inorg. & Nuclear Chem., 2, 196 (1956).

[50] Wille, R. G., and Good, M. L., J. Am. Chem. Soc., 79, 1040 (1957).

the other oxidation states of iodine because it does not undergo rapid isotopic exchange with elemental iodine[51] or iodate[52] and does not coprecipitate with barium iodate;[53] nor does iodate coprecipitate with potassium periodate.[53] Musakin and Puchkov[54] have used paper chromatography to distinguish carrier-free periodate from iodide or iodate.

-1 Oxidation state. The preparation of carrier-free iodide solutions has been described in Sec. 3-D. According to the aforementioned criteria, no more than 90 per cent of the activity was in the form of iodide even in the presence of 0.005 $\underline{f}$ sodium sulfite.

0 Oxidation state. Kenney and Spragg[24] have suggested that elemental iodine rather than hydrogen iodide distills in the procedures described for the separation of carrier-free I^{131} from tellurium targets. Accordingly, the purification procedure previously described (see Sec. 3-D) should yield a solution of carrier-free elemental I^{131} in water. However, it is noteworthy that Eiland[43] found the composition of these solutions to vary over a wide range when subjected to analysis by extraction with pure benzene and benzene containing carrier iodine.

+5 Oxidation state. Solutions of carrier-free $I^{131}O_3^-$ have been prepared by oxidation of I^{131} with potassium chlorate in warm dilute nitric acid,[51] with cerium(IV) in 0.5 $\underline{f}$ sulfuric acid at 105° C,[13] or at pH 7 with hot manganese(VII).[54] In the last instance, alcohol was used to reduce the residual manganese(VII) to manganese dioxide, which was coagulated by boiling and subsequently filtered off.

Solutions of carrier-free $I^{131}O_4^-$ free of metal cations have been prepared by oxidation of I^{131-} in 5.76 $\underline{f}$ nitric acid at 150° C for 3 hours.[55] The resulting solution of iodate-131 was evaporated to dryness at room temperature in the dark under reduced pressure, and the residue was dissolved in distilled water.

+7 Oxidation state. Good et al.[51] oxidized carrier-free I^{131-} to periodate with chlorine in alkaline solution. Musakin and Puchkov[54] employing electrolytic oxidation of I^{131-} in alkaline solution produced periodate-131 in yields of about 30 per cent.

[51] Good, M. L., Purdy, M. B., and Hoering, T., J. Inorg. & Nuclear Chem., 6, 73 (1958).

[52] Cottin, M., and Haissinsky, M., Compt. rend., 224, 1636 (1947).

[53] Appelman, E. H., doctoral dissertation, University of California, Berkeley, 1960, p. 48 (UCRL-9025).

[54] Musakin, A. P., and Puchkov, L. V., Zhur. Neorg. Khim., 4, 483 (1959).

[55] Perkins, H., and Kahn, M., J. Inorg. & Nuclear Chem., 14, 288 (1960).

6. PREPARATION OF INORGANIC COMPOUNDS OF IODINE LABELED WITH I^{131}

The preparations described below deal with macro amounts of iodine and, therefore, are not subject to considerations of the anomalous behavior of carrier-free iodine discussed previously. Such anomalies should however be considered in all procedures prior to the addition of carrier iodine in the appropriate oxidation state.

-1 Oxidation state. The initial step in the preparation of most inorganic compounds of iodine labeled with I^{131} requires an alkali iodide-I^{131}. Dry potassium iodide-I^{131} suitable for dissolution in water or nonaqueous solvents can be prepared as follows[56,57]: A small amount of aqueous potassium iodide, inoculated with carrier-free I^{131} tracer, is oxidized to elemental iodine with chromium(VI) in acid solution; the iodine is subsequently extracted into a small volume of benzene, which is then washed with several portions of water. This active dilute solution of iodine in benzene is shaken with an aqueous solution of inactive potassium iodide whereby, via rapid isotopic exchange, a major portion of the I^{131} is transferred to the potassium iodide, which is then obtained in a pure dry form on evaporation of the aqueous layer. It is important to note the order of addition of reagents in this procedure. If carrier-free I^{131} is treated with chromium(VI) before the addition of carrier iodide, the anomalous oxidation products of carrier-free iodine that do not readily react nor undergo exchange with carrier iodide will be formed.

Leden and Parck[58] precipitated silver iodide-I^{131} from aqueous sodium iodide-I^{131} by addition of silver perchlorate. Presumably, other insoluble iodides could be prepared in a similar manner

Fialkov and Nazarenko[59] reported complete isotopic exchange between molten iodine or iodine vapor and aluminum iodide, tin(IV) iodide, arsenic(III) iodide, or antimony(III) iodide during 1 to 2 hours at 150° C in a sealed tube. Nazarenko and Vouk[60] observed complete exchange between silicon tetraiodide and molten iodine at 130° C in less than 1 hour. These results suggest a general procedure for the preparation of inorganic radioactive iodides that exchange rapidly with elemental iodine. Thus, after isotopic

56 Stillson, P., and Kahn, M., J. Am. Chem. Soc., 75, 3579 (1953).

57 Leary, J. A., and Kahn, M., J. Am. Chem. Soc., 81, 4173 (1959).

58 Leden, I., and Parck, C., Acta Chem. Scand., 10, 535 (1956).

59 Fialkov, Ya. A., and Nazarenko, Yu. P., Ukrain. Khim. Zhur., 19, 356 (1953); C.A., 49, 9365f (1955).

60 Nazarenko, Yu. P., and Vouk, T. V., Ukrain. Khim. Zhur., 21, 16 (1955); C.A., 49, 13003b (1955).

exchange between inactive inorganic iodide and active molecular
iodine has been effected, the labeled inorganic iodide could be obtained in pure form by subsequent removal of the molecular iodine
by distillation.

Labeled tetrammineplatinum(II) iodoplatinite has been precipitated by the addition of tetrammineplatinum(II) chloride to a solution
initially containing ammonium iodide-I^{131} and inactive potassium
iodoplatinite; the iodoplatinite exchanged rapidly[61] at 15° C with the
I^{131-}. Labeled cesium iodoplatinate was prepared in a similar
manner using cesium chloride to precipitate the labeled iodoplatinate
from the exchange mixture.[61, 62]

Labeled tetrammineplatinum(II) tetraiodomercurate(II) was precipitated with tetrammineplatinum(II) chloride from an aqueous
solution of potassium tetraiodomercurate(II) that had been labeled[63]
through rapid exchange with I^{131-}.

0 Oxidation state. Crystals of elemental iodine labeled with I^{131}
have been prepared by treating an acidified solution of sodium
iodide-I^{131} with an excess of sodium nitrite.[64] The crystals were
centrifuged from the ice-cold solution and washed with cold water.

Darbee and Harris[65] prepared active elemental iodine by exposing crystals of inactive iodine to an aqueous solution of carrier-
free sodium iodide-I^{131}. The iodine, which became active through
rapid isotopic exchange, was washed with water and then dried by
distillation through a glass wool-phosphorus pentoxide mixture.

Dilute aqueous solutions of radioactive molecular iodine have
been prepared by oxidation of sodium iodide-I^{131} in acid media with
iodate[5] or nitrite.[2] Elemental iodine dissolved in carbon tetrachloride[66] or benzene[67] has been labeled by shaking with an aqueous
solution containing a small quantity of potassium iodide-I^{131}.

+1 Oxidation state. An aqueous solution of iodine cyanide-I^{131}
has been prepared by allowing inactive iodine cyanide to undergo
isotopic exchange with active molecular iodine in n-hexane; the
iodine cyanide-I^{131} was subsequently extracted from the n-hexane

[61] Grinberg, A. A., Kozlova, L. I., Nikolskaya, L. E., and
Shagisultanova, G. A., Zhur. Priklad. Khim., 28, 5 (1955).

[62] Poë, A. J., and Vaidya, M. S., J. Chem. Soc., 1960, 187.

[63] Grinberg, A. A., and Mironov, V. E., Radiokhimiya, 2, 249
(1960), C.A., 54, 17140d (1960).

[64] Hamilton, C. F., Power, M. H., and Albert, A., J. Biol.
Chem., 178, 213 (1949).

[65] Darbee, L. R., and Harris, G. M., J. Phys. Chem., 61,
111 (1957).

[66] Kahn, M., and Freedman, A. J., J. Am. Chem. Soc., 76,
929 (1954).

[67] Zeltmann, A. H., and Kahn, M., J. Am. Chem. Soc., 76,
1554 (1954).

with water. [4] Alternatively, if exchange is allowed to occur in water between iodine cyanide and sodium iodide-I^{131}, the iodide may be removed by precipitation with silver nitrate. Solutions of iodine cyanide-I^{131} in acetone or ethanol were similarly prepared by removing the iodide ion with Amberlite MB-1 resin.

Kaufmann and Budwig[68] prepared a solution of iodine bromide-I^{131} in absolute methanol by treating dry sodium iodide-I^{131} with a stoichiometric quantity of bromine dissolved in methanol; the sodium bromide which forms precipitates out of solution, and can be removed by filtration.

Fialkov and Pavlov[69] observed a rapid isotopic exchange between iodine monochloride and radioactive iodine in dilute hydrochloric acid. The iodine was separated from the aqueous layer by extraction with chloroform, leaving behind a dilute aqueous acid solution of iodine monochloride-I^{131}.

Swartz and Christian[70] prepared labeled iodine monochloride by treating a glacial acetic acid solution of sodium iodide-I^{131} and elemental iodine with dry chlorine gas. Distillation of the mixture through anhydrous calcium chloride yielded a glacial acetic acid solution of iodine monochloride-I^{131} free of elemental iodine.

+5 *Oxidation state.* Labeled alkali iodate can be prepared by simply inoculating an aqueous solution of carrier alkali iodate with carrier-free $I^{131}O_3$ prepared as described previously. This solution can be evaporated to dryness to yield the labeled salt or treated with various metal cations to precipitate out insoluble labeled iodates.

Oxidation of carrier I^{131-} in 5.76 f nitric acid for 3 hours at 150 C in a sealed tube produces carrier $I^{131}O_3^-$ in approximately 85 per cent yield; under the same conditions oxidation of carrier-free I^{131} to $I^{131}O_3^-$ is essentially quantitative.[55] The labeling of iodate through isotopic exchange with elemental I^{131} in aqueous solutions is possible but the reaction is slow.[5]

+7 *Oxidation state.* Mach[71] oxidized carrier I^{131-} in sodium bicarbonate solution to periodate-131 with sodium hypochlorite at 100° C. The periodate was purified by paper electrophoresis. A similar procedure was employed by Good et al.[51] and Glendenin et al.[2,46]

---

[68] Kaufmann, H. P., and Budwig, J., Fette, Seifen, Anstrichmittel, 53, 253 (1951).

[69] Fialkov, Yu. Ya., and Pavlov, V. L., Zhur. Obsechi. Khim., 26, 1711 (1956).

[70] Swartz, H. A., and Christian, J. E., Can. Pharm. J., 91, 369 (1958).

[71] Mach, M., Chem. prumsyl, 8 (33), 303 (1958); C. A., 52, 19580b.

Index

Note: In this index, the compounds are arranged in a purely alphabetical manner, as if the formula represented a normal word (i.e., D_3BO_3 is followed by DBr, DCl*, $DClO_4$, etc.), without regard to subscripts except where needed to avoid confusion. The nuclides H^2 and H^3 are indexed as D and T, respectively. All other isotopic nuclides are indicated by a superscript asterisk (*).